THE ROTATION DIET COOKBOOK

BOOKS BY MARTIN KATAHN, PH.D.

The Rotation Diet

THE ROTATION DIET

COOKBOOK

Martin Katahn, Ph.D.

Director, Vanderbilt Weight Management Program

and Terri Katahn

GUILD PUBLISHING LONDON

Typeset by Phoenix Photosetting, Chatham
Printed in Great Britain by
Mackays of Chatham Ltd, Kent

To Enid Katahn,
wife and mother to this team,
with much love.

Contents

STANDARD MEASURES FOR THE BRITISH EDITION

Since Dr Katahn's *Rotation Diet Cookbook* originated in Nashville, Tennessee, some of the measurements for servings are given by volume using the American cup. Measurement by volume is often the most sensible way, for a serving of vegetables or cooked rice, for example, and to give an idea of the appropriate quantity of fruit. To be accurate, measure a 'cup' up to the 8-fluid-ounce (225-ml) mark in a standard measuring jug; you will soon be able to judge the proper amounts. As a rough guide, 3 stalks of raw celery (sliced), 2 medium carrots (sliced) or 3 ounces (80 g) of raw sliced mushrooms all approximate 1 cup. Again as a rough guide, 1 piece of fruit – a small apple or orange, half a large banana, 3 ounces (80 g) of grapes (about 20), a small slice of melon or two thin (½-inch/1-cm) slices of pineapple each approximates half a cup. A normal serving of any cooked vegetable approximates one cup; a small serving or 3 rounded tablespoons half a cup. Men are often allowed vegetable servings half as big again. These approximate the 'average' and 'small' helpings that a man could expect in a restaurant or at home. Accurately the greens or marrow would come up to the 12-fluid-ounce (330-ml) level in your measuring jug (for 1½ cups), the peas or carrots to the 6-fluid-ounce (180-ml) level (for ¾ cup).

Rice and pasta such as macaroni will roughly double in volume on cooking; for porridge, use the volume of water that you require and add the appropriate quantities of oatmeal or rolled oats according to the instructions for your usual brand – i.e. for one cup of porridge use 8 fluid ounces (225 ml) of water and 3 to 4 level tablespoons of rolled oats.

In the recipes most of the American cup measurements have been converted to British Imperial and Metric weights on the scales given overleaf, the criterion being in each case: which is the easiest measurement to use? Spoonfuls are always level unless 'rounded' or 'heaped' is specified; and please remember that all teaspoons, including ½ and ¼ teaspoon, should be scant measures – just a little less than level.

Weights	Volume/Liquids
1 kg = 2 lbs 3 oz	1 litre = 1¾ pints/35 fluid oz
450 g = 1 lb	700 ml = 1¼ pints/24 fluid oz
350 g = 12 oz	(3 American cups)
300 g = 10 oz	570 ml = 1 pint/20 fluid oz
225 g = 8 oz	450 ml = 16 fluid oz
175 g = 6 oz	(2 American cups)
145 g = 5 oz	330 ml = 12 fluid oz
110 g = 4 oz	(1½ American cups)
80 g = 3 oz	225 ml = 8 fluid oz
56 g = 2 oz	(1 American cup)
40 g = 1½ oz	180 ml = 6 fluid oz
28 g = 1 oz	(¾ American cup)
	110 ml = 4 fluid oz
	(½ American cup)
	25 ml = 1 fluid oz
	15 ml = 1 tablespoon
	10 ml = 1 dessertspoon
	5 ml = 1 teaspoon

PREFACE:
WHY WRITE A COOKBOOK?

Wherever I go to give a talk about the problem of obesity, the most frequently asked personal question is, 'Have you been following the Rotation Diet ever since you lost your own weight?' And, of course, the answer is no. I haven't dieted for twenty-four years, except for research purposes in the Vanderbilt Weight Management Program.

I think the question reflects a common attitude to dieting. Evidently, most people believe that if you are overweight and go on a weight-loss diet, whether it's the Rotation Diet or any other diet, and if you are successful in losing weight, you must resign yourself to 'dieting' for the rest of your life.

Nothing is farther from the truth, and that is why I'm writing a cookbook.

I would like to show you how I, as a former fat man, have learned to prepare just about anything my heart desires, from soup to nuts, without 'dieting'. This is how I keep the 5½ stone (34 k) that I lost twenty-four years ago from creeping back around my hips, which, by the way, used to be 55 inches (140 cm) round.

I would also like to show you how my daughter, Terri, and a small army of friends learned to cook and plan menus in accordance with my low-fat, low-salt principles, as they jumped in to help me create recipes of all kinds that would also be in accordance with *their own* tastes. The results, as you will discover as you experiment with the recipes in this book, are proof positive: all low-calorie cooking does not have to be bland and taste the same! You can adapt your favourite recipes, using the same principles, to suit *your* tastes.

You will find as you examine the book that not one dietetic food, artificial sweetener or any other artificial ingredient is used in any of the recipes. I have always felt that such concoctions do no good when it comes to weight management. And now there is research to support my claims that, if anything, people who use artificial sweeteners tend to gain more weight in a given time than those who don't.* I want to show you how to use the 'good stuff' – the genuine, tasty foods – in a way that will help you control your weight.

The approach to food preparation and menu planning that you will find in *The Rotation Diet Cookbook* is designed to have other health benefits. By being low in overall fat and salt content and high in vitamins, minerals and dietary fibre, the approach I take follows the most up-to-date guidelines for preventing heart disease and cancer.

There is, however, one important, indisputable fact that you must accept if you are going to lose weight and keep it off for ever. If you are an overweight person and want to weigh even five pounds less for the rest of your life, you must DO SOMETHING DIFFERENT from what you have been doing, for the rest of your life. You cannot return to your present life-style after losing even five pounds, without going right back to square one.

If you are a sedentary person, an increase in physical acitivity can give you a reasonable margin in your calorie intake. It's a margin of several hundred calories that's lacking in your present life-style. That's why this may be one of the only cookbooks in history that has a chapter devoted to physical activity! Just taking a brisk walk for 45 minutes each day will permit you to enjoy one of our dessert recipes every day, or a couple of glassses of wine with dinner, with no fear of gaining weight.

But my goal in writing this cookbook goes beyond simple weight management. The increase in physical activity that I recommend, important as it is in helping to control your weight, does not ensure the health benefits of reducing fat (and possibly sodium) in your diet. When it comes to reducing the risk of heart disease and cancer, the meal plans and style of food preparation that I sug-

---

* For instance, the summary of the research findings of the American Cancer Society in the September 1986 edition of *Wellness Letter* (volume 2, no. 12), a health newsletter published by the University of California at Berkeley.

gest are *at least as important*, and possibly even more important, than an increase in physical activity. Fortunately, when you learn to reduce the fat content of your diet, you accomplish both objectives: you reduce the risk of disease and at the same time make it much easier to control your weight.

The basic principles that Terri and I have used in developing our recipes are:

1. Keep fat at a minimum but still come up with tasty dishes. Our goal here is to show you how to design a meal plan and then prepare the foods so that you end up with about 25 to 30 per cent of your daily calories, on average, coming from fat. If we were to go further than that in reducing fat calories, we don't think it would be possible to develop tasty recipes and to design a comprehensive dietary plan that a majority of people (including ourselves) could live with for the rest of our lives.
2. Reduce the amount of sugar. Rather than use any artificial sweetener, we prefer to use moderate amounts of sugar as a sweetener (or honey or molasses, when appropriate). It tastes better and it is more satisfying.
3. Demonstrate how the wise use of herbs and spices can add to the attractiveness of your dishes, while avoiding such an exotic or complicated approach to cooking that no-one but a professional cook would have the time to pursue it. So, we focus on the use of spices and herbs, the latter used in their most easily found form, which is often dried rather than fresh. Of course, if fresh is available, all the better.

As for salt (sodium), we include minimal amounts because salt helps bring out the flavour of other ingredients. You can prove this to yourself by mixing up a blend of herbs, tasting the mixture, then adding just a pinch of salt. Suddenly, there is an explosion of flavour.

In general, our recipes include about half the salt that a salt-adapted taste might expect, so you may find yourself taking a little time getting used to the new blend of tastes. Do take the time, because, as you reduce salt in your diet, your sensitivity to its flavour will probably increase. You'll want less as you get used to using less!

In our opinion, the weight of scientific evidence suggests that healthy people who do not have a familial tendency to hypertension can use salt in moderation without danger to their health. However, if you are on a salt-restricted diet, be sure to check with your doctor about the use of salt in our recipes before including the recommended amount.

4. Finally, we wanted dishes that are, for the most part, relatively simple and quick to prepare. Although we were fortunate to obtain the enthusiastic cooperation of several professional chefs and bakers in the development of our recipes, we ourselves are not professionals. Both Terri and I work full-time and we rarely wish to put a great deal of time into preparing meals at the end of a long working day. (We do, of course, enjoy spending several hours creating special meals for festive occasions.) If you learn to organize your approach to cooking as we suggest, you will find that most dishes that we have included in this book take less than 20 or 25 minutes to prepare (not including final cooking time). A few of the more elaborate may take an hour, although some of the preparation can be done in advance so that the time required for the final steps just before meal time is reduced.

Think of this book as a course in healthy food preparation as well as a cookbook. We show you a number of daily meal plans with different calorie totals. Try our way of low-fat cooking, then adapt any of your own favourite recipes and design your own healthy meal plans.

Martin Katahn, Ph.D.
Nashville, Tennessee
January 1987

ACKNOWLEDGEMENTS

Just as the Rotation Diet itself became a community-wide weight-loss programme, first in our home town of Nashville and then in hundreds of other cities all over America, so this cookbook has become, in some ways, a community-wide effort. So many devoted people helped to make this book possible that it is difficult for us to know where to begin to express our appreciation. Perhaps we should start with the three people who, in addition to ourselves, created, cooked and tested most of the recipes.

Joyce Weingartner, friend, master baker, and enthusiastic teacher of the art of baking fine breads, has contributed her bread recipes in the past (to *The Rotation Diet*), and really entered into the present project by testing, and in part creating, over one hundred of the recipes. Joyce and her family were some of our best taste-testers, as were several of her friends who were on the Rotation Diet, and who would drop in to her house each week for the plunder, armed with bags full of plastic containers.

Donna Kamler and Patty Smith, chefs at Robert Orr/Sysco, cooked, tested, sampled, and retested over two-hundred recipes in the Robert Orr/Sysco Kitchen. We deeply appreciate both the friendship and cooperation of Burt Hummell, president of Robert Orr/Sysco, for making the company kitchen and his staff available to us, and for seeing to it that we had the very finest quality meat and produce at our fingertips for all of our recipes.

Many others responded to our calls for help in illustrating specific approaches to food preparation. Margaret Nofziger Dotzler prepared most of our tofu recipes and several meatless dishes. Jewel Coburn brought us a number of exciting recipes from around the world, including her native Australia. Patti Bereyso, Kim Harrison, Trey Kuhn, Patricia Lipman, Denni Llovet, Patricia Sommers, George and Betty Schnitzer and June Stevenson also contributed their favourite low-calorie, low-fat recipes.

We also want to thank the Kellogg Company for providing some of the recipes for breakfast foods, muffins and breads, several of which were created especially for this book. In particular, we'd like to thank Dr Shirley Chen, research nutritionist at the Kellogg Company, for providing important information on recent research in nutrition.

Several Nashville restaurants answered our requests for illustrations of how they prepare low-calorie, low-fat dishes for their customers who wish to order such foods when eating out. The recipes that they provided for this cookbook are unique and instructive, and appear in print for the first time. In some cases we had to adjust the recipes for home preparation (not many of us will prepare Court Bouillon by the gallon!) But we can testify that, with a little practice, we can all become adept at recreating what the finest chefs have originated. So thanks to Mr Jaime Camara and Chef Tom Allen at Arthur's; Mr John Haggard, Head Chef Sylvain le Coguic, and Maître d'Hoyt Hill at Julian's; Ms Bonnie Chen and Chef Wang Chia Hsin at Peking Gardens; Chef Kem Ramovich at Villa Romano; and Manager Casey Ishida at Kobe Steak House.

Jamie Pope, MS, RD, now the nutritionist at the Vanderbilt Weight Management Program, gave willingly of her time and energy in compiling the substitution and fibre lists that appear at the end of this book. She also got into the spirit of things and helped create some great recipes.

Mary Bomar performed indispensible work, especially in analysing all our recipes at least once on one of our Tandy 1200HD computers, using *The Food Processor* Computerized Nutrition System from ESHA Research. Marilyn Blair was our all-around 'do-anything-and-everything' production assistant, who helped us keep our overflowing files in order and kept mountains of food and paperwork moving between our offices, the post office (and hence, the publisher), Robert Orr/Sysco, Vanderbilt, and so on, throughout Nashville.

Enid Katahn, wife and mother, and David Katahn, son and brother, also helped either by cooking in every spare moment or by tasting (and tasting twelve to fifteen dishes at a time requires quite a taste tolerance!). David also pitched in with analysing recipes when we needed extra help at the last minute. Enid has our special thanks, along with master carpenter and designer Mitch MacKay, for remodelling the kitchen at the 'Katahn Homestead' into what must be the most beautiful and efficient kitchen anyone could wish for.

Once again, it's a pleasure to thank our literary agents, Arthur and Richard Pine, for all they have done for us during the writing of this book, and for their help with our health-promotion activities in general. What began as a professional relationship between literary agents and author six years ago has developed into a valued friendship.

And thanks once again to our editor at W. W. Norton, Starling Lawrence. This is his fourth book with one or more of the Katahn family, and he provided, as usual, invaluable advice on format, style and content. Star loves to cook as much as we do, and we share an interest in improving the quality of our diets without sacrificing the enjoyment found in good food, tastefully prepared. As with our literary agents, our relationship with Star has gone far beyond the usual business and professional relationship between publishing company, author and editor. It is wonderful to work with all of the friendly and helpful people at W. W. Norton, and we want to express our appreciation to Fran Rosencrantz, publicity director, Eddie Gunn, publicity associate, Anthony Levintow, Debra Makay, Nancy Palmquist and Patty Peltekos of the editorial department, art director Hugh O'Neill and production manager Andy Marasia for the special roles they have played in making this book a reality.

Finally, an undertaking such as this would have taken at least four times longer and caused fifty times the headaches without the help of our friendly Tandy computers. From a single Model II in 1981, we have grown to a 'fleet' of twelve various models (in our home offices and the Weight Management Office at Vanderbilt University). We want to thank Doug Stallings in particular for his personal attention to our needs during the past six years, and our thanks to Ralph Kirkland, Rita Baughman and Andrew McCluskey of the Tandy Area Training and Support Group, who answer the 'crisis' telephone number when any of us call for advice in an emergency.

THE ROTATION DIET COOKBOOK

What Is the Rotation Diet?

Although *The Rotation Diet Cookbook* is designed to show you how to maintain desirable weight for the rest of your life without depriving yourself of the enjoyment of good food, we're sure at least some of our readers may want to lose a few pounds at the outset. And what better way than with the Rotation Diet!

So, let's start with an explanation of that diet.

The Rotation Diet has certain unique features and several advantages over other approaches to losing weight. It's a quick-weight-loss plan that:

1. does not lower the metabolic rate;
2. is time limited and highly motivating;
3. includes a wide variety of healthy foods from all four food groups;
4. and is safe for overweight adults who are otherwise in good health.

When you make up your mind to lose weight using the Rotation Diet, you set a target of time – three weeks – in which you rotate caloric intake. In addition, if you are a sedentary person, you GET ACTIVE. This is what protects you from the 'starvation response,' that is, a lowering of your metabolic rate. When you use other

3

low-calorie diets and neglect to increase physical activity, your need for food can drop 35 or even 40 per cent in the space of three weeks. You can't eat like a normal human being after those diets without gaining weight even faster that you lost it!

During the Rotation Diet, women follow a core diet of approximately 600 calories for three days, 900 for four and 1200 for a week. Then, in the third week, you return to the calorie levels of the first week. The version for men contains 600 calories more at each level. You eat a wide variety of healthful foods: fruits, vegetables, whole grains, low-fat milk products, lean meat, fish and poultry. Although there are recommended menus, you can substitute freely, as long as you stay within the same food group. Using the substitution rules and the guidelines for food preparation, you design the diet to suit your personal tastes and food preferences.

In addition to the core diet, there is an 'insurance policy' that greatly increases the nutritional value of the diet. The insurance policy (explained on pages 295–6) enables most people to follow the diet for the full three weeks and obtain an average weight loss of two-thirds of a pound (300 g) a day. At any meal (or for snacks, if you choose) you can eat all you want of just about any vegetable. I call these *free vegetables* because your consumption can be virtually unlimited. In addition, you choose a *safe fruit*, one that you really like so that you don't feel deprived because you're dieting. Any time you need a lift or are in need of a snack for any reason, have a *safe fruit*.

In the original version of the Rotation Diet, I suggested that you choose only one fruit (apples, for example) as your *safe fruit* so as not to be tempted to overeat. I suggested that you set an upper limit on the fruit at three servings per day. The reason for these suggestions about *free vegetables* and the *safe fruit* is that the vegetables listed in the original version contain 10 calories or less per average portion, while the fruit might average 60 calories for a medium-size piece. I have, however, relaxed the rule on the *safe fruit* as a result of the experience people have had on the diet. As long as you keep to three fruit snacks a day, in addition to the meals on the core menu, it is perfectly all right to vary the fruit and enjoy yourself.

I also relaxed the restrictions on the *free vegetables*. Experience showed that just about any vegetable could be used as a *free vegetable*, including all those that contain fewer than 25 calories per average portion. Perhaps the most important thing that people who use the Rotation Diet learn is that they – and you – can't get fat on fruits and vegetables! These foods, together with whole grains, should comprise 55 to 60 per cent of your total daily calorie intake. The complete *free vegetable* and *safe fruit* lists are given on pages 295 and 296.

On pages 303–10 are some suggestions for 600-, 900-, 1200-, 1500- and 1800-calorie menus, as well as directions for men, and for couples who want to diet together. When friends and families that need to lose some weight do it together, they have more fun, and are generally more successful because of the support they can give one another.

The menus refer to specific recipes, but all of our recipes list the caloric values as well as other important nutrient information, so that you can easily choose the recipes that are especially good for low-calorie days in case you want to make substitutions and design your own weight-loss plan.

I want to repeat, however, that this is a cookbook designed to illustrate a way of 'cooking for life' – not 'dieting for life'. The 1800-calorie menus on pages 307–10 illustrate basic maintenance menus, and instructions are given for increasing portion sizes for men, who will end up needing an average of between 2100 and 2400 calories per day.

Our recipes show you how to eat just about everything, maximizing flavour and sound nutrition while cutting back on fat, sugar and salt, so that you have a nutrition plan you can live with. Just take a look at some of the recipe headings: there are recipes for everything from appetizers to desserts. We really concentrated on developing desserts, because they are what most people expect to give up the moment anyone says 'weight management'.

We recognize that many others have created healthful dietary plans for weight reduction and the permanent control of obesity, as well as for the prevention of those diseases that are related to an overconsumption of fat. The problem with these plans (and we are sure you know what we mean when we say this) is that the 'cure' is often worse than the disease! They require sacrifices that are just too hard to live with. If the recommendations don't 'feel good' – and in the case of a cookbook, if the recipes don't taste good – and if the payoff is not worth whatever sacrifices are involved, there is no way you will stick with the programme.

The Rotation Diet has a BIG payoff. And the recipes taste so good we think you will be able to stick with our suggestions for a lifetime of good cooking whether you use them for weight reduction or not.

So, enjoy!

NUTRITION NOTE

With each recipe we include information on calorie content, cholesterol, dietary fibre, total fat and sodium. Thus if you use our recipes for your daily menus you will find it easy to calculate totals and design a special diet should you wish to limit calories for weight reduction, or determine whether your diet falls within the guidelines for cholesterol, fat, sodium and dietary fibre recommended by the major health organizations. Our sample menus, (pp. 303–10) are designed with these guidelines in mind although on a given day they can be a little above or below the exact recommendations for any given nutrient (as would be typical of a normal approach to eating in which no one can be expected to tie a calculator to one's fork!)

We feel that, on the average, no more than 30 per cent of calories should come from fat; about 55 to 60 per cent should come from carbohydrate, and about 15 per cent from protein.

An average of 300 milligrams of cholesterol per day is a goal to aim for, with the American Heart Association now suggesting that it is even better to regulate cholesterol in relation to your total daily caloric intake, with no more than 100 miligrams cholesterol per 1000 calories. But we think this latest recommendation will be difficult, and certainly tedious, to implement. Unless there is existing heart disease or a familial history, the general goal of 300 milligrams per day seems reasonable.

According to the American National Cancer Institute, dietary fibre should fall between 20 and 35 grams per day, with many health authorities suggesting that you gradually increase to the upper level of this range provided that amount of fibre does not make you uncomfortable. We, too, think this is a good idea since consumption of foods relatively high in dietary fibre has extra value for weight control, because of their bulk and the tendency of fibre to bind with and prevent the absorption of a small amount of the fat in your diet.

A healthy range for sodium lies between 110 and 3300 milligrams per day, although the American Heart Association now ties sodium intake to total daily calories, suggesting 1000 milligrams per 1000 calories. In the past, most medical authorities considered moderate sodium intake to mean 2000 milligrams per day. One teaspoon of salt contains about 2200 milligrams of sodium, so we tend to use very little in our recipes and add a bit to taste at the table.

A 'no' in our nutrient analyses indicates less than 0.5 gram fat or fibre, and less than 0.5 milligrams cholesterol or sodium. We round up in other cases (0.5 to 1.49 will be listed as 1, 1.5 to 2.49 will be listed as 2, etc.). Recipes that contain tiny bits of fibre (for example, from small amounts of vegetables or nuts) will thus say 'no' fibre even though up to 0.49 gram is present, and the same will be true of fat up to 0.49 gram. The decision to round up or down was arbitrary and was made to avoid confusing decimal values that would contain a small amount of error anyway due to the way nutritional analyses are performed in the laboratory.

We used standard varieties of soy sauce and bouillon in our analyses, since these are the most easily available in all supermarkets. However, compared with commercial bouillons (powders and cubes) which contain from 900 to 1500 milligrams of sodium in the quantities used per cup of water, plus sweeteners, homemade stock will tend to be much lower in sodium, sugars and other additives. You may always substitute a low-sodium soy sauce or bouillon if you wish, and you will reduce the sodium content of the relevant recipes by a significant amount. Read the labels of the substitute products, since these · products usually contain more sweetener than the meat or soy product named on the label. They may also use potassium chloride in place of sodium chloride (table salt) and some people find this flavour objectionable. Please check our Basic Soup Stocks (pages 35–8) for several simple recipes that can be used whenever bouillon or stock is called for. Once you discover how good your homemade stock can be, we think you will rarely fall back on the commercial product.

Many of our recipes call for skim or low-fat milk. Our analyses are based on 2% 'semi-skimmed' milk, when the choice is given, since that is what we find most palatable. Per cup of milk, each per cent butterfat adds roughly 20 calories to the recipe or slightly over 2 grams of fat. When you divide this by 4 to 8 servings, we think this is an insignificant amount of fat for a significant increase in flavour and texture.

All preparation times listed are rough estimates, since everyone cooks at a different pace. The second or third time you prepare a recipe will not take as long as the first. Cooking times also vary slightly, since some ovens run hotter than others. If you find a dish takes significantly longer to cook than indicated, make a note to increase the oven temperature next time. Finally, we hope our advice on how to organize your kitchen, and to assemble all ingredients prior to starting meal preparation, will help move things along more quickly if you tend to be somewhat inefficient.

The Efficient Kitchen

The joy of cooking begins in an efficient kitchen that makes the preparation of food as pleasurable in the doing as in the eating. It's so much easier to prepare healthful meals for yourself and for your family when you work in an environment that's equipped to facilitate your efforts and that gives you the rewards creative cooking so richly deserves.

Ask yourself this question:

How many times have you started to prepare a meal, whether it's after a long, late day at work when you're tired and hungry, or whether it's a joyously anticipated holiday celebration when you have the whole day to cook, and found yourself getting tense and irritable?

Your change in mood may have occurred for several reasons, all of which are easily corrected if you take a little time to examine what happened.

Did you run out of worktop space? Couldn't find the oregano? The knife was so dull you couldn't trim the meat without trimming your fingers? You twisted your back when you bent over and tried to crawl into the corner of a bottom cabinet to reach the roasting pan? You cut into a lemon and it squirted all over the toaster, which, for some reason, has for twenty years managed to stay smack at the rear of your work space and is still

10

splattered with a sprinkle from yesterday's grapefruit?

Annoyances like these can quickly destroy the joy of cooking. We know it as well as anyone. *Every single one of these aggravations has happened to us!*

Finally, since we really love to cook, we learned to pay a little attention to the organization of our kitchens and the preparation process itself. There's no question about it: inferior utensils, a poorly laid-out kitchen, inefficient storage, lack of essential ingredients and poor cooking strategies can all make meal preparation an aggravating chore.

Here are some suggestions that have helped make meal preparation easier and a source of pleasure for us.

EQUIPMENT

Knives and Related Utensils

When it comes to knives, buy the very best you can afford! For years I was as susceptible to cheap promotions as anyone. For example, I only recently disposed of a set of impossible kitchen carving knives and steak knives that I received at a petrol service station for a dollar and ten gallons of gasoline during a promotion when our family first came to Nashville twenty-five years ago! We tried them once. They didn't have enough body to cut a hamburger, and for ugliness they couldn't be beaten, so they were stuck in the back of a drawer, taking up space needed for more important household goods.

There is a tremendous difference between fine knives and inferior knives. Haven't you always marvelled at the ease with which your butcher trims a steak or roast, or skins a chicken? You can do the same if you treat yourself to first-class knives. Keep them sharp with a good steel.

Our most used knives are:

10-inch (25-cm) chef's knife (for the heavy duty jobs such as splitting a turnip or carving a big roast);
10-inch (25-cm) slicing knife (thinner blade more convenient for slicing turkey, for example);

11

6½-inch (16-cm) utility knife (better on carrots, potatoes, and larger vegetables than a paring knife); and

4-inch (10-cm) paring knives (I like to have two since they are in constant use).

It pays to keep your knives right next to the point of use in a wooden knife block. With this set up, you won't have to leave your work area or reach across sink or stove whenever you need one.

Never put your knives in the dishwasher. This will ruin the handles and dull the blades as well, since they knock up against the other cutlery while washing.

I keep a large assortment of serving spoons, spatulas (mostly wooden, a few plastic, all of which will not scratch our pots and pans) and other implements stored upright in a canister, as a 'bouquet', on a counter near the stove. Terri keeps hers in a large drawer right next to the stove. So small utensils such as the can opener and corkscrew don't jam and jumble, they fit in a deep drawer near the stove.

Pots and Pans

We have had a set of copper-bottom cookware in the family for thirty-five years, and while I may still occasionally use a saucepan, or the large covered stockpot when I cook spaghetti, I feel that lightweight copper- or aluminium-clad stainless cookware is just not suitable for either simple or serious cooking.

I prefer pots and pans made of an extra-thick, heavy-duty aluminium alloy, while Terri has a set of pots and pans made of heavy-duty enamelled steel. A heavy-cast aluminium with a nonstick interior also works well. My 10-inch (25-cm) and 12-inch (30-cm) lidded frying pans have received lots of use, and I keep a complete set of nonstick pans in my motor home, since it is so much easier to clean when I am travelling.

Recently we were introduced to 7-ply stainless steel, which is excellent for waterless cooking; a 2-quart (2-litre) saucepan and a 10-inch (25-cm) lidded frying pan

12

are now the mainstays for food preparation in my household. A 5- or 7-ply stainless-steel bottom spreads the heat evenly and, once the pan is hot, you can continue cooking on very low heat. I use these two pots for covered dishes, as the 'whistle' vent on the cover, which lets steam escape, tells me when the interior is maintaining the right temperature. Even when dry-frying food does not stick in the 7-ply pan as it will in a thinner one. Let the pan get hot before you add any oil, and then add the meat, poultry or other ingredients.

Most people will find that 2- and 4-quart (2- and 4-litre) covered saucepans and a 10-inch (25-cm) and 12-inch (30-cm) frying pan are indispensable. We have never needed a stockpot larger than 6 quarts (6 litres). As with your knives, buy the best you can afford, but keep function in mind, and your own preference for equipment. Don't buy things you won't use and don't keep things that you aren't using. Look in your cupboard right now – you may find pots you haven't used for years! I just got rid of two very heavy cast-iron frying pans that many chefs swear by, but they didn't 'feel right' or suit my style.

We use a variety of deep, enamelled, covered roasting pans, ranging in interior size from $9\frac{1}{2} \times 14$ inches (24 × 33 cm) to $11\frac{1}{2} \times 17$ inches (29 × 42 cm). Those extra inches really make a difference, since the smallest is right for roasting a chicken, while the largest takes care of a 22-pound (10-kilo) turkey. A heavy weight enamelled roasting pan can be used on top of the stove, since it will spread the heat quite evenly. My smallest roaster has a rack, which makes it excellent for steaming everything from fish to vegetables. And the largest one comes in handy for mixing great batches of stuffing when I prepare that large turkey for Christmas. I also use a covered roasting pan to make stews (as well as roasts) in the oven, with a low heat setting.

Terri uses a plain carbon-steel wok for stir-frying, while I prefer a frying pan, mainly because my electric-stove instructions warn against burning out the elements when using a stove-top wok. The frying pan works fine, but the texture and flavour always seem to be better in the wok, as it heats faster and the 'hot spot' makes for crisper vegetables in the stir-fry.

Casseroles and Other Pots

Our favourite earthenware casseroles and baking dishes, as well as soup bowls and coffee mugs, are made by two of Nashville's fine potters, Burneta Clayton and Lenore Vanderkooi. I also find a 3½-quart (3-litre) glass casserole very useful, and for the biggies I use a 5-quart (4½-litre) stoneware casserole, one of those brown monstrosities that have been around for generations. Earthenware, glassware and stoneware are also excellent for microwave cooking.

Miscellaneous

We have a few other items in both our kitchens that do special jobs particularly well.

A **microwave oven** is particularly useful for cooking vegetables. Microwave cooking requires little water, while more nutrients are retained in microwave cooking than through any other cooking method. The microwave is also useful for reheating foods, making cheese toast, baking a potato or two and making scrambled eggs and omelettes. We do not rely on it for most of our food preparation, however. Most of our main courses, roasts, stews, casseroles and poached and steamed foods, are best prepared on the stove top or in the convection oven.

We have both a **blender** and **food processor**. The food processor does everything from grating Parmesan to slicing vegetables when we have great quantities to slice (we still prefer our fine knives and a manual approach for a few stalks of celery or an onion or two). It also works well for chopping something like a large quantity of Brazil nuts, or for making bread or biscuit crumbs. But when it comes to *blending* or *pulverizing*, the blender does a better job than the food processor.

Big wooden salad bowls are essential. Salads don't look right and don't seem to taste as well in glass or metal. A modest-size walnut bowl, about 4 inches (10 cm) deep and 14 inches (35 cm) across the top, is fine

14

for a family and for small dinner parties, but for a buffet, a festive way to serve a gigantic salad is in a truly generous bowl, 8 inches (20 cm) deep and 18 inches (45 cm) across at the summit!

Serving plates have been passed along in our family since our ancestors emigrated from Russia and Lithuania at the turn of this century. Among them is an English porcelain serving plate (the imprint of origin is now illegible) and another is a gold-leafed one whose finish is beautifully cracked. What a joy it is to display a large glistening turkey or a beef bourguignon, surrounded by an arrangement of colourful vegetables, new pototoes and mushrooms, on one of these before serving dinner to family and friends! The platters have held such a wealth of goodness over the years that, each time we use them, we experience again feelings of thanksgiving at being together as a family and living in the United States.

For many years I always chopped, never pressed, fresh garlic. Of course, in my recipes, minced or chopped garlic is just fine. Finally, however, my wife Enid got tired of finding surprise pieces of garlic in her food and purchased a **garlic press**. It is now a mainstay in Terri's kitchen as well as ours. It handles cloves of all sizes, presses easily and completely and, thank goodness, is easy to clean. You should have a fine garlic press since fresh garlic is a completely different experience from garlic powder. The powder will do at a pinch, as we demonstrate in some of our recipes, but fresh is best!

An offcut of two-by-four wood is quite serviceable for pounding meat (I've done it) but it's not quite as good as an honest-to-goodness **meat tenderiser** when it comes to our wonderful veal recipes. It's worth the investment, and you can use it for poultry and beef as well. A large **wooden cutting board**, well seasoned and used for all pounding and cutting, is a must. I have a built-in oak board, 24 × 27 inches (60 × 68 cm) next to the sink, and its convenience makes these jobs a joy. Some bakers prefer a marble slab for pastry-making, but we have never used one.

Other utensils that we find useful include a **pepper mill** (fresh-ground is far more flavourful than ground pepper, which we never use); a **coffee grinder**, since fresh-ground coffee is also a completely different experience from pre-ground; and a **mortar and pestle**, which we use for grinding herbs, spices and seeds when we mix recipes such as Herb Salt (pp. 244–5). I have a mortar and pestle of attractive black marble, and Terri has a small lightweight wooden one. If you don't wish to buy a mortar and pestle, you can use a bowl and a heavy spoon.

GENERAL INSTRUCTIONS FOR BAKING AND ROASTING

We specifically indicate the instances in which baking or roasting requires a preheated oven. Although the probability is very low, earthenware or heat-resistant glass can crack when exposed to an extreme change in temperature. Therefore, we do not preheat our oven when we plan to use china or glass cookware.

Many recipes indicate greasing baking tins and frying pans with a vegetable non-stick spray. If you have difficulty obtaining this, warm the tin or pan before greasing it with a trace of oil on a small wad of paper. You will need very little fat.

HERBS AND SPICES

Here is a guide to the use of herbs and spices that can add to your cooking and eating pleasure. I keep my herbs and spices handy in a rack on the worktop at the rear of my work area, together with garlic and onion powder and a few homemade blends that I use frequently. I keep others on three revolving shelves in the cupboard over the work area: one shelf for seeds of various kinds, another for liquid seasonings and the third for infrequently used items. We have not tried all the various foods with all the suggested herbs and spices in the following list. But we think you will find one or two uses for each of them, as we do. You will find what we think are some particularly good suggestions in our recipes.

Allspice – Meats, fish, gravies, chutneys, tomato sauce
Anise – Fruit
Basil – Green beans, onions, peas, potatoes, tomatoes, lamb, beef, shellfish, eggs, sauces
Bay Leaves – Artichokes, beetroot, carrots, onions, potatoes, tomatoes, meats, fish, soups and stews, sauces and gravies
Caraway Seeds – Asparagus, beetroot, cabbage, carrots, cauliflower, coleslaw, onions, potatoes, sauerkraut, turnips, beef, pork, pasta, cheese dishes
Cardamom – Melon, sweet potatoes
Cayenne Pepper – Sauces, curries
Celery Seed – Cabbage, carrots, cauliflower, sweetcorn, potatoes, tomatoes, turnips, salad dressings, beef, fish dishes, sauces, soups, stews, cheese
Chervil – Carrots, peas, salads, tomatoes, salad dressings, poultry, fish, eggs
Chilli Powder – Sweetcorn, aubergine, onions, beef, pork, chilli con carne, stews, shellfish, sauces, egg dishes
Chives – Carrots, sweetcorn, sauces, salads, soups
Cinnamon – Stewed fruits, apple or pineapple dishes, sweet potatoes, toast
Cloves – Baked beans, sweet potatoes, pork and ham roasts
Cumin – Cabbage, rice, sauerkraut, chilli con carne, minced beef dishes, cottage or Cheddar cheese
Curry Powder – Carrots, cauliflower, green beans, onions, tomatoes, pork and lamb, shellfish, fish, poultry, sauces for eggs and meats
Dill Seed – Cabbage, carrots, cauliflower, peas, potatoes, spinach, tomato dishes, turnips, salads, lamb, cheese
Dillweed – Vegetables, salads, poultry, soups
Ginger – Stewed apple, melon, baked beans, carrots, onions, sweet potatoes, poultry, beef, veal, ham, lamb, teriyaki sauce
Mace – Carrots, potatoes, spinach, beef, veal, fruits, sauces

17

Marjoram – Asparagus, carrots, aubergine, greens, green beans, peas, spinach, lamb, pork, poultry, fish, stews, sauces

Mustard – Asparagus, broccoli, Brussels sprouts, cabbage, cauliflower, green beans, onions, peas, potatoes, meats, poultry

Mustard Seed – Salads, curries, pickles, ham, corned beef, chutneys

Nutmeg – Beetroot, Brussels sprouts, carrots, cabbage, cauliflower, greens, green beans, onions, spinach, sweet potatoes, sauces

Oregano – Baked beans, broccoli, cabbage, cauliflower, green beans, onions, peas, potatoes, spinach, tomatoes, turnips, beef, pork, veal, poultry, fish, pizza, chilli con carne, Italian sauces, stews

Paprika – Salad dressings, shellfish, fish, gravies, eggs

Parsley – All vegetables, soups, sauces, salads, stews, potatoes, eggs

Pepper – Most vegetables

Poppy Seeds – Salads, pasta

Rosemary – Mushrooms, peas, potatoes, spinach, tomatoes, salads, beef, lamb, pork, veal, poultry, stews, cheese, eggs

Saffron – Rice

Sage – Aubergine, onions, peas, tomato dishes, salads, pork, veal, poultry, ham, cheese

Savory – Baked beans, beetroot, cabbage, carrots, cauliflower, potatoes, rice, egg dishes, roasts, minced meat dishes

Sesame Seed – Asparagus, green beans, potatoes, tomatoes, spinach

Tarragon – Asparagus, beetroot, cabbage, carrots, cauliflower, mushrooms, tomatoes, salads, macaroni and vegetable combinations, beef, poultry, pork

Thyme – Artichokes, beetroot, carrots, aubergine, green beans, mushrooms, peas, tomatoes, pork, veal, poultry, cheese and fish dishes, stuffings

Turmeric – Mustards and curries, chicken

ORGANIZING THE KITCHEN

We know a number of people who unpacked their china and kitchen utensils when they moved into their homes and put things away 'temporarily' until they could find the time 'to get organized'. Twenty years later they are still scrambling all over the kitchen for things they use every day and reaching over things they haven't used for a year.

Here are some hints that can increase your efficiency and decrease some of the frustrations that can arise during food preparation.

1. Keep frequently used items as close as possible to their point of use (pots and pans by the stove, glasses near the sink, and so on).
2. Rearrange your kitchen so that cooking utensils, dishes and other paraphernalia you use every day, or almost every day, are up front, at eye level in their storage areas and where you don't have to move anything else to reach them. Then, take the items you use perhaps once or twice a year, and put them in the farthest, least convenient reaches of your storage areas. Everything left over, those items you might use once or twice a month, should be put in intermediate space. (While reorganizing your kitchen, you might consider throwing out anything you haven't used for a year or more. Or, if you have an attic or basement that you don't mind cluttering, stick these little-used items there and throw them out next year if you haven't used them by then!)
3. Don't clutter work space on your worktops with kitchen equipment. Pick a space at least two feet wide and keep it completely clear for working. This spot is usually best placed either to the right or left of the sink. If at all possible, it should be a hardwood cutting-board surface of oak or maple. Then clear another space yourself, to be used as a holding area for the cooking ingredients you

19

assemble prior to cooking, and clear a third spot to be used, if necessary, as a holding area for partly finished dishes that are not yet ready to pop on or into the stove or microwave. If your worktops are deep enough, you can store canisters and frequently used small appliances in less used areas, but don't let them cramp your preparation space.

4. If your stove top is not large enough for hot pots when you take them off burners or out of the oven, prepare another area right next to the stove with a fully heat-resistant surface, such as a portable slab of stainless steel. If you are lucky enough to be able to design your own kitchen, build it in (along with that cutting board next to your sink).

5. Efficient kitchen work-centres have sink, refrigerator and stove all within a step or two of one another but on different walls, forming a triangle of space for you to work in.

6. Set up a logical system for storing tinned goods and packets of foods. Arrange spices in alphabetical order (some people find an alphabetical order good for tinned things too). The best storage systems for spices have the jars laid on their sides, wine-storage style, with removable, replaceable labels on the tops so that you can add and delete spices when necessary. You can save a great deal of money buying frequently used spices in reasonable amounts from a shop that sells them in bulk. Keep the spices in your own jars.

7. Always assemble the ingredients you will need for cooking and lay them out, in order of use, in your holding area before starting to prepare your meal.

8. I have already mentioned that a convenient way to store serving spoons, spatulas and other large items in constant use is as a 'bouquet' in an open vase or jug near the stove. Silverware needs a drawer only about 2½ inches (6 cm) deep, while small utensils, such as can openers, corkscrews, jar openers, etc., can be kept in one deep drawer, about 4 inches (10 cm) deep, set aside for this purpose, using drawer organizers or cigar box

bottoms to group them so they won't jumble and jam as you open the drawer.

9. Open wall space can be used to hang utensils, or hang them from the ceiling.

10. Label and date foods that you put in the freezer, and organize the freezer so that you know where things are. Some foods are best used within a few months, while others may last up to a year. Use a reliable cookbook for advice on how long frozen foods last.

11. A butcher's-block-topped table on lockable castors, at worktop height, can do double- or even triple-duty and is one of the most useful things you can have in your kitchen: the table is extra work space, it can be used to cart things from kitchen to eating area(s), and it can serve as a kitchen table for light meals. Attaching a 2-inch (5-cm) thick maple top, 24 × 36 or 48 inches (60 × 90 or 120 cm) to a trestle base will allow room for your knees and thighs underneath. Lightweight, easily movable stools can serve as seating for meals or food preparation.

Breakfast Foods

Many nutritionists consider breakfast the most important meal of the day. I think eating in the morning is important in a very special way for persons who are trying to manage their weight: when you skip breakfast, you tend to build up a 'hidden hunger' that shows itself in overeating at night.

There is some research evidence that people who eat breakfast are more alert and better problem-solvers in the morning, and that eating a nutritious breakfast helps to avoid an afternoon attack of glooms.

Although some people who wake early really don't feel comfortable if they eat before ten or eleven, or even noon, we think you should give breakfast a try. Experiment for two weeks with a breakfast such as you will find on one of our menus (pp. 303–10) and see if you feel and work better. If you tend to eat from the moment you get home from work until you go to bed, that tendency to nibble all night might decrease once you start eating breakfast. You must, however, give the experiment a full two weeks to take effect, since it can take your system that long to readjust if you have been skipping breakfast for a long time. There are many hormones and enzymes that mobilize our bodies for the day and that aid in digesting food. They may be slightly out of rhythm, and it can take a while to retrain them. If you find yourself uncomfortable at the end of two weeks, well, go back to what you were doing! It must be right for you.

I like cereal with fruit and milk, or bread and cheese along with a piece of fruit, as my two 'standard' breakfasts. Terri prefers yogurt and fresh fruit. Both of us like a good cup of fresh-ground coffee, followed by a second cup! In order to keep our caffeine intake at reasonable levels, we often mix decaffeinated with regular coffee; I usually drink only a half cup at a time. We rarely have eggs, and I cannot remember the last time I had bacon or sausages, although it might have been about a year and a half ago on a camping trip. (Yes, I must admit it: there is something wonderful about the smell and the taste of bacon cooked out in the open and I don't intend to forego that pleasure permanently!) But these foods are too high in fat and cholesterol to be part of my daily diet.

We include here some 'special' breakfast foods for special occasions: French toast; yogurt and fruit; and unusual ways to make eggs.

If you like plain fried or scrambled eggs for breakfast, you can prepare them with very little added fat by using a nonstick vegetable cooking spray or a nonstick pan. Then, too, a plain boiled egg can be delectable if you know how to boil it properly. As you will see below, there really is a trick to it!

BOILED EGG

PREPARATION TIME: 5 MINUTES.   COOKING TIME: 15 MINUTES.

Place the egg in a saucepan with enough water to cover. Bring to a boil. Then cover immediately, *remove from the heat*, and let stand 15 minutes for a hard-boiled egg with a light, almost fluffy texture and no sulphurous green ring. (The green ring results from the interaction of continuous high heat with the sulphur in the egg.) Soft-boiled eggs should stand about 4 to 5 minutes when prepared this way.

Per Egg: 79 calories, 274 mg cholesterol, no dietary fibre, 6 g fat, 69 mg sodium.

FRENCH TOAST

PREPARATION TIME: 5 MINUTES.   COOKING TIME: 7 TO 10 MINUTES.

This is good served with fresh or stewed fruit or, of course, a dessertspoon or two of real maple syrup or runny honey.

1 egg
1 dessertspoon skim milk
¼ teaspoon cinnamon

2 slices whole-grain bread
Nonstick vegetable
*   cooking spray*

1. Beat the egg and the milk with the cinnamon. Dip the bread in the egg mixture, coating both sides.
2. Spray a frying pan with nonstick cooking spray, and heat over medium heat. Fry the bread in the pan, turning once, until golden brown on both sides.

VARIATIONS: Omit the cinnamon, and substitute ¼ teaspoon of grated lemon or orange peel.

1 serving.

Per Serving (without syrup): 247 calories, 279 mg cholesterol, 3 g dietary fibre, 10 g fat, 399 mg sodium.

YOGURT AND FRESH FRUIT

PREPARATION TIME: 2 TO 3 MINUTES.

Plain low-fat yogurt mixed with fresh fruit is one of Terri's standard foods for breakfast or for lunch. You can take it with you to work in a plastic container, if there is a refrigerator available for storing it until lunchtime.

Commercial varieties of yogurt containing fruit usually also contain large amounts of sugar. Mixing your own means your fruit is fresh, and you can control the amount of sugar. Terri never uses any sweetener besides dried fruit or an occasional bit of sweetened coconut – which actually tastes too sweet to her now.

Her favourite combinations include sultana-apple-almond, and raisin-orange-banana with a dash of coconut.

You can use tinned fruit, as long as it is unsweetened and canned in fruit juice. Tinned pineapple with coconut is very good.

You may like to experiment with spices. A dash of cinnamon, nutmeg, allspice, cardamom, clove or mace, or a combination of a couple of these, will heighten the sweetness without adding calories.

Some fruits, however, such as apples or bananas, turn brown when exposed to air, so they are best eaten right away.

Here's the basic recipe:

8 fluid ounces (225 ml) plain low-fat yogurt
1 medium-sized piece of fruit, chopped OR *4-fluid-ounce (110-ml) measure of sliced mixed fruit*

1 dessertspoon sultanas, raisins or other chopped dried fruit
1 dessertspoon chopped nuts of choice

1. Combine all the ingredients in a serving bowl, and it's ready to eat.

1 serving.

Per Serving: 296 calories, 14 mg cholesterol, 4 g dietary fibre, 8 g fat, 161 mg sodium.

SCRAMBLED EGGS AND CHEESE

PREPARATION TIME: 3 TO 5 MINUTES.   COOKING TIME: 5 MINUTES.

By using an extra egg white you can extend the amount of egg, without the cholesterol of a second yolk. By using very little fat and a low-fat cheese, you also save calories. The difference? 140 calories versus 300!

25

1 egg
1 egg white
1 ounce (28 g) low-fat hard
  cheese, grated

Nonstick vegetable
  cooking spray (optional)

1. Beat together the egg and egg white. Pour into a nonstick pan or a pan sprayed with nonstick vegetable cooking spray, and cook over medium-low heat, stirring occasionally.
2. After a minute, add the cheese. Keep cooking and stirring occasionally until done.

1 serving.

Per Serving: 175 calories, 289mg cholesterol, no dietary fibre, 10 g fat, 269 mg sodium.

Appetizers

I have a confession to make: it's been ages since my wife and I have served anything except fruit as an appetizer at our dinner parties. So, Terri and I had to start from scratch to create appetizers that we would be comfortable serving to our friends at our own dinner and cocktail parties.

For informal dinner parties, I enjoy serving a large bowl of fruit on the coffee table, with individual plates and knives for our guests to use for carving up their own apples, pears or peaches as we talk in the den before dinner.

For large parties and other occasions when you need many different appetizers, consider using a monster-size Creative Fruit Salad (see page 54) as your centrepiece. Hollow out half a watermelon, if available, or use a large punch bowl filled with various fruits, such as melon balls, sliced apples, chunks of fresh pineapple or pears or both, strawberries or raspberries, grapes and sections of a citrus fruit. Mix in a few ounces of lemon juice to preserve the colour, and then add a bottle of white wine or champagne. If you don't care to use an alcoholic beverage as a mixer, use ginger ale. The beverage serves as a marinade for the fruit. Guests can use cocktail sticks to spear the fruit. If watermelon is not available, we use a large clear glass brandy snifter to hold our assortment.

You can feature your fruit bowl along with some of the other hors d'oeuvres from this chapter at cocktail parties, but we assure you, a creation of this kind will easily compete for attention with any appetizers that might surround it!

Some of the appetizers in this section are lowered-fat modifications of standard recipes (the Stuffed Mushrooms), while others are quite unusual. Our version of Aubergine Caviar has an appropriately rich and luxurious flavour, but without any fat at all. As well as a dip, use it as a filling for hard-boiled eggs or tomato shells.

There are recipes in other sections of this book that can easily be adapted for use as appetizers. Two that seem particularly appropriate are Spinach Pizza (see pp. 171–2) and Courgette Pizza (see pp. 172–3). If you try these as appetizers, serving size can be determined by cutting the pie into quarters and then cutting each quarter into eighths; the caloric and nutritional values here would be about one-eighth of those listed under the main-course recipes.

One final word of caution. Many dips and appetizers are unavoidably high in fat, and we all know how hard it is to resist a bowl or plate of those goodies, *especially* when we are hungry! A sure way to ruin a good dinner is to encourage your guests to satisfy their appetite before they even get to the table. So try making individual servings of your appetizers, or perhaps pass them a couple of times and leave the plate in the kitchen. Remember that you can do yourself and your friends a favour by at least providing the alternative of fresh fruit.

We also cut calories when serving dips by using fresh, sliced vegetables or whole-grain crispbread for dipping, instead of potato crisps and other high-fat snacks.

AVOCADO DIP

PREPARATION TIME: 5 MINUTES.

Though avocados are high in fat, they are nutritious and can be eaten sparingly. Mixed with yogurt, the protein

28

level is boosted. Go easy on the salt if you are watching your sodium intake.

Often the avocados in the supermarkets are not yet ripe. Simply leave them on the kitchen worktop or a windowsill for a day or two until they feel slightly soft. You can speed the process by putting them in a brown paper bag.

2 medium avocados
8 fluid ounces (225 ml)
 plain low-fat yogurt

Garlic, cumin, salt and
 fresh-ground black
 pepper to taste

1. Peel and mash the avocados in a medium-sized bowl. Add the remaining ingredients and mix well with a fork or, for a very smooth consistency, use a wire whisk or blend in a blender. Serve with cut up fresh vegetables or whole-grain crispbread.

Serving size is 1 dessertspoon.

Per Serving: 33 calories, no cholesterol, 1 g dietary fibre, 3 g fat, 31 mg sodium (with ¼ teaspoon salt used in the complete recipe).

CHEESE AND OLIVE PARTY TOAST

PREPARATION TIME: 8 TO 10 MINUTES.   COOKING TIME: 2 MINUTES.

4 tablespoons black olives,
 chopped
4 tablespoons chopped
 spring onion
1 ounce (28 g) Emmenthal
 or Gruyère cheese, grated
1 dessertspoon
 mayonnaise

¼ teaspoon Indian Spice
 Blend (p. 244) or other
 curry powder
¼ teaspoon salt
¼ teaspoon black pepper
1 dessertspoon Parmesan
 cheese, grated
14 slices rye bread

1. Combine all ingredients except bread, and mix well.
2. Spread a scant teaspoon of the mixture on each slice of bread. Grill for 2 minutes, until the cheese melts.

Makes 14 rounds. 14 servings.

Per Serving: 38 calories, 3 mg cholesterol, 1 g dietary fibre, 2 g fat, 120 mg sodium.

AUBERGINE CAVIAR

PREPARATION TIME: 1 HOUR AND 15 MINUTES.   COOKING TIME:
35 TO 40 MINUTES.

Aubergines are thought to have been cultivated first in India over four thousand years ago. Though popular in Middle Eastern countries, they made their way westward slowly, being regarded with some suspicion by Europeans, who thought they might be dangerous. John Gerard wrote in his *Herball* in 1597 that aubergines had 'a mischievous quality'. We are not sure precisely what he meant by that, but he admonished his readers to 'forsake' the aubergine.

For those who don't mind making a little mischief, serve this tasty spread chilled, with whole-grain, low-salt crispbread, or wedges of pita bread.

1 large aubergine
8 spring onions, chopped
  fine
1 small pepper (red,
  green, or yellow),
  minced
2 cloves garlic, minced or
  crushed
1 dessertspoon olive oil
2 medium tomatoes,
  chopped

½ teaspoon fresh-ground
  black pepper
⅛ teaspoon cayenne
  pepper
½ teaspoon cumin
½ teaspoon salt
Dash of Tabasco (optional)
2 dessertspoons lemon
  juice

1. Preheat oven to 400°F (Gas Mark 6/200°C). Pierce the aubergine several times with a fork, and place on a foil-covered baking sheet. Bake for about 1 hour, turning occasionally.
2. When the aubergine is done, the skin will be wrinkled and soft. Take it out of the oven and let it cool. Cut it in half, scoop out the pulp, and chop it finely. Place it in a colander in the sink to drain while you prepare the other ingredients.
3. Sauté the onion, pepper and garlic in the oil over medium heat until the onion is translucent. Add all the other ingredients except the lemon juice, stirring the aubergine in last.

4. Cover and let simmer on low heat for about 30 minutes, stirring occasionally. Then remove the cover, and let simmer until liquid is reduced.
5. Let cool, then stir in the lemon juice, and refrigerate.

Serving size is 1 dessertspoon.

Per Serving: 10 calories, no cholesterol, 1 g dietary fibre, no fat, 287 mg sodium.

STUFFED MUSHROOMS

PREPARATION TIME: 20 MINUTES.   COOKING TIME: 15 MINUTES.

Here is an example of how to combine a small amount of butter, for flavouring, with other fats (in this case, olive oil) and herbs. The combination of parsley, garlic and onions is basic to many recipes and here provides for a mild, noticeably buttery stuffing. If you prefer a spicier appetizer, add to the stuffing recipe below freshly ground black pepper, your favourite herb blend to taste, or just ONE splash of Tabasco.

24 large mushrooms
(about 8 to 10 ounces
225–300 g)
1 small clove garlic,
crushed
1 small onion, finely
minced
¼ teaspoon dried parsley
2 teaspoons olive oil

2 heaped tablespoons
Whole-Wheat
Breadcrumbs (p. 219)
1 dessertspoon egg white
(save the rest of the egg
for another recipe)
small knob of butter,
melted

1. Rinse the mushrooms and remove the stems. Dice six of the stems and reserve.
2. Sauté the garlic, onion and parsley in the oil, stirring constantly until onion is translucent. Carefully drain any liquid from the pan.
3. Stir in the breadcrumbs, egg white and butter, and mix thoroughly.
4. Fill the mushrooms with this mixture. Place on a

31

foil-covered baking pan, and bake at 350°F (Gas Mark 4/180°C) for 15 minutes.

6 servings. Serving size is 4 mushrooms.

Per Serving: 48 calories, 2 mg cholesterol, 1 g dietary fibre, 3 g fat, 36 mg sodium.

CHICK PEA DIP

PREPARATION TIME: 10 MINUTES.

A low-fat alternative to traditional hummous. And, by the way, if you can find the unhulled sesame seeds, they are an excellent source of calcium. They are sometimes available in health food shops. See page 160 for instructions on how to toast seeds without added fat.

1 15-ounce (435-g) tin chick peas
1 teaspoon onion powder
2 to 3 cloves garlic, crushed
¼ teaspoon salt

4 fluid ounces (110 ml) plain low-fat yogurt
2 dessertspoons toasted sesame seeds, ground with mortar and pestle

1. Drain the chick peas and pour into a blender or food processor.
2. Add the onion powder, garlic, salt and yogurt, and blend until smooth.
3. Pour the mixture into a serving bowl, and top with the sesame seeds. Chill until serving time.

Serving size is 1 dessertspoon.

Per Serving: 28 calories, no cholesterol, 1 g dietary fibre, 1 g fat, 20 mg sodium.

SALMON MOUSSE

PREPARATION TIME: 10 MINUTES.

Serve this as an appetizer on whole-grain crispbread or use it as a sandwich spread. It is also good on whole-grain bread and grilled for a couple of minutes. This is one of our new appetizers that are slightly higher in fat, but it is so delicious that it's worth showing off on occasion. The use of Neufchatel cheese in place of cream cheese helps lower the saturated fat content, and salmon is a good source of the 'good' Omega III fatty acids that we discuss on page 134.

1 (16-ounce/450-g) tin salmon, drained and flaked
8 ounces (225 g) Neufchatel cheese
2 tablespoons lemon juice
2 dessertspoons diced red onion
1 dessertspoon fresh parsley, minced

2 scant teaspoons horseradish sauce
4 tablespoons chopped nuts (walnuts are good)
Black olive or teaspoon of nuts for garnish (optional)

1. In a blender or food processor, combine all ingredients except the nuts, and blend until smooth.
2. Stir in the nuts, then pour the mousse into a serving bowl. Chill until serving time. Garnish with a black olive in the centre, or decorate with a further teaspoon of nuts, if desired, and serve.

Serving size is 1 dessertspoon.

Per Serving: 45 calories, 11 mg cholesterol, no dietary fibre, 3 g fat, 102 mg sodium.

Soups

As a main meal or a first course, soups are always in season: refreshing cold soups for the summer, invigorating hot soups for the winter.

We like to start most of our soups with our own homemade chicken or vegetable stock, and we have included some basic stock recipes (see Basic Soup Stocks, pp. 35–8).

Another trick we like is to save the liquid from steaming or simmering vegetables for use in soups. Pour the liquid into a plastic freezer container, seal it, and freeze. Whenever you cook vegetables, simply add the leftover juices to the container. Then, when you want to use the stock for soups or for cooking grains or any other dish, run the container under warm water to loosen the sides, and pop the whole cube into a saucepan. Heat until you melt as much as you need for your recipe; if you don't need it all, put the rest of the cube back in the freezer for another time. We use most vegetable juices for this purpose, but we avoid stronger ones, such as asparagus, which tend to overpower the flavour of milder ingredients.

We realize that many people don't want to take the time to make their own stock and, at a pinch, we, too, will use instant bouillon granules or stock cubes. If you use instant, you should be aware that *the* primary ingredient in commercial preparations is *salt*. A single cube or teaspoon of granules, the measure ordinarily used to create one cup of bouillon, can contain 900 to 1500 milligrams of sodium.

Clear soups are generally lower in calories than cream soups, but we have found that substituting skim or low-fat milk in place of cream works very well.

Cornflour is a good thickener, so is a *roux* made with flour and butter or margarine. It should be cooked over low heat long enough to turn golden brown or you will have a floury flavour in your food. Arrowroot is good, but it doesn't reheat well. Cornflour should be mixed with a small amount of water or stock to make a thin paste then added to soups or sauces. Vegetable soups can be thickened by whirring a few of the vegetables in a blender or food processor until puréed and stirring the mixture back into the soup.

Making a meal out of a hearty soup or stew is a standard winter dinner for us, along with a bountiful salad and a slice of whole-grain bread. Thus, we've included a couple of chilli recipes and other warm, filling soups in this section. Also check the Beef, Lamb, Poultry, Fish and Veal sections for some wonderful casseroles.

Finally, soup appears to be an excellent aid in preventing overeating. People who frequently include soup with their meals find it easier to lose weight and maintain their losses.

BASIC SOUP STOCKS

SOUP BASE

PREPARATION TIME: 15 TO 20 MINUTES.   COOKING TIME: 2 HOURS.

This is the basic stock that we use for making soups of various kinds and for cooking rice and boiled potatoes. It is excellent for soaking and cooking beans.

Save all chicken and turkey giblets (necks, hearts, gizzards, but *not* livers). Freeze these parts immediately, first trimming skin and any fat from the necks, and hold in your freezer until you have accumulated the parts of 4 to 6 birds.

You may substitute a beef soup bone or two for the giblets, but we prefer the lighter flavour and lower cholesterol of chicken stock.

You can also freeze the soup stock in plastic containers for later use as needed.

Giblets of 4 to 6 birds
1 large bay leaf
Salt and pepper to taste
1 teaspoon each:
  rosemary, sage, thyme,
  tarragon
1 large onion, coarsely
  chopped

2 large stalks celery, cut
  into 2-inch (5-cm) pieces
  (include leaves)
2 large carrots, cut into
  2-inch (5-cm) pieces

1. Place the giblets in a deep saucepan with enough water to cover (about 3 to 4 pints/2 litres). Bring to a boil and skim as necessary. When finally clear of fat scum, add the remaining ingredients. You may also throw in any other greens or wilted vegetables you have in your refrigerator (except for asparagus, cabbage, broccoli and cauliflower, which taste too strong).
2. Bring to a boil once again, then reduce heat and simmer for at least 2 hours.
3. Separate the giblets and vegetables from the water. Blend the vegetables in a blender or food processor until smooth, and return to the stock. Save the cooked giblets for low-calorie snacks.

Makes about 4–5 pints (2¼ to 3 litres) depending on how many giblets and vegetables you add.

Per 8 fluid ounces (225 ml): 31 calories, 20 mg cholesterol, 1 g dietary fibre, 1 g fat, 82 mg sodium.

BASIC VEGETABLE STOCK

PREPARATION TIME: 10 MINUTES.   COOKING TIME: 1 HOUR.

Here's a basic recipe for a stock made from water and a variety of fresh vegetables. You can add other vegetables, such as parsnips, turnips, leeks, etc., if desired.

*3 medium carrots, cut in
    chunks*
*2 stalks celery, cut in
    chunks*
*3 medium onions, cut in
    chunks*
3 cloves garlic, minced

*small handful fresh
    parsley, minced*
1 bay leaf
6 whole peppercorns
*½ teaspoon tarragon
    and/or other dried herbs*
2½ pints (1½ litres) water

1. Combine all ingredients in a large soup pot, and bring to a boil. Reduce heat to simmer, cover, and let cook for about 1 hour.
2. You may strain the vegetables out and use the clear broth, or put the stock in a blender and purée for a thicker stock, adding more water if necessary.

Makes about 3 pints (1¾ litres).

Per 8 fluid ounces (225 ml): 24 calories, no cholesterol, 2 g dietary fibre, no fat, 23 mg sodium.

ONION STOCK

PREPARATION TIME: 15 MINUTES.   COOKING TIME: 5 MINUTES.

If you are out of vegetable or other stock, try making a quick onion broth for soups, as follows:

*1 large onion, sliced
1 dessertspoon vegetable
    oil*

2 pints (1 litre) water

1. Sauté the sliced onion in the oil over medium heat until golden brown, stirring often.
2. Add the water, bring to a boil, then reduce heat and let simmer for about 5 minutes. You may strain the onion out, depending on the type of dish you are

planning to combine with the stock. We usually prefer to leave the onion in, as it provides added fibre, vitamins and minerals.

Per 4 fluid ounces (110 ml): 15 calories, no cholesterol, no dietary fibre, 1 g fat, 1 mg sodium.

SOUPS

ASPARAGUS SOUP

PREPARATION TIME: 25 MINUTES. COOKING TIME: 10 TO 15 MINUTES.

You may substitute tinned asparagus if necessary, but, as usual, fresh is best.

1 pound (450 g) fresh asparagus
1 pint (570 ml) skim milk
1 teaspoon onion powder
½ teaspoon salt
½ teaspoon dry mustard
Fresh-ground black pepper to taste
Fresh parsley sprigs or chives

1. Wash and trim asparagus spears, and steam until just tender.
2. Chop the asparagus into 1-inch (2.5-cm) pieces, and place in a blender or food processor. Add the milk, onion powder, salt and mustard, and blend at high speed until smooth.
3. Pour the soup into a pot, and heat over medium heat. Do not boil.
4. Pour into 4 serving bowls, grind some black pepper on top, and garnish with a couple of parsley sprigs.

4 servings.

Per 12 fluid ounces (330 ml): 85 calories, 2 mg cholesterol, 2 g dietary fibre, 1 g fat, 351 mg sodium.

CHUNKY TOMATO SOUP

PREPARATION TIME: 10 TO 15 MINUTES.   COOKING TIME:
                                           45 MINUTES.

This is a spicy soup if you use the cumin. You may also prefer to reduce the amount of onion if you find it too strong.

1 dessertspoon olive oil
1 small bunch of spring
*   onions, minced*
2 cloves garlic, crushed
¼ teaspoon cumin
*   (optional)*
Black pepper to taste

3 28-ounce (800-g) tins
*   tomatoes, plus their*
*   juice*
2 medium tomatoes, diced
2 tablespoons fresh
*   parsley, minced*

1. Heat the olive oil in a large saucepan over medium heat. Add the onion and garlic, cover, and sauté, stirring occasionally. Add a little water if necessary to keep the ingredients from sticking.
2. Add the cumin and pepper, turn heat to low, and cover.
3. Drain the tinned tomatoes and reserve the juice. In a blender or food processor, whir the tinned tomatoes until smooth. Add tomatoes to the onion mixture, along with the reserved juice and the fresh tomatoes. Cover and let simmer over low heat for about 45 minutes.
4. Sprinkle with parsley and serve.

6 servings.

Per 16 fluid ounces (450 ml): 123 calories, no cholesterol, 5 g dietary fibre, 3 g fat, 646 mg sodium.

DAVID'S CHILLI

PREPARATION TIME: 35 MINUTES TOTAL.   COOKING TIME:
                                           4½ HOURS.

This is my son David's multi-bean chilli. The beans and rice combination provides protein, boosted by the judicious use of a small amount of beef.

8 ounces (225 g) haricot
  beans
4 ounces (110 g) black
  beans
2 pints (1¼ litres) water
4 to 5 cloves garlic,
  minced or crushed
2 teaspoons salt
2 dessertspoons olive oil
4 tablespoons uncooked
  brown rice

4 tablespoons lentils
8 fluid ounces (225 ml)
  water
2 medium onions,
  quartered
2 dessertspoons chilli
  powder
8 ounces (225 g) lean
  minced beef
1 10-ounce (300-g) tin
  tomato purée

1. Rinse the white and black beans. Place them in a large saucepan with the 2 pints (1¼ litres) of water. Bring to a boil, then reduce heat to simmer.
2. Add the garlic, salt and oil. Cover and simmer for about 2½ hours, stirring occasionally.
3. Add the rice and the lentils, along with the 8 fluid ounces (225 ml) of water. Bring to a boil again, then reduce the heat to simmer.
4. Add the onions and chilli powder.
5. Cover and simmer for about 2 more hours, stirring occasionally, and adding extra water if necessary to keep the beans covered.
6. Meanwhile, brown the mince. Drain off any excess fat, and stir in the tomato purée. Simmer for about 15 minutes.
7. When most of the water has cooked away from the beans, add the meat sauce, and mix well.

8 servings.

Per 8 fluid ounces (225 ml): 266 calories, 25 mg cholesterol, 8 g dietary fibre, 10 g fat, 590 mg sodium.

FRENCH ONION SOUP

PREPARATION TIME: 15 TO 20 MINUTES.   COOKING TIME: 30 MINUTES.

One bowl of onion soup for dinner in a restaurant can tip the scales a couple of pounds higher in the morning. This is due to the large amount of salt usually found in these soups; the salt makes you retain water. Here's a recipe using no- or low-salt bouillon or homemade stock that eliminates some of the sodium without eliminating the soup. (The cognac helps make up for some of that lost salt flavour.)

2 medium onions, sliced in
   rounds
⅓ ounce (10 g) butter or
   margarine
1½ pints (800 ml) beef
   stock
1 bay leaf
1 teaspoon dried basil
½ teaspoon dried thyme
½ teaspoon salt
½ teaspoon fresh-ground
   black pepper

Dash of cognac or dry
   sherry (optional)
4 slices Whole-Wheat
   French Bread
   (pp. 221–3)
4 slices Emmenthal or
   Gruyère cheese, ½
   ounce (15 g) each
2 dessertspoons Parmesan
   cheese, grated

1. Sauté the onions in the butter or margarine until they are translucent, stirring occasionally. Add a little water if necessary to keep the onions from sticking.
2. Add the bouillon, seasonings, and the cognac if desired, and bring to a low boil. Reduce heat, and let simmer for 30 minutes.
3. Meanwhile, toast the bread on a foil-covered grill until crisp. Top each slice of bread with a slice of cheese, and grill for several minutes more, until cheese is melted. (Keep your eye on it!)
4. Divide the grated Parmesan between four soup bowls. Pour in onion soup and float the bread slices on top.

4 servings.

Per 12 fluid ounces (330 ml): 232 calories, 24 mg cholesterol, 5 g dietary fibre, 11 g fat, 1382 mg sodium.

POTATO AND CHEESE SOUP

PREPARATION TIME: 10 MINUTES. COOKING TIME: 45 MINUTES.

Use Gruyère, Jarlsberg or Emmenthal cheese for this one.

16 fluid ounces (450 ml)
  stock – vegetable,
  chicken or beef
12 fluid ounces (330 ml)
  water
1 bay leaf
½ teaspoon salt
Fresh-ground black
  pepper to taste
1 medium onion, diced
2 large potatoes, diced

2 stalks celery, diced
4 ounces (110 g) fresh
  mushrooms, sliced
1 ounce (28 g) butter or
  margarine
2 dessertspoons whole-
  wheat flour
2 tablespoons fresh
  parsley, minced
4 ounces (110 g) grated
  cheese

1. Combine stock, water, bay leaf, salt, pepper, onion, potatoes, celery and mushrooms in a large pot, and bring to a boil. Reduce heat, and let simmer covered for 30 minutes, or until potatoes are tender.
2. In a small saucepan, melt the butter or margarine over medium heat, and stir in the flour. Stir constantly until golden brown, add a little of the hot soup liquid then stir the mixture into the soup.
3. Raise the heat to medium high, and stir the soup until it bubbles and thickens. Sprinkle with parsley and cheese, and serve.

8 servings.

Per 12 fluid ounces (330 ml): 164 calories, 21 mg cholesterol, 3 g dietary fibre, 7 g fat, 405 mg sodium.

PATTI'S VEGETABLE SOUP

PREPARATION TIME: 30 MINUTES. COOKING TIME: 1 HOUR.

2 dessertspoons vegetable
  oil
4 medium white onions,
  peeled, halved and
  sliced

3 leeks, trimmed, halved
  lengthwise and sliced
4 medium carrots, sliced
2 small turnips, peeled,
  quartered and sliced

4 stalks celery, sliced
5 large cloves garlic,
  minced
½ teaspoon dried thyme
¼ teaspoon dried
  tarragon
5 large potatoes, skins on,
  sliced
3¼ pints (2 litres) chicken
  stock

6 fluid ounces (180 ml)
  skim milk
¼ teaspoon nutmeg
Fresh-ground black
  pepper to taste
½ bunch watercress, well
  rinsed, shredded
2 ounces (56 g) Parmesan
  cheese, grated

1. Heat the oil in a large pan over medium-high heat.
   Add the onions, leeks, carrots, turnips, celery, garlic,
   thyme and tarragon, tossing to coat. Cover and cook
   vegetables, stirring occasionally, until they begin to
   soften, about 10 minutes.
2. Stir in the potatoes and the stock. Cover and bring to
   a boil, then simmer, partially covered, for 45 minutes,
   stirring occasionally.
3. With a slotted spoon, transfer half the vegetables to a
   food processor or blender, and purée until smooth.
   Return the purée to the pan. If the soup seems thin,
   purée a few more vegetables.
4. Add the milk, the nutmeg and a generous grinding
   of black pepper. Return the soup to a low boil. If soup
   seems too thick, add a little more stock.
5. Scatter the watercress on the surface of the soup,
   cover, and simmer about 5 minutes. Stir, and serve,
   with 1 rounded teaspoon of grated Parmesan
   sprinkled on top of each serving.

12 servings.

Per 12 fluid ounces (330 ml): 146 calories, 4 mg cholesterol, 3 g dietary fibre, 4 g fat, 621 mg sodium.

BARLEY CHICKEN SOUP

PREPARATION TIME: 10 TO 15 MINUTES.   COOKING TIME:
                                                2½ HOURS.

A complete meal in one pot. Omit the cayenne pepper

and chilli powder if you don't like spicy food. You can also decrease or omit the salt if you are trying to cut down on your sodium intake.

4 chicken breasts (or 8 thighs or drumsticks), skinned
4 ounces (110 g) pearl barley
1½ pints (850 ml) water
3 large carrots, cut in ¼-inch (½-cm) slices

1 large stalk celery, sliced
1 medium onion, diced
1 teaspoon salt
½ teaspoon thyme
¼ teaspoon cayenne pepper (optional)
pinch chilli powder (optional)

1. Combine all ingredients in a large pan. Bring to a boil, then reduce heat and simmer for 2½ hours.

4 servings.

Per 16 fluid ounces (450 ml): 205 calories, 73 mg cholesterol, 4 g dietary fibre, 4 g fat, 656 mg sodium.

COLD TOMATO SOUP (JULIAN'S)

PREPARATION TIME: 10 MINUTES.   COOKING TIME: 45 MINUTES.

This delicious soup is the first course of a full meal prepared by the chef at Julian's, in Nashville, that contains fewer than 600 calories for the whole meal. The main course is the Grilled Duck Breast (pp. 128–9), followed by the Crêpe with Fresh Strawberries (pp. 270–1) for dessert.

¼ ounce (7 g) unsalted butter
4 small to medium carrots, diced
2 onions, diced
1 clove garlic, minced
3 pounds (1 kg 350 g) fresh tomatoes
1½ pints (850 ml) chicken stock

1 dessertspoon chopped fresh basil
1 tablespoon chopped fresh parsley
½ teaspoon black peppercorns
Pinch of thyme

1. Melt the butter in a large pot, add the carrots, onions

44

and garlic, and cook over low heat for 2 minutes. Add all the remaining ingredients, and bring to a boil. Simmer for 45 minutes.
2. Put the soup in a blender and purée. Cool, then chill in the refrigerator. Garnish with a leaf of fresh basil, if available.

8 servings.

Per 8 fluid ounces (225 ml): 91 calories, 2 mg cholesterol, 6 g dietary fibre, 2 g fat, 60 mg sodium.

CUCUMBER SOUP

PREPARATION TIME: 10 TO 15 MINUTES.   REFRIGERATION TIME: 4 HOURS.

You may garnish this soup with a dessertspoon per serving of either chopped hard-boiled egg, finely chopped spring onion, chives, croutons (preferably whole-grain), or thin slices of avocado.

2 cucumbers
1¼ pints (700 ml) chicken
  stock
1¼ pints (700 ml) plain
  low-fat yogurt
2 tablespoons white wine
  vinegar
1 garlic clove
1½ teaspoons salt
½ teaspoon white pepper
  (or black)

1. Wash but do not peel the cucumbers. Cut them into 1-inch (2.5-cm) chunks, and purée along with the remaining ingredients in a blender or food processor.
2. Refrigerate at least 4 hours.

8 servings.

Per 8 fluid ounces (225 ml): 86 calories, 6 mg cholesterol, 2 g dietary fibre, 2 g fat, 888 mg sodium.

GAZPACHO

PREPARATION TIME: 10 MINUTES.   REFRIGERATION TIME:
                                                                24 HOURS.

Serve this chilled soup in bowls with one of the following garnishes: chopped hard-boiled egg, finely chopped spring onions, chives, croutons or avocado (1 dessertspoon per serving; the avocado will add more fat and calories than the other choices).

1 large tomato
½ small onion
½ medium cucumber
½ medium green pepper
1 celery stalk
2 teaspoons fresh parsley, finely chopped
2 cloves garlic, minced or crushed
16 fluid ounces (450 ml) tomato juice
2 tablespoons red wine vinegar

4 fluid ounces (110 ml) white wine
1½ tablespoons basil
1 dessertspoon lemon juice
1 teaspoon salt
½ teaspoon white pepper
1 teaspoon Worcestershire sauce
Dash of Tabasco sauce

1. Finely chop all vegetables. (A food processor is ideal for this.) Combine all remaining ingredients and refrigerate for 24 hours.

6 servings.

Per 6 fluid ounces (180 ml) (without garnishes): 42 calories, no cholesterol, 2 g dietary fibre, no fat, 658 mg sodium.

MINESTRONE SOUP

PREPARATION TIME: 25 MINUTES.   COOKING TIME: 2 HOURS.

You may use 2 teaspoons or more of Traditional Italian Herb Blend (p. 245) in place of the garlic, basil, salt and pepper in this recipe. Another handy feature is that you don't have to soak the beans overnight before cooking as there is plenty of cooking time in the recipe itself. Try it with our Italian Whole-Wheat Bread (pp. 219–21).

1¼ pints (700 ml) chicken stock
1¼ pints (700 ml) water
4 ounces (110 g) uncooked haricot beans
1 bay leaf
2 medium carrots, sliced
1 medium potato, diced
½ small head of cabbage, shredded
1 16-ounce (450-g) tin unsalted tomatoes
1 medium onion, diced
1 stalk celery, sliced
1 dessertspoon olive oil
1 medium courgette, cut into chunks
2 cloves garlic, minced or crushed
½ teaspoon dried basil leaves
¼ teaspoon salt
¼ teaspoon fresh-ground black pepper
2 tablespoons fresh parsley, minced
2 ounces (56 g) whole-wheat macaroni, uncooked

1. In a large soup pot, combine the stock, water, beans and bay leaf. Bring to a boil, then reduce heat and let simmer for 1 hour.
2. Add the carrots, potato, cabbage and tomatoes, and let cook another 30 minutes.
3. Meanwhile, sauté the onions and celery in the oil over medium heat, until onions are translucent. Stir in the courgette, garlic and the other seasonings, including the parsley. Cover, and let sauté/steam until tender. Add this mixture to the beans, and let simmer together for 15 to 20 minutes.
4. Add the macaroni, and cook until tender, about 10 minutes, adding more water if necessary.

8 servings.

Per 12 fluid ounces (330 ml): 107 calories, no cholesterol, 5 g dietary fibre, 3 g fat, 464 mg sodium.

SPLIT-PEA SOUP WITH VEGETABLES

PREPARATION TIME: 15 MINUTES.   COOKING TIME: 2 TO 2½ HOURS.

Here is a basic recipe for meatless split-pea soup. Instead

of the usual ham hock or pork (and fat) that is customarily added to split-pea soup, we recommend adding to this recipe a couple of whole cloves and/or about ¼ teaspoon of sage, and/or ¼ teaspoon of rosemary. We think these additional seasonings complement the taste of the peas best, though of course you can use any other herbs that you like.

This is delicious served with Breadsticks (p. 231).

*1 pound (450 g) dried split
  peas
Water or vegetable stock
6 stalks celery, sliced into
  ½-inch (1-cm) pieces
8 small to medium carrots,
  thinly sliced*

*3 medium red potatoes,
  cut into eighths
1½ teaspoons salt
⅛ teaspoon black pepper*

1. Rinse the peas and combine with 4 pints (2¼ litres) of water or stock. Bring to a boil, then reduce the heat and let simmer for 1 hour, stirring every 15 minutes.
2. Add another 16 fluid ounces (450 ml) of water, the celery, carrots, potatoes, salt, pepper and other seasonings if desired. Return to a boil, then reduce heat again, and simmer another hour, stirring every 15 minutes. The soup is done when the peas are creamy, the vegetables are soft but hold their shape, and the soup is thick but not stiff. If necessary, add more water and simmer an additional 20 minutes.

6 servings as a main course.

Per 16 fluid ounces (450 ml): 322 calories, no cholesterol, 13 g dietary fibre, 1 g fat, 779 mg sodium.

VICHYSSOISE

PREPARATION TIME: 30 MINUTES.   COOKING TIME: 30 MINUTES.

Again, yogurt and low-fat milk come to the rescue. Vichyssoise is a traditional French delicacy, heavy on the cream. Here's our low-fat version to be served hot or cold.

2 medium potatoes
1 pound (450 g) leeks
1 ounce (28 g) butter or
  margarine
1 pint (450 ml) chicken or
  vegetable stock
1¼ pints (700 ml) low-fat
  milk

8 fluid ounces (225 ml)
  plain low-fat yogurt
Fresh-ground black
  pepper to taste
2 tablespoons chives

1. Scrub the potatoes and dice them finely. Wash and trim the leeks and dice them finely.
2. Melt the butter in a large saucepan over medium heat. Add the potatoes and leeks, and turn the heat to low. Cover and let sauté/steam for about 10 minutes, stirring often. You may wish to add a little bit of the stock to keep the vegetables from sticking.
3. Pour in the stock, and bring to a boil. Add the milk, and reduce the heat to medium low. When milk is heated through, cover and reduce the heat to low. Let simmer for about 30 minutes, then set aside to cool for another 30 minutes.
4. Pour the soup into a blender or food processor, and add the yogurt and pepper. Blend until smooth. Chill for several hours in the refrigerator, or serve hot, sprinkled with a teaspoon of chopped chives per serving.

6 servings.

Per 14 fluid ounces (350 ml): 213 calories, 24 mg cholesterol, 3 g dietary fibre, 8 g fat, 457 mg sodium.

WINTER BEAN SOUP

PREPARATION TIME: 15 MINUTES.   COOKING TIME: 2 HOURS.

Another hearty soup to warm you up in chilly weather.

1 pound (450 g) haricot
  beans
2½ pints (1 litre 330ml)
  water
2 lean soup bones

2 small leeks, chopped OR
  ½ bunch spring onions
1 large clove garlic,
  crushed
½ green pepper, diced

49

2 stalks celery, diced
12 small or 8 medium
carrots, sliced
4 ounces (110 g)
mushrooms, sliced

1 teaspoon chilli powder
1 teaspoon salt
½ teaspoon black pepper
¼ teaspoon cumin
1 bay leaf

1. Soak the beans overnight in the water.
2. The next day, add all the other ingredients, and bring to a boil. Reduce heat to simmer, cover, and let cook for 2 hours or until the beans are tender.

6 servings.

Per 10 fluid ounces (275 ml): 182 calories, no cholesterol, 14 g dietary fibre, 1 g fat, 412 mg sodium.

SPINACH EGG-DROP SOUP

PREPARATION TIME: 10 MINUTES.   COOKING TIME: 10 MINUTES.

2½ pints (1 litre) chicken
stock
10 ounces (300 g) frozen
spinach
1 dessertspoon sesame
seeds, ground with
mortar and pestle
1 tablespoon chives

2 eggs, lightly beaten
1 teaspoon Traditional
Italian Herb Blend
(p. 245)
Dash ginger
¼ teaspoon salt
¼ teaspoon fresh-ground
black pepper

1. Bring the stock to a boil in a large pan. Add the spinach and bring back to a boil.
2. Reduce heat and let simmer until spinach is cooked.
3. Stir in the sesame seeds and chives, and bring to a boil again. Remove the pot from the heat, and slowly pour in the beaten eggs, stirring slightly. Add the seasonings, and serve.

8 servings.

Per 8 fluid ounces (225 ml): 66 calories, 69 mg cholesterol, 1 g dietary fibre, 3 g fat, 697 mg sodium.

Salads

In America, salads are traditionally eaten before the meal, while in Europe they are served after the main courses and before the dessert to clear the palate and aid the digestion.

Salads as full meals, or on the side as appetizers, can be among the most attractive dishes on your table. We enjoy seeing the contrasting colours of the various vegetables, grains, legumes, cheeses or meats we toss into a salad, sprinkled with an array of herbs and glistening with our favourite dressing.

Our recipes vary from the everyday side salad to the more exotic Middle Eastern tabbouli, which uses bulgur wheat as its base. We include a couple of Greek-style salads, one using lettuce and one with black-eyed peas. There are more; some originate from other countries, and some from our imaginations. For Europeans some of the salads containing fruit will serve as delicious healthy desserts.

Nutritionists recommend that approximately half the vegetables you eat each day should be raw. Eating vegetables uncooked preserves both bulk and nutrient content. For people using the Rotation Diet to lose weight, we do, of course, recommend unlimited *free vegetables* with every meal and as snacks. We hope the suggestions

51

we give will prompt you to increase your consumption of vegetables, both cooked and raw, and to create some of your own salads to make it interesting.

ARTICHOKE-SPINACH SALAD

PREPARATION TIME: 12 TO 15 MINUTES.

12 ounces (350 g) fresh
  spinach
4 ounces (110 g) radishes
1 14-ounce (400-g) tin
  artichokes, drained

½ medium red onion,
  sliced

1. Wash carefully and trim the spinach, and tear the leaves into bite-sized pieces. Wash, trim, and slice the radishes.
2. Toss all ingredients in a salad bowl, and serve with your favourite dressing.

4 servings.

Per Serving: 124 calories, no cholesterol, 7 g dietary fibre, 8 g fat, 599 mg sodium.

APPLE-CARROT SALAD

PREPARATION TIME: 10 MINUTES.

A delicious variation on the usual carrot-raisin salad.

2 medium apples, diced
8–12 small to medium
  carrots, grated
1½ ounces (40 g) raisins or
  sultanas

1½ ounces (40 g) walnuts,
  chopped
4 ounces (110 g) plain low-
  fat yogurt
1 dessertspoon honey

1. Combine apples, carrots, raisins and walnuts.
2. Blend the yogurt with the honey and pour over the other ingredients, mixing thoroughly.

8 servings.

Per Serving: 87 calories, 1 mg cholesterol, 2 g dietary fibre, 3 g fat, 18 mg sodium.

CHICK PEA SALAD

PREPARATION TIME: 10 MINUTES.

REFRIGERATION TIME:
3 TO 4 HOURS.

12 ounces (350 g) cooked
chickpeas (5 ounces/
150 g) raw
1 medium onion, diced
½ medium red pepper,
diced
2 medium tomatoes, diced

1 tablespoon olive oil
½ teaspoon fresh-ground
black pepper
¼ teaspoon salt
Herb and Onion Dressing
(pp. 68–9)

1. Combine all ingredients in a large bowl, and refrigerate for several hours before serving.

8 servings.

Per Serving: 96 calories, no cholesterol, 4 g dietary fibre, 4 g fat, 77 mg sodium.

CHEF'S SALAD

PREPARATION TIME: 8 TO 10 MINUTES.

The calorie content of this salad will range between 300 and 400, depending on whether you include the egg, and how much dressing you use.

¼ head of lettuce,
shredded
1 medium tomato,
quartered
1 slice (ring) of green
pepper
small wedge of cabbage,
shredded
1–2 carrots, coarsely
grated

1 ounce (28 g) Emmenthal
OR Gruyère cheese, cut
in narrow strips
1 ounce (28 g) white meat
of turkey OR chicken, cut
in strips
1 egg, quartered
(optional)
Choice of free vegetables
(see p. 295)

53

Herb Salt (pp. 244–5) Your favourite no- or low-
Fresh-ground black cal dressing
  pepper
Several large leaves of
  lettuce

1. Arrange your vegetables attractively on the large
   lettuce leaves and sprinkle with seasonings to taste.
   Use 1 to 2 tablespoons of dressing.

1 serving.

Per Serving (with egg): 338 calories, 324 mg cholesterol,
10 g dietary fibre, 16 g fat, 748 mg sodium.

CREATIVE FRUIT SALAD

PREPARATION TIME: 5 MINUTES.

This is called *Creative Fruit Salad* because you can
create a different salad every time you make it, using
whatever fruits, spices or nuts you have on hand. Cut the
fruit into chunks, and sprinkle with lemon juice to keep
the fruit looking fresh and to add a bit of tang. Then, for
every portion of fresh fruit, add 1 dessertspoon of any one
of the following:

Grated coconut Raisins, sultanas OR
Chopped unsalted nuts of chopped dates
  any kind

Then add a sprinkle of any of the following spices:

Cinnamon Ginger
Nutmeg Anise
Allspice Cardamom

A main-course serving is a 16-fluid-ounce (450-ml)
measure of any combination of fresh fruit, plus the dessertspoon of nuts or raisins. The spices, of course, add few
or no calories.

Per Serving: 205 calories, no cholesterol, 7 g dietary fibre,
3 g fat, 8 mg sodium.

CUCUMBER-RADISH SALAD

PREPARATION TIME: 12 MINUTES.

½ *large cucumber*
12 *radishes*
¼ *large red onion, thinly*
  sliced
4 *ounces (110 g) hard*
  cheese, grated
small handful fresh
  parsley, minced
1 *dessertspoon red wine*
  vinegar

1 *dessertspoon Dijon* OR
  spicy brown mustard
4 *tablespoons (60 ml) plain*
  low-fat yogurt
1 *dessertspoon*
  mayonnaise
1½ *teaspoons dried basil*
⅛ *teaspoon celery seed*

1. Scrub cucumber clean, removing waxy substance if necessary; it is preferable not to peel it. Slice the cucumber as thinly as possible. Clean, trim and slice the radishes as thinly as possible.
2. Combine the cucumbers, radishes and onions in a bowl, along with the cheese.
3. Add the remaining ingredients, tossing lightly. Serve chilled.

4 servings.

Per Serving: 157 calories, 31 mg cholesterol, 1 g dietary fibre, 11 g fat, 339 mg sodium.

SIDE SALAD

PREPARATION TIME: 10 MINUTES.

Since salads are usually a mainstay for most dieters, and are certainly used frequently in the Rotation Diet, people often ask what constitutes a 'side salad'. Actually, you can eat unlimited quantities of almost any vegetable, so you can feel free to create your own side salad, but generally we tell people this is what you would normally get along with a meal in a typical restaurant – asking for your dressing to be served separately, of course.

The basic side salad is as follows:

½ *carrot, thinly sliced*
1 *stalk celery, thinly sliced,* OR ¼ *green pepper, diced*
small wedge shredded red cabbage OR 4 *sliced mushrooms*

2 *thin slices sweet red onion*
Lettuce or greens (free vegetables, see p. 295)

1. Arrange all ingredients in a bowl or on a plate. Add your favourite no- or low-cal dressing (see pp. 72–3, 67–8) and flavour with Herb Salt (pp. 244–5) or other seasonings if you like.

1 *serving. Serving size is about a 12-fluid-ounce (330-ml) measure.*

Per Serving (without dressing): 44 calories, no cholesterol, 4 g dietary fibre, no fat, 46 mg sodium.

GREEK BLACK-EYED PEA SALAD

PREPARATION TIME: 6 MINUTES.

REFRIGERATION TIME: 6 TO 8 HOURS.

8 *ounces (225 g) black-eyed peas, cooked*
1 *pepper, diced (red or yellow is attractive)*
½ *bunch spring onions, diced*
1 *small clove garlic, crushed*

½ *teaspoon dried oregano*
2 *tablespoons olive oil*
3 *tablespoons red wine vinegar*
1 *teaspoon lemon juice*
2 *tablespoons fresh parsley, minced*
¼ *teaspoon salt*

1. Combine all ingredients in a large bowl. Marinate 6 to 8 hours in the refrigerator, stirring occasionally.

8 *servings.*

Per Serving: 123 calories, no cholesterol, 4 g dietary fibre, 5 g fat, 75 mg sodium.

FENNEL SALAD WITH PECANS OR WALNUT HALVES

PREPARATION TIME: 10 MINUTES.

If you like licorice, you will love fennel. Raw fennel smells and tastes strongly of licorice when served alone. However, diced and added to a salad, it blends delectably, adding a touch of sweetness to a vinaigrette dressing (along with a healthy dose of potassium and vitamin A).

Look for firm fennel bulbs in the produce section of your supermarket. Test the bulbs with your thumb for firmness.

½ head iceberg OR *cos lettuce*
½ head radicchio, escarole OR *other lettuce*
½ medium fennel bulb
1 ounce (28 g) pecan or walnut pieces
2 tablespoons red wine vinegar
1½ tablespoons vegetable oil
1 dessertspoon water
1 teaspoon mustard seed, ground with mortar and pestle
¼ teaspoon dried tarragon
¼ teaspoon salt
¼ teaspoon fresh-ground black pepper

1. Wash and dry the lettuce. Tear the leaves into bite-size pieces, and place in a large salad bowl.
2. Trim the tough outer leaves of the fennel. Wash and core the bulb. Dice, and add to the bowl. Add the nuts.
3. Combine the remaining ingredients in a jar. Cover and shake, then pour into the salad. Toss and serve.

4 servings.

Per Serving: 95 calories, no cholesterol, 1 g dietary fibre, 9 g fat, 141 mg sodium.

ORIENTAL SPINACH-SESAME SALAD

PREPARATION TIME: 12 MINUTES.

This salad is good served chilled or at room temperature. It is at its best served the same day it is made. See pages 159–60 for instructions on how to toast seeds.

2 fluid ounces (55 ml) water
1½ pounds (675 g) fresh spinach, washed thoroughly and trimmed
1 dessertspoon honey

2 dessertspoons tamari OR *soy sauce*
2 tablespoons toasted sesame seeds, ground with mortar and pestle

1. Bring the water to a boil in a saucepan, toss in the spinach, cover, and cook about 30 *seconds*, until wilted.
2. Drain the spinach (reserve the liquid for other recipes, such as a soup, if you like) and rinse it in a colander in cold water. Drain well, and transfer to a serving bowl.
3. In a small bowl, combine the honey, tamari sauce and sesame seeds. Pour this dressing over the spinach, toss, and serve.

4 servings.

Per Serving: 97 calories, no cholesterol, 7 g dietary fibre, 4 g fat, 649 mg sodium.

VEGETABLE SLAW

PREPARATION TIME: 10 MINUTES.   REFRIGERATION TIME: ½ HOUR.

The onion and garlic can be pulverized in a food processor with the lemon juice, mayonnaise, yogurt and salt, if desired. A food processor is wonderful for grating vegetables!

½ small onion, grated
1 clove garlic, grated
Juice of 1 lemon (1½ to 2
  tablespoons)
3 tablespoons mayonnaise
4 ounces (110 g) plain low-
  fat yogurt

½ teaspoon salt
Fresh-ground black
  pepper to taste
1 small head cabbage,
  grated
1 large carrot, grated
1 medium pepper, grated

1. Combine all ingredients and mix well. Refrigerate for at least ½ hour. Mix well before serving.

6 servings.

Per Serving: 119 calories, 7 mg cholesterol, 3 g dietary fibre, 8 g fat, 270 mg sodium.

POTATO-VEGETABLE SALAD

PREPARATION TIME: 20 TO 25 MINUTES.   REFRIGERATION TIME:
                                                  1 HOUR.

Simply the best potato salad we have ever tasted! Thanks to my wife Enid for coming up with this low-calorie version of an all-time favourite.

6 medium potatoes, boiled
  and cubed
3 hard-boiled eggs, diced
½ small onion, grated
2 medium carrots, diced
1 medium pepper, diced
2 stalks celery, sliced thin
8 ounces (225 g) plain low-
  fat yogurt

3–4 tablespoons (50–60 ml)
  mayonnaise
¼ teaspoon garlic powder
Fresh-ground black
  pepper to taste
1 teaspoon tarragon
1 dessertspoon Dijon
  mustard
1 teaspoon salt

1. Combine all ingredients, chill for at least an hour, and serve.

12 servings.

Per Serving: 124 calories, 35 mg cholesterol, 2 g dietary fibre, 5 g fat, 258 mg sodium.

GREEK SALAD

PREPARATION TIME: 8 MINUTES.

*4 ounces (110 g) feta
  cheese*
20 cherry tomatoes OR *2
  medium tomatoes, sliced*
*1 large pepper, thinly
  sliced*
*1 medium onion, thinly
  sliced*

*1 clove garlic, minced or
  crushed*
1 teaspoon dried oregano
Fennel Dressing (p. 68)
*16 Greek olives (or use
  regular black olives)*
16 large lettuce leaves

1. One hour before preparation time, cut the feta cheese into chunks and soak in cold water for 1 hour to reduce salt content.
2. Cut the cherry tomatoes in half, or slice the regular tomatoes into wedges. Combine the tomato, pepper, onion, garlic and oregano. Drain the feta cheese, pat dry with paper towels, and toss with the vegetables.
3. Divide into 8 servings, place on lettuce leaves, and garnish with 2 olives and 1 dessertspoon of Fennel Dressing (p. 68) per serving.

8 servings.

Per Serving: 64 calories, 12 mg cholesterol, 1 g dietary fibre, 5 g fat, 231 mg sodium.

MARINATED BROCCOLI AND CAULIFLOWER

PREPARATION TIME: 15 TO 20 MINUTES.   REFRIGERATION TIME:
                                        2 HOURS.

2 dessertspoons olive oil
*2 dessertspoons red wine
  vinegar*
*8 fluid ounces (225 ml)
  water*
2 cloves garlic, crushed
*1/2 teaspoon fresh-ground
  black pepper*
1 bay leaf
1 teaspoon dried basil

1/4 teaspoon salt
*1/2 medium cauliflower,
  cut into florets*
*3 medium stalks broccoli,
  cut into florets*
*1 medium red onion,
  chopped*
1/2 teaspoon oregano
Fresh parsley
8 cherry tomatoes

1. Combine all the ingredients except the oregano, parsley and tomatoes in a large saucepan. Bring to a slight boil, reduce heat and simmer, covered, until broccoli and cauliflower are cooked *al dente* – just barely tender; about 5 to 7 minutes.
2. Chill 2 hours, then garnish each serving with a sprinkle of oregano, parsley sprigs and 2 tomatoes.

4 servings.

Per Serving: 98 calories, no cholesterol, 3 g dietary fibre, 7 g fat, 146 mg sodium.

JAPANESE-STYLE CRAB SALAD

PREPARATION TIME: 12 MINUTES.

The 'light soy sauce' and rice-wine vinegar can be found in some Oriental shops. They have a unique, delicate flavour, but if you wish to substitute, you may: use tamari or regular or low-sodium soy sauce for the soy sauce, and white wine vinegar for the rice-wine vinegar.

2 medium cucumbers, unpeeled, sliced very thin
6 ounces (175 g) crab meat
1 teaspoon peanut oil
2 tablespoons light soy sauce or tamari
2 dessertspoons rice-wine vinegar
1 dessertspoon toasted sesame seeds, ground with mortar and pestle

1. Drain the sliced cucumbers well; also drain the crab.
2. Heat a small pan over medium-low heat, and brush with the oil. Add the sesame seeds and toast, stirring constantly, until lightly browned.
3. Lightly toss all ingredients together in a bowl and serve.

6 servings.

Per Serving: 58 calories, 28 mg cholesterol, 1 g dietary fibre, 3 g fat, 800 mg sodium.

RED BEAN AND PASTA SALAD

PREPARATION TIME: 10 MINUTES.   COOKING TIME: 1 HOUR.

All you have to do is look at the restaurant salad bars to know that pasta salads are 'in'. The problem with most pasta salads, when it comes to weight control, is not the pasta but the dressings that are used. If you use our Italian Dressing or the oil and vinegar dressing in the amount we suggest, you will be adding very few fat calories to this salad. If you find that the flavour is too mild, use additional seasoning (such as Herb Salt or a commercial no- or low-salt seasoning) at the table, or add another splash of vinegar.

8 ounces (225 g) dried red beans
8 ounces (225 g) pasta
1 10-ounce (300-g) pack frozen peas, defrosted in time for mixing
4 tablespoons Italian Dressing (p. 73) OR *Basic Lo-Cal Salad Dressing (pp. 67–8)*
1 tablespoon lemon juice
1 teaspoon Traditional Italian Herb Blend (p. 245)
Dash of salt
Fresh-ground black pepper to taste
Fresh parsely for garnish

1. Soak beans overnight, cook for about 1 hour or until just tender, and drain.
2. Cook pasta, drain, and cool in cold water.
3. Mix beans, pasta and peas with dressing in large bowl, and add lemon juice, Herb Blend, salt and pepper.
4. Serve garnished with parsley.

12 servings. Serving size is a 4-fluid-ounce (110-ml) measure.

Per Serving: 153 calories, no cholesterol, 7 g dietary fibre, 1 g fat, 103 mg sodium.

TABBOULI

PREPARATION TIME: 10 MINUTES.

There are almost as many versions of this tradional Middle Eastern recipe as there are cooks. Some people like to add tomato, fresh mint leaves or other ingredients. This is how Terri usually makes it.

The salad:

12 ounces (350 g) bulgur wheat
Water
6 carrots, grated OR finely chopped

¾ cucumber, grated or finely chopped
small bunch fresh parsley, minced

The dressing:

4 tablespoons (60 ml) safflower oil
4 tablespoons (60 ml) red wine vinegar
4 tablespoons (60 ml) tamari OR soy sauce

1½ tablespoons lemon juice
3 to 4 garlic cloves, crushed

1. Soak the bulgur wheat in a bowl in enough water to cover for 3 to 4 hours. The wheat will soak up the water and become puffy and chewable.
2. In the meantime, combine all dressing ingredients and set aside. Chop the vegetables as directed.
3. When the bulgur is ready, add the vegetables, mixing well, then add the dressing. Toss and serve.

6 servings as a main course. Serving size is a 10-fluid-ounce (275-ml) measure.

Per Serving: 301 calories, no cholesterol, 6 g dietary fibre, 10 g fat, 696 mg sodium.

VEGETABLE-CHEESE SALAD WITH HERB DRESSING

PREPARATION TIME: 15 TO 20 MINUTES.   REFRIGERATION TIME: ½ HOUR.

Combine two or more of your favourite cheeses: Cheddar, Emmenthal, Gruyère, mozzarella, Gouda – whatever you prefer. Swiss, part-skim mozzarella and other mild white cheeses are lowest in fat. Try this with Patti's Vegetable Soup (pp. 42–3).

12 ounces (350 g) cheese, cut in julienne strips
1 medium cucumber, diced
1 medium tomato, diced
1 medium pepper, diced
½ small onion OR *1 shallot, minced*
⅓ cup fresh parsley, chopped
Juice of one medium lime
Juice of one medium lemon

2 dessertspoons mayonnaise
4 ounces (110 g) plain low-fat yogurt
1 teaspoon Dijon mustard
½ teaspoon horseradish
½ teaspoon dillweed
½ teaspoon tarragon
½ teaspoon marjoram
½ teaspoon basil
1 teaspoon paprika

1. Combine cheese, vegetables and parsley in a large bowl.
2. In another bowl, blend together the remaining ingredients to make the dressing.
3. Pour the dressing over the cheese and vegetables, chill for about ½ hour, and serve.

8 servings as a main course. Serving size is an 8-fluid-ounce (225-ml) measure.

Per Serving: 213 calories, 43 mg cholesterol, 1 g dietary fibre, 16 g fat, 246 mg sodium.

Dressings

A good dressing is a blessing. Here's why.

As we said in our introduction to salads, most nutritionists agree that a good percentage of our vegetables, **perhaps even 50** per cent, should be eaten raw. Although many vegetables taste very good raw and without adornment, most of us prefer salad vegetables with some kind of dressing. Plain lemon juice or plain vinegar can take you only so far!

So, we place a major emphasis in this cookbook on salad dressings. Ours are generally relatively low in fat, but not all. Being fans of blue cheese dressing, we struck a compromise in order to include one here. We have experimented with the use of yogurt, together with higher calorie ingredients such as mayonnaise, looking for blends that considerably reduce the fat calories below those contained in mayonnaise alone.

We feel that olive oil is the best oil for salads. Fortunately, olive oil may be pretty good for you in reasonable amounts. Olive oil, as well as peanut oil, is primarily monounsaturated, and oils of this kind may have a cholesterol-reducing effect. We blend olive oil with vinegars of various kinds and water, and add herbs and spices, of course. For the most part, we aim for a low-calorie dressing which averages around 35 calories or so per dessertspoonful.

Every so often we are able to obtain extra-virgin olive oil, which is quite green in colour and more than delicious in salads. But normally we use any brand of oil available in supermarkets.

We use wine vinegar most often in our salads, but if you can find some of the fruit vinegars, especially the strawberry and raspberry flavours, give them a try. They are not as popular as they were a few years ago, but some salads, such as a spinach salad, are especially good with a fruit vinegar, as are the more delicate varieties of lettuce.

You can make your own herb vinegars at home by heating vinegar and bottling it with a wide assortment of herbs. However, our No-Cal Salad Dressing (pp. 72–3) illustrates an easy herb vinegar that requires no heating, bottling or straining.

MUSTARD SEED DRESSING

PREPARATION TIME: 5 MINUTES.

In ancient times, people apparently ate mustard seeds whole, especially as a condiment with meats, with no grinding, combining, cooking or diluting whatsoever. We sometimes add whole mustard seeds to this dressing; they provide a pleasant burst of flavour that is not as strong as you might think. However, for the less adventurous, we suggest grinding them first, which distributes the flavour throughout the dressing.

2 fluid ounces (55 ml) olive oil
2 fluid ounces (55 ml) red wine vinegar
2 fluid ounces (55 ml) water
2 large cloves garlic, crushed
1 teaspoon whole mustard seeds

1 teaspoon thyme
½ teaspoon oregano
½ teaspoon basil
¼ teaspoon dillweed
Salt and fresh-ground black pepper to taste
Dash tamari OR soy sauce

1. Grind the mustard seeds with mortar and pestle if you desire, and then blend all ingredients together. Store in the refrigerator.

Makes about 6 fluid ounces (180 ml). Serving size is 1 dessertspoon.

Per Serving: 42 calories, no cholesterol, no dietary fibre, 5 g fat, 48 mg sodium.

BASIC LO-CAL SALAD DRESSING

PREPARATION TIME: 5 MINUTES.

To create a basic low-calorie dressing, one with about 35 calories per dessertspoon, mix equal parts olive oil, vinegar and water. Then, you can begin to get creative! You can make an Italian-style dressing by crushing a small amount of garlic and onion and adding the juice – or by using onion and garlic powder – plus Italian herbs (see our Traditional Italian Herb Blend, p. 245).

If you want to get a feel for the individuality of your herbs, you might try using only one at a time, such as tarragon (as we do here) or basil or oregano. We add a modest amount of salt, as in the recipe below, to help bring out the flavours of the other ingredients, as well as freshly ground black pepper. A tangier dressing is obtained by adding a teaspoon of Dijon mustard, and it gets tangier still with a teaspoon of dry mustard! A dash of cayenne pepper also seems to have a stimulating effect on the other flavourings in the dressing, and we almost always finish our blend with a dash of cayenne or Tabasco.

2 fluid ounces (55 ml) fine olive oil
2 fluid ounces (55 ml) water
2 fluid ounces (55 ml) wine or fruit vinegar
1 clove garlic, crushed
½ teaspoon salt
1 teaspoon dried tarragon

1. Blend by shaking in a jar and let stand for several hours before using. Shake before using. This will

keep for several weeks in the refrigerator, but it won't last nearly that long, because you'll want to eat it! If the oil solidifies in the refrigerator, let the jar sit on the worktop to warm before serving or briefly run the jar under lukewarm water.

Makes about 6 fluid ounces (180 ml). Serving size is 1 dessertspoon.

Per Serving: 41 calories, no cholesterol, no dietary fibre, 5 g fat, 89 mg sodium.

FENNEL DRESSING

PREPARATION TIME: 5 MINUTES.

4 fluid ounces (110 ml) water
4 fluid ounces (110 ml) olive oil
4 fluid ounces (110 ml) red wine vinegar
2 tablespoons lemon juice
2 teaspoons fennel seed, ground with mortar and pestle
1 teaspoon mustard seed, ground with mortar and pestle
2 tablespoons fresh parsley, minced
¼ teaspoon salt
½ teaspoon fresh-ground black pepper

1. Combine all ingredients in a medium-size bowl and store in a jar in the refrigerator.

Makes about 16 fluid ounces (450 ml). Serving size is 1 dessertspoon.

Per Serving: 31 calories, no cholesterol, no dietary fibre, 3 g fat, 17 mg sodium.

HERB AND ONION DRESSING

PREPARATION TIME: 5 MINUTES.

This makes a light, tart dressing that goes equally well with a salad of your favourite greens and vegetables or over a fruit dish.

2 spring onions, diced
(bulbs and green stems)
4 tablespoons fresh
parsley
4 ounces (110 g) plain low-
fat yogurt

1 dessertspoon
mayonnaise
1 clove garlic, crushed
2 tablespoons red wine
vinegar
¼ teaspoon salt

1. Blend all ingredients in blender or food processor. Store in the refrigerator in an airtight container.

Makes about 6 fluid ounces (180 ml). Serving size is 2 dessertspoons.

Per Serving: 33 calories, 3 mg cholesterol, no dietary fibre, 2 g fat, 120 mg sodium.

RED WINE-BLUE CHEESE DRESSING

PREPARATION TIME: 7 MINUTES.   REFRIGERATION TIME: 12 HOURS.

It is not possible to make a truly low-fat, low-sodium blue cheese dressing since blue cheese is a high-fat, high-sodium cheese. This is our compromise, achieved by using yogurt rather than sour cream or greater amounts of mayonnaise. Blue cheese dressing, however, cannot be recommended for everyday use except in very small quantities.

2 ounces (55 g) crumbled
blue cheese
1 clove garlic, crushed
¼ teaspoon salt
¼ teaspoon fresh-ground
pepper
1 spring onion, minced

2 tablespoons plain low-
fat yogurt
1 teaspoon mayonnaise
1 teaspoon red wine
1 teaspoon fresh parsley,
minced

1. Combine all ingredients in a small bowl. Chill overnight and serve cold.

Makes about 4 fluid ounces (110 ml). Serving size is 2 dessertspoons.

Per Serving: 44 calories, 7 mg cholesterol, no dietary fibre, 3 g fat, 247 mg sodium.

COTTAGE CHEESE DRESSING

PREPARATION TIME: 5 MINUTES.

Another popular dressing from *The Rotation Diet*, this one is excellent with salads or on baked potatoes. For variety, add onions or substitute blue for cottage cheese.

*4 ounces (110 g) low-fat
    cottage cheese*
*4 ounces (110 g) plain low-
    fat yogurt*
*½ medium green pepper,
    chopped*
4 radishes, sliced
2 dessertspoons chives
*1 dessertspoon poppy
    seeds*
*Herb Salt (pp. 244–5) to
    taste*

1. Mix all ingredients in a blender or food processor.

Makes about 12 fluid ounces (330 ml). Serving size is 1 dessertspoon.

Per Serving: 10 calories, 1 mg cholesterol, no dietary fibre, no fat, 33 mg sodium.

HONEY-MUSTARD DRESSING

PREPARATION TIME: 5 MINUTES.

Good with a spinach or other green salads.

*2 fluid ounces (55 ml) olive
    oil*
*2 fluid ounces (55 ml) white
    wine or fruit vinegar*
1 teaspoon honey
1 teaspoon dry mustard
*¼ teaspoon ground fennel
    seed (optional)*
1 teaspoon lemon juice
*Dash of salt and freshly
    ground black pepper to
    taste*
*1 tablespoon of chopped
    fresh parsley or
    watercress*

1. Blend the dry mustard with a small amount of vinegar, and then combine all ingredients, shake and serve. Store in the refrigerator.

Makes a little over 4 fluid ounces (110 ml). Serving size is 1 dessertspoon.

Per Serving: 63 calories, no cholesterol, no dietary fibre, 7 g fat, 27 mg sodium.

DILL SEED AND WALNUT DRESSING

PREPARATION TIME: 3 TO 4 MINUTES.   REFRIGERATION TIME:
                                                          12 HOURS.

This tart-sweet dressing is delicious on a salad of thinly sliced cucumber, or try it with any combination of your favourite greens or raw vegetables.

8 ounces (225 g) plain low-
   fat yogurt
2 ounces (56 g) seedless
   raisins or sultanas
1 teaspoon dill seed
2 ounces (56 g) chopped
   walnuts

1 clove garlic, minced
¼ teaspoon salt
⅛ teaspoon fresh-ground
   black pepper

1. Combine all ingredients in a small bowl. Chill 12 hours, and serve cold.

Makes about 12 fluid ounces (330 ml). Serving size is 2 dessertspoons.

Per Serving: 39 calories, 1 mg cholesterol, no dietary fibre, 2 g fat, 58 mg sodium.

PAPRIKA DRESSING

PREPARATION TIME: 5 MINUTES.

This dressing serves double-duty as a salad dressing or as a sauce for meat. You can also try using it as a moistener for sandwiches instead of mayonnaise. It's best to use a brand of horseradish sauce with little or no added sugars, dextrose, oils or mayonnaise.

8 ounces (225 g) plain low-
   fat yogurt
½ teaspoon salt

¼ teaspoon fresh-ground
   black pepper
1 clove garlic, crushed

2 teaspoons paprika
1 teaspoon pure
   horseradish sauce

1 spring onion, diced
2 dessertspoons sour
   cream

1. Combine all ingredients and chill.

Makes about 10 fluid ounces (275 ml). Serving size is 1 dessertspoon.

Per Serving: 12 calories, 1 mg cholesterol, no dietary fibre, 1 g fat, 63 mg sodium.

VINAIGRETTE DRESSING

PREPARATION TIME: 4 MINUTES.

4 fluid ounces (110 ml)
   olive oil
2 dessertspoons wine
   vinegar
2 dessertspoons lemon
   juice
1 teaspoon dry mustard

4 fluid ounces (110 ml)
   water
Herb Salt to taste
   (pp. 244–5)
Fresh-ground black
   pepper to taste

1. Blend the mustard with a small amount of the vinegar, place all the ingredients in a jar, and shake well.

Makes about 10 fluid ounces (275 ml). Serving size is 1 dessertspoon.

VARIATIONS: Add other herbs or the juice of pressed garlic or onion.

Per Serving: 49 calories, no cholesterol, no dietary fibre, 5 g fat, 32 mg sodium (using 1 teaspoon Herb Salt).

NO-CAL SALAD DRESSING

PREPARATION TIME: 4 MINUTES.

4 fluid ounces (110 ml)
   wine vinegar
½ teaspoon Herb Salt (see
   pp. 244–5)
1 dessertspoon fresh
   parsley, chopped

1 clove garlic, crushed, OR
   ¼ teaspoon garlic
   powder

72

1. Mix all ingredients well. Store in the refrigerator.

VARIATIONS: Use other vinegars and herbs for variety. Tarragon is one of our favourite herbs for salad dressing. If available, try fruit vinegars, such as raspberry or strawberry. Add water to this recipe if you find it too vinegary for your taste.

Makes about 4 fluid ounces (110 ml). Serving size is 1 dessertspoon.

Per Serving: 2 calories, no cholesterol, no dietary fibre, no fat, 13 mg sodium.

ITALIAN DRESSING

PREPARATION TIME: 5 MINUTES.

3 fluid ounces (90 ml) water
3 fluid ounces (90 ml) olive oil
3 fluid ounces (90 ml) white vinegar
1 tablespoon lemon juice

1 clove garlic, minced
1 teaspoon basil leaves, crushed
¼ teaspoon salt
¼ teaspoon Worcestershire sauce

1. Combine all ingredients in a jar, cover and shake until the salt dissolves. Store in the refrigerator. Shake before serving.

Makes about 10 fluid ounces (275 ml). Serving size is 1 dessertspoon.

Per Serving: 41 calories, no cholesterol, no dietary fibre, 5 g fat, 12 mg sodium.

LIME DRESSING

PREPARATION TIME: 5 MINUTES.

Try this dressing with the Artichoke-Spinach Salad (p. 52).

2 fluid ounces (55 ml) olive
  oil
2 fluid ounces (55 ml)
  water
2 fluid ounces (55 ml) lime
  juice
1 teaspoon ground
  coriander

¼ teaspoon basil
⅛ teaspoon ground
  ginger
¼ teaspoon salt
¼ teaspoon fresh-ground
  black pepper

1. Whisk together all ingredients. Store in an airtight container in the refrigerator.

Makes about 6 fluid ounces (180 ml). Serving size is 1 dessertspoon.

Per Serving: 42 calories, no cholesterol, no dietary fibre, 5 g fat, 45 mg sodium.

POPPY SEED DRESSING

PREPARATION TIME: 4 TO 5 MINUTES.

This dressing is both sweet and tart. Pour it over fruit salads or a wedge of honeydew or cantaloupe melon, or use it with chicken, tuna or other seafood salads served with or on a bed of lettuce.

8 ounces (225 g) plain low-
  fat yogurt
2 teaspoons honey
Juice of 1 lime (about 2
  dessertspoons)

1 dessertspoon poppy
  seeds

1. Combine all ingredients in a bowl. Serve chilled.

Makes about 10 fluid ounces (275 ml). Serving size is 2 dessertspoons.

Per Serving: 25 calories, 1 mg cholesterol, no dietary fibre, 1 g fat, 16 mg sodium.

Beef

Beef receives bad marks from some health experts because it is high in saturated fat, and consumption of saturated fat in large amounts appears to be related to a higher incidence of heart disease and certain forms of cancer.

I have a very simple philosophy when it comes to beef: use low-fat cuts in moderation. What's moderation? For me, it's once or twice a week, although I don't feel there is strong evidence against eating low-fat cuts of beef three or four times a week, provided your cholesterol level is normal and there is no history of heart disease in your family.

If you like beef in your diet more than once or twice a week, I think you can help protect yourself against possible ill effects by including plenty of dietary fibre, which will help keep you regular and can help lower cholesterol. That is why I place such a strong emphasis on increasing the fruits, vegetables and whole grains in your diet. In addition, you should include fish at least once a week, preferably twice, since the oil contained in certain fatty fish – tuna, mackerel, sardines, trout, salmon and herring – also seems to help reduce cholesterol levels. As a general dietary principle, no matter what the source of fat in your diet, I think it's best to stay within the limits of 30 per cent total calories from fat.

Choose low-fat cuts of beef: topside, silverside, sirloin, fillet, skirt and, of course, extra-lean mince. But, watch out for that mince and, particularly, hamburgers. Some of them contain a very high proportion of fat.

Trim the fat from other cuts of beef before cooking, not after, as a general rule. If you don't find well-trimmed beef in the shop, don't be shy: ask the butcher to trim your meat specially. I recommend that you make friends with your butcher, if you haven't already, and explain what you want and why. I have never met a meat manager in a supermarket who did not want to cooperate with me and I think you will find that to be the case, too. Good supermarkets will go out of their way to keep your business!

Our Oriental recipes are examples of how to use modest amounts of beef, as well as other meats, more as a garnish or condiment accompanying vegetables and other foods than as main courses. My wife, Enid, and I began doing this several years ago, after a visit to San Francisco. We had such memorable Chinese and Indian dinners there that, before returning to Nashville, we purchased some Chinese and Indian cookbooks that appeared to have recipes for some of the dishes we had eaten. To add a pleasant variety to your meals, try using a few Oriental techniques with meat if you aren't already doing so.

BAKED SKIRT STEAK

PREPARATION TIME: 12 MINUTES.   COOKING TIME: 30 MINUTES.

*1½ pounds (675 g) skirt or
   rump steak*
*1 dessertspoon vegetable
   oil*
*8 fluid ounces (225 ml) hot
   water*
1 bay leaf
*1 large clove garlic,
   crushed*

1 teaspoon salt
2 stalks celery, minced
*⅛ teaspoon fresh-ground
   black pepper*
2 teaspoons lemon juice
1 medium carrot, diced
¼ medium pepper, diced

1. Trim away any visible fat from the steak. Sear the steak in the oil over medium to medium-high heat. Remove the pan from the heat. Place the steak in a casserole dish.
2. For extra flavouring, pour the water into the cooled pan you seared the meat in, and stir. Pour this over the meat, than add all the other ingredients.
3. Cook uncovered at 350°F (Gas Mark 4/180°C) for 30 minutes, or longer if you prefer your meat well-done.

LIGHT GRAVY (OPTIONAL): To make the *roux*, heat 1 dessertspoon vegetable oil and stir in 2 dessertspoons of whole-wheat flour. Cook gently for two to three minutes, stirring all the while. Take 8 fluid ounces (225 ml) of liquid from the meat and stir into the *roux*. Stir until thickened, and serve over the meat.

4 servings of 4½ ounces (125 g) each (cooked weight), plus gravy.

Per Serving (with gravy): 273 calories, 88 mg cholesterol, 1 g dietary fibre, 12 g fat, 630 mg sodium.

AUBERGINE BEEF CASSEROLE

PREPARATION TIME: 15 MINUTES.   COOKING TIME: 45 MINUTES.

Serve this with a side salad for a complete meal.

2 pounds (900 g) lean mince
1 medium onion, chopped
1 small green pepper, chopped
1 dessertspoon whole-wheat flour
½ teaspoon fresh-ground black pepper
½ teaspoon salt

1 teaspoon dried oregano
16 fluid ounces (450 ml) tomato sauce (try Real Italian Tomato Sauce, pp. 206–7)
1 large aubergine
4 ounces grated low-fat mozzarella or Cheddar cheese

1. Brown the mince. Remove it from the pan and pour off excess fat, if any, leaving just enough pan-juices to sauté the onion and green pepper.

2. When the onion is translucent, return the mince to the pan. Add the flour, spices and tomato sauce, and let simmer until thick.
3. Meanwhile, slice the aubergine into ½-inch (1-cm) rounds, and layer half of them in a casserole. Add half the beef mixture, then half the cheese. Repeat layers.
4. Bake covered in a slow oven, around 325°F (Gas Mark 3/170°C) for 45 minutes.

12 servings.

Per Serving: 227 calories, 61 mg cholesterol, 2 g dietary fibre, 15 g fat, 451 mg sodium.

FAJITAS

PREPARATION TIME: 15 MINUTES.   COOKING TIME:
                                                 5 TO 10 MINUTES.

You can prepare this Mexican dish (pronounced fah-hee-tuhs) a day ahead, by dicing your vegetables, grating the cheese, and so on, after you put the meat in to marinate. Store the prepared ingredients in the refrigerator until the next day. Then cook the meat, slice in on a serving platter, put the prepared vegetables and cheese in individual serving bowls, and let everyone make their own *fajitas.*

1 pound (450 g) lean topside or silverside, cut ½-inch (1-cm) thick
Juice of two limes (about 3 fluid ounces (80 ml) of juice)
2 cloves garlic, minced
½ teaspoon fresh-ground black pepper
¼ teaspoon chilli powder
¼ teaspoon cumin

6 Whole-Wheat Tortillas (see pp. 227–8)
½ lettuce, cut fine (don't use a food processor or it will not be the right texture)
6 tomatoes, diced
6 spring onions, chopped
6 dessertspoons grated Cheddar cheese

1. Trim any visible fat from the beef. Pound it with a mallet or wooden spoon to about ¼-inch (5-mm) thickness.

78

2. In a shallow bowl, combine the lime juice, garlic, pepper, chilli powder and cumin. Add the steak, toss lightly, and marinate in the refrigerator overnight or for about 6 or 7 hours, turning the meat occasionally.
3. Barbecue the steak on a grill over medium-hot coals for about 3 minutes a side, or fry for 5 to 10 minutes, turning occasionally. Add some of the marinade if necessary to prevent it from sticking. Meanwhile, warm the tortillas briefly on each side in a dry frying pan or a warm oven.
4. Slice the beef across the grain into thin slices. Spread lengthwise in the centre of each tortilla equal amounts of beef. Then top each serving with 2 dessertspoons each of lettuce and tomato, and 1 dessertspoon each of onions and cheese. Roll the tortillas up lengthwise and serve.

6 servings. Serving size is 1 tortilla with fillings.

Per Serving: 257 calories, 62 mg cholesterol, 2 g dietary fibre, 11 g fat, 213 mg sodium.

BRISKET WITH TOMATO SAUCE

PREPARATION TIME: 10 MINUTES.   COOKING TIME: 1½ HOURS.

*2 pounds (900 g) topside
  or silverside
1 clove garlic, crushed
1 teaspoon salt
½ teaspoon fresh-ground
  black pepper
¼ teaspoon marjoram*

*1 14½-ounce (415-g) tin
  no-salt-added tomatoes,
  with juice
1 tablespoon lemon juice
1 medium onion, chopped
1 pound (450 g) carrots,
  sliced*

1. Trim all visible fat from the beef. Combine the garlic, salt, pepper and marjoram, and rub the mixture all over the beef.
2. Pour the juice from the tin of tomatoes into your roasting pan or casserole. Add the meat and lemon juice. Arrange the vegetables around the meat.
3. Cover the pan, place it in a cold oven, and turn the heat to 425°F (Gas Mark 7/220°C). Bake 1½ hours or until done to your taste.

4. Heat the tomatoes in a pan, and serve alongside the roast.

6 servings of 4 ounces (110 g) each (cooked weight), plus vegetables.

Per Serving: 258 calories, 109 mg cholesterol, 3 g dietary fibre, 12 g fat, 562 mg sodium.

STEAK MARINADE

PREPARATION TIME: 3 TO 5 MINUTES.

Here are two marinade sauces for any lean cut of meat that you might want to use for frying, grilling or a barbecue. Both the wine and soy sauce have a tenderizing effect, so marinate overnight in the refrigerator, in a large covered bowl or plastic bag. Turn the meat once or twice while it is marinating, to be sure all of it has been well covered.

These amounts will do nicely for 2 pounds (900 g) of meat.

Basic Marinade
1 dessertspoon olive oil
4 fluid ounces (110 ml) dry red wine (use white wine for light-coloured meats)
¼ teaspoon Herb Salt (pp. 244–5)
1 bay leaf
1 teaspoon chives
1 small onion, minced

Oriental Marinade
1 dessertspoon olive oil
2 fluid ounces (55 ml) tamari OR soy sauce
2 fluid ounces (55 ml) dry red wine
4 cloves garlic, minced
4 spring onions, minced
6 whole peppercorns
⅛ teaspoon ground coriander
1-inch (2.5-cm) cube fresh ginger root, peeled and grated or minced

Olive oil contains approximately 120 calories per dessertspoon. The other ingredients provide negligible calories, including the wine, since the alcohol will evaporate

80

and the sugar content is very low. Soy sauce is quite high in sodium, but it is difficult to predict how much will penetrate or adhere to the meat. Our guess is that the sodium content per serving, e.g., 4½ ounces (125 g) of steak, would be moderate, perhaps 500 mg.

JAPANESE BEEF STIR-FRY

PREPARATION TIME: 5 TO 10 MINUTES.　　　　COOKING TIME:
15 TO 20 MINUTES.

Here is an example of Oriental-style cooking in which meat is only part of the 'main course'. Serve this dish as soon as it's ready. If you are making enough for a second day use ordinary or Chinese cabbage instead of red, as the red cabbage tends to turn other ingredients purple when cooked and stored.

4 fillet steaks (about 4 ounces (110 g) each)
1 dessertspoon peanut oil
12 ounces (350 g) mange-tout peas
¼ head red cabbage, thinly sliced

¼ inch (5 mm) fresh ginger root, minced, OR *ground ginger to taste*
1 dessertspoon saké (optional)
Dash tamari OR *soy sauce*

1. Heat a wok or heavy frying pan over medium-high heat for several minutes. Meanwhile, trim the beef of all visible fat and slice the beef into thin slices.
2. Add the oil to the pan, then the beef. Cook, stirring constantly, until browned.
3. Lower the heat to medium, remove the meat from the pan, and set aside.
4. Add the peas, cabbage and ginger root to the wok, and cook for five minutes, stirring constantly.
5. Return the meat to the wok, and stir in the saké and the soy sauce. Cover, and let simmer for a few more minutes, until the vegetables are just tender and the meat is cooked the way you like it.

4 servings of 3 ounces (90 g) each (cooked weight), plus vegetables.

Per Serving: 281 calories, 82 mg cholesterol, 8 g dietary fibre, 13 g fat, 81 mg sodium.

HUNGARIAN GOULASH

PREPARATION TIME: 15 TO 20 MINUTES.   COOKING TIME: 15 TO 20 MINUTES.

Serve this with an 8-fluid-ounce (225-ml) measure of cooked pasta or grain per serving.

3 pounds (1 kilo 375 g) lean beef
4 leeks, diced
1 dessertspoon olive oil
2 medium carrots, diced
1 16-ounce (450-g) tin no-salt-added tomatoes
8 fluid ounces (225 ml) beef stock
1 dessertspoon paprika
1 teaspoon salt
½ teaspoon black pepper
¼ teaspoon ground cloves (optional)
1 dessertspoon cornflour
2 fluid ounces (55 ml) water
2 fluid ounces (55 ml) sour cream
2 fluid ounces (55 ml) plain low-fat yogurt

1. Trim the beef of all visible fat, and cut the beef into 1-inch (2-cm) chunks. Brown the beef in a pan, then remove the beef and drain any excess fat. In the same pan, sauté the leeks in the oil.
2. When the leeks are tender, return the beef to the pan. Add the carrots, tomatoes, stock, paprika, salt, pepper and cloves.
3. Combine the cornflour with the water, and stir in with the beef. Cover, and let simmer until meat is tender. Then stir in the sour cream and yogurt and heat through.

8 servings of 4½ ounces (125 g) each (cooked weight), plus sauce.

Per Serving (meat with sauce): 311 calories, 126 mg cholesterol, 2 g dietary fibre, 17 g fat, 546 mg sodium.

THAI STIR-FRY

Here is an example of how to use nuts or seeds (in this case, sesame) in small amounts as a flavourful garnish. See pages 159–60 for instructions on how to toast them without added fat.

1 pound (450 g) skirt or
  flank steak
2 fluid ounces (55 ml)
  tamari OR soy sauce
2 tablespoons honey
½ inch (1 cm) ginger root,
  minced
1 clove garlic, minced or
  crushed
2 dessertspoons toasted
  sesame seeds, ground
  with mortar and pestle

1 dessertspoon oil
  (preferably peanut)
1 small aubergine, cut in
  thin strips
¼ to ½ teaspoon crushed
  red pepper (optional)
2 fluid ounces (55 ml)
  stock

1. Cut the beef across the grain into strips about ¼ inch (5 mm) thick. Pound lightly with a meat hammer. Place in a bowl or sealable plastic bag with the tamari, honey, ginger and garlic.
2. Add the oil to a wok or large frying pan, let it heat through, and add the beef. Cook, stirring constantly, until beef is browned, then remove the beef and reserve.
3. Add the aubergine, the crushed red pepper and the stock to the pan. Cover, and steam for 5 to 10 minutes, until the aubergine softens, stirring occasionally.
4. Add the beef, cover, and let simmer for several minutes, until done.
5. Sprinkle with sesame seeds and serve.

4 servings of 3 ounces (90 g) each (cooked weight), plus vegetables.

Per Serving: 313 calories, 82 mg cholesterol, 5 g dietary fibre, 15 g fat, 1037 mg sodium.

EASY BEEF STROGANOFF

PREPARATION TIME: 10 MINUTES.   COOKING TIME: 10 MINUTES.

1 small onion, diced

3 to 4 ounces (80–110 g)
fresh mushrooms, diced

1 dessertspoon vegetable
oil

1½ pounds (675 g) cooked
beef, minced or sliced

3 fluid ounces (90 ml)
plain low-fat yogurt

3 fluid ounces (90 ml) sour
cream

3 fluid ounces (90 ml) dry
white wine

½ teaspoon salt

¼ teaspoon fresh-ground
black pepper

½ teaspoon nutmeg

1. Sauté the onions and mushrooms in the oil over medium-low heat until the onions are translucent. Stir in the remaining ingredients, and let simmer for 10 minutes, covered, until heated through. Do not boil.

6 servings.

Per Serving: 199 calories, 50 mg cholesterol, 1 g dietary fibre, 15 g fat, 233 mg sodium.

EASY BEEF AND RICE

PREPARATION TIME: 10 MINUTES.   COOKING TIME:
                                                 45 TO 50 MINUTES.

With her full schedule as a concert pianist and professor of music at Vanderbilt's Blair School of Music, my wife Enid doesn't often have time for elaborate cooking. Here is one of her many quick-and-easy recipes. Serve with a side salad for a complete, tasty meal. You may substitute homemade stock for the bouillon and water if you like.

12 ounces (350 g) brown
rice

1½ pints (850 ml) water

4 shallots or spring onions,
chopped

4 bouillon cubes

1 pound (450 g) lean mince

1 pound 4 ounces (550 g)
pulped tomatoes

1 teaspoon mixed herbs

1. Combine the first 4 ingredients in a large pot. Bring to a boil, lower the heat, and simmer until tender, about 35 to 40 minutes.
2. In a large frying pan, sauté the minced beef. Drain off any excess fat, then add the tomato pulp and seasoning. Add the cooked rice. Heat through, and serve.

8 servings of about an 8-fluid-ounce (225-ml) measure.

Per Serving: 275 calories, 38 mg cholesterol, 3 g dietary fibre, 9 g fat, 727 mg sodium.

LEMON-PEPPER BEEF

PREPARATION TIME: 5 MINUTES.   COOKING TIME:
18 TO 20 MINUTES.

We first made this dish with 3 tablespoons of lemon juice and it had a decidedly sharp aftertaste of lemon! So we reduced the amount. Use the lesser amount of lemon juice if you prefer a less intense lemon flavour. Reduce or increase cooking time depending on how you like your meat cooked. This dish goes well with cooked pasta, such as vermicelli, and a side salad.

1 pound (450 g) lean topside or silverside, well-trimmed
2 fluid ounces (55 ml) dry red wine
1 to 2 tablespoons lemon juice

½ teaspoon salt
1 bay leaf
2 yellow or red sweet peppers, cut in eighths
Fresh-ground black pepper to taste

1. Combine all ingredients in a large bowl or pan, and marinate overnight or at least 6 hours in the refrigerator. Turn beef and peppers occasionally.
2. Place beef on grill pan about 4 inches (10 cm) from heat and grill about 8 minutes. Turn, and add the pepper pieces to the pan. After six minutes or so, turn the peppers over, then grill about 4 minutes more for medium-well-done beef. Slice the beef thinly across the grain, and serve with the peppers.

4 servings of 3 ounces (80 g) each (cooked weight).

Per Serving: 187 calories, 82 mg cholesterol, no dietary fibre, 9 g fat, 316 mg sodium.

Veal

When well-trimmed, cuts of veal are 20 to 40 per cent lower in calories than similar cuts of mature beef. In addition veal's delicate flavour makes it a fine vehicle for carrying the tastes of different sauces. The economy of calories, together with the interest that can be generated by many different blends of herbs and spices, can make veal an excellent alternative to mature beef in your diet. Look for pale pink-coloured flesh and very white fat when you buy veal. The best cuts are the fillet, loin and upper leg.

We include several recipes for *scaloppine* (very thin, beaten slices of veal) in sauces, plus a variety of other ways to prepare veal, which can be used in meat loaves, for meatballs, in stews and as steak.

Perhaps you will notice that many of our veal recipes seem to be of Italian origin. That's because the Italians have perfected the art of preparing delicate sauces to complement the delicacy of veal.

Because veal is such a lean and delicate meat, many cooks add an unconscionable amount of butter and oil in its preparation, in the mistaken belief that adding fat is the way to enhance the flavour. From our recipes, you will discover that preparing veal requires very little fat; we find a judicious use of herbs, spices and wine is the best way to bring out veal's flavour. Our Herb Salt (pp. 244–5) and Traditional Italian Herb Blend (p. 245) complement veal; keeping some ready-made herb blends on hand for the times when you don't have time to start from scratch will save on preparation time.

But veal invites experimentation and every one of the following herbs and spices, alone or in combination, will enhance your pleasure of this delicious meat: rosemary, thyme, sage, bay leaf, chervil, parsley, mustard seed, coriander, tarragon, chives, basil, allspice or, in place of allspice, a blend of cinnamon, nutmeg and cloves, which is especially good in meatballs.

Experiment with wine in the sauces: dry sherry, Marsala, Madeira, dry vermouth and white wine with the *scaloppine*, and dry red when you want a richer marinade. White wines add little colour to the pale meat, while reds, of course, darken it.

When you beat veal to make *scaloppine*, place it on a wooden board and cover it with wax paper to prevent your pounder from sticking and the meat from splattering. I have used everything from a piece of scrap wood to the bottom of a wooden salad bowl to pound meat, but your best implement is a metal beater made especially for that purpose. I have one that has a flat side for veal and a serrated side for tenderizing tougher cuts of beef. You can find one at a cookware shop.

BROCHETTES OF VEAL

PREPARATION TIME: 50 MINUTES.   COOKING TIME: 10 MINUTES.

Though we recommend a barbecue for this recipe, you can also grill the kebabs indoors.

*1½ pounds (675 g)
    boneless veal roast,
    well-trimmed, cut into
    1-inch (2-cm) cubes
12 ounces (350 g) white
    mushrooms
2 dessertspoons olive oil*

*½ teaspoon salt
Fresh-ground black
    pepper to taste
2 dessertspoons dry red
    wine
Juice of ½ lemon*

¼ *teaspoon thyme*
1 bay leaf, crushed
1 teaspoon tarragon
3 cloves garlic, minced

2 medium sweet red
peppers OR *any other*
sweet peppers, cut into
1-inch (2-cm) pieces

1. Place the cubed veal in a large mixing bowl and add all the remaining ingredients. Cover and marinate in the refrigerator for about 2 hours. Stir the mixture at least twice.
2. About ½ hour before grilling time, prepare a charcoal fire.
3. While the coals are warming, arrange the cubed veal, mushrooms and peppers on 6 skewers.
4. When the charcoal fire is hot, place the kebabs on the grill and cook, turning occasionally, until done (about 10 minutes, depending upon the heat of the grill).

6 servings of 3 ounces (80 g) each (cooked weight), plus vegetables.

Per Serving: 297 calories, 109 mg cholesterol, 2 g dietary fibre, 19 g fat, 238 mg sodium.

LEMON VEAL *SCALOPPINE*

PREPARATION TIME: 10 TO 12 MINUTES.

COOKING TIME:
5 TO 10 MINUTES.

1 pound (450 g) veal,
sliced thin (8 slices)
Fresh-ground black
pepper to taste
1 dessertspoon olive oil
2 fluid ounces (55 ml) dry
white wine

2 fluid ounces (55 ml)
chicken stock
Juice of 1 lemon
2 tablespoons chopped
fresh parsley

1. Pound the veal to about half its original thickness, or as thin as possible without tearing the meat. Sprinkle the meat with pepper.
2. Heat the olive oil in a large nonstick frying pan and, when it is quite hot, brown the veal 1 minute per side.

3. Add the wine, chicken stock, lemon juice and parsley and continue to cook the veal, occasionally turning the slices, until the sauce has reduced to desired consistency (from 5 to 10 minutes).

4 servings of 3 ounces (80 g) each (cooked weight), plus sauce.

Per Serving: 218 calories, 109 mg cholesterol, no dietary fibre, 13 g fat, 150 mg sodium.

VEAL (OR CHICKEN) FLORENTINE

PREPARATION TIME: 25 MINUTES.   COOKING TIME: 25 MINUTES.

'Florentine' indicates that a dish is made with spinach. It is an Italian style of cooking that works well with veal, chicken or fish. This is good served with cooked pasta.

1 pound (450 g) veal cutlets (4 slices) OR *4 chicken breasts, skinned, boned*
¼ teaspoon black pepper
1 10-ounce (300-g) pack frozen chopped spinach, thawed, drained
1 egg OR *2 egg whites*
2 ounces (56 g) low-fat ricotta cheese

2 dessertspoons grated Parmesan
1 clove garlic, minced or crushed
½ teaspoon oregano
2 dessertspoons olive oil
8 fluid ounces (225 ml) dry white wine

1. Pound the veal or chicken to ¼-inch (5-mm) thickness. Sprinkle with the pepper.
2. In a medium bowl, combine the spinach, egg, cheeses, garlic and oregano. Spread this mixture over the veal.
3. Roll the veal, Swiss-roll fashion, around the spinach filling, securing the rolls with toothpicks or string.
4. Add the oil to a small pan, over medium to medium-low heat and lightly brown the rolls on all sides. Place the rolls in a casserole dish, add the wine, and bake at 350°F (Gas Mark 4/180°C) for 25 minutes.

4 servings of 1 roll 3 ounces (80 g) each (cooked weight), plus vegetables.

Per Serving (with veal): 319 calories, 184 mg cholesterol, 2 g dietary fibre, 20 g fat, 201 mg sodium.

Per Serving (with chicken): 276 calories, 148 mg cholesterol, 2 g dietary fibre, 13 g fat, 209 mg sodium.

VEAL STEW

PREPARATION TIME: 30 MINUTES.　　　COOKING TIME (WITHOUT BROWNING): 1¾ HOURS.

I generally prefer not to brown my meat when I make stews. Skipping the browning step results in a lighter gravy and you save a couple of hundred calories of fat content in the total recipe. I also don't normally add any flour or cornflour to thicken the gravy. It will thicken somewhat during the final minutes of cooking in an uncovered pot.

If you wish to brown the meat (which will take out some of the moisture in the meat but won't really 'seal in' the juices), do it in the same cooking pot, using a minimum of oil, say one dessertspoon. As for a gravy, if you prefer it thick, make a *roux* (p. 207) and blend it in during the last 30 minutes of cooking, or simply sprinkle a bit of flour into the stew about a minute before it finishes cooking, and stir frequently until done.

*1 dessertspoon oil
(optional, for browning)
4 pounds (1 kilo 800 g)
lean veal roast, cut into
1½-inch (4-cm) cubes
3 medium onions,
chopped
4 cloves garlic, chopped
½ teaspoon salt
Fresh-ground black
pepper to taste*

*1 bay leaf
½ teaspoon dried thyme
¼ teaspoon rosemary
3 tablespoons chopped
fresh parsley
8 fluid ounces (225 ml) dry
white wine
1¼ pints (700 ml) chicken
stock
4 medium ripe tomatoes,
cut into eighths*

5 *medium carrots*	2 *tablespoons chopped*
5 *small courgettes*	*fresh parsley for garnish*
4 *celery stalks*	

BROWNING METHOD

1. If you want to brown the meat, heat the oil in a large cooking pot or Dutch oven and add veal cubes, turning until brown.
2. Add onions and garlic; heat until translucent. Add all seasonings, wine, stock and tomatoes. Cover and simmer for 30 minutes.
3. As the stew is simmering, cut the carrots, courgettes and celery into bite-size pieces (about 1 inch (2 cm) long), add to the pot, cover, and simmer another 45 minutes. Uncover and continue to simmer until the gravy is reduced to the desired consistency.
4. Skim any fat that appears on the surface of the liquid, and serve, garnished with the extra parsley.

TO OMIT BROWNING

1. Prepare the vegetables, and then add all the ingredients to the pot, except for the parsley garnish, cover, and bring to the boiling point. Immediately reduce heat and simmer for about 1½ hours on low heat. Uncover to reduce liquid and skim off the fat. When gravy is of desired consistency, serve with parsley garnish.

10 servings of about 16-fluid-ounce (450-ml) measure.

Per Serving (without oil): 339 calories, 131 mg cholesterol, 5 g dietary fibre, 18 g fat, 670 mg sodium. (Oil will add about 10 calories per serving in the form of another gram of fat.)

VEAL POTROAST WITH FENNEL AND LEEKS

PREPARATION TIME: 15 MINUTES.   COOKING TIME: 1½ TO 2 HOURS.

4-*pound (1-kilo 800-g)*	4 *leeks*
veal roast, bone in	16 *small new potatoes*
3 *bulbs fennel*	½ *teaspoon sage*

92

½ teaspoon rosemary	1 tablespoon lemon juice
¼ teaspoon coriander	2 fluid ounces (55 ml)
Fresh-ground black	white wine or water
pepper to taste	

1. Trim all visible fat from the roast and place it in a Dutch oven or large casserole dish.
2. Trim the tough outer leaves from the fennel. Wash and core the bulbs and cut in chunks. Arrange around the veal.
3. Carefully wash and trim the leeks. Cut the white portion in large pieces and add to the roasting pan, along with the washed new potatoes.
4. Sprinkle with seasonings, lemon juice, and wine. Cover, and bake at 350°F (Gas Mark 4/180°C) for 1½ to 2 hours.

8 servings of 4½ ounces (125 g) each (cooked weight), plus vegetables.

Per Serving: 469 calories, 175 mg cholesterol, 3 g dietary fibre, 23 g fat, 97 mg sodium.

VEAL MARSALA

PREPARATION TIME: 10 TO 12 MINUTES.   COOKING TIME:
                                                                            3 MINUTES.

1½ pounds (675 g) thinly	1 dessertspoon olive oil
sliced veal (12 slices)	2 fluid ounces (55 ml)
¼ teaspoon salt	Marsala wine
Fresh-ground black	2 tablespoons chopped
pepper to taste	fresh parsley

1. Between waxed paper, pound the meat to ¼-inch (5-mm) thickness and sprinkle with the salt and pepper.
2. Heat the oil in a large nonstick frying pan. When it is hot, brown half the veal for 1 minute on each side, remove to an oven-proof plate warmed in the oven, and hold in reserve. Brown the other half of the veal and then immediately return the meat from the plate to the pan.

93

3. Add the Marsala and parsley and cook for 3 minutes. Serve at once.

6 servings of 3 ounces (80 g) each (cooked weight).

Per Serving: 206 calories, 109 mg cholesterol, no dietary fibre, 12 g fat, 145 mg sodium.

VEAL *SCALOPPINE*

PREPARATION TIME: 10 TO 12 MINUTES.   COOKING TIME: 15 MINUTES.

1½ pounds (675 g) veal scaloppine in 6 pieces
1 clove garlic, minced
½ teaspoon salt
¼ teaspoon pepper
¼ teaspoon oregano

¼ teaspoon dried basil
2 ounces (56 g) fresh mushrooms, sliced
3 tablespoons Marsala or sherry

1. Pound veal to ¼-inch (5-mm) thickness. In a Teflon-coated pan or a heavy frying pan sprayed with non-stick vegetable cooking spray, brown the veal on both sides over medium-high heat.
2. Reduce heat to low, and add other ingredients. Cover and cook until veal is tender, about 15 minutes.

6 servings of 3 ounces (80 g) each (cooked weight), plus sauce.

Per Serving: 202 calories, 109 mg cholesterol, no dietary fibre, 9 g fat, 235 mg sodium.

VEAL *SCALOPPINE* DIJON

PREPARATION TIME: 10 MINUTES.   COOKING TIME: 5 MINUTES.

1½ pounds (675 g) veal scaloppine (about 18 thin pieces)
Fresh-ground black pepper to taste

1 dessertspoon olive oil
½ ounce (15 g) butter
4 cloves garlic, minced
2 dessertspoons dry white wine

2 dessertspoons chicken
  stock
1 dessertspoon Dijon
  mustard

2 teaspoons Herb Salt
  (pp. 244–5)
3 tablespoons chopped
  fresh parsley

1. Pound the meat and then sprinkle with pepper.
2. Heat the oil in a large nonstick frying pan over medium heat, and when it is hot, cover the bottom of the pan with meat. Lightly brown the meat on each side (about 30 seconds), remove it to a warm plate and continue with the remaining meat until all is done.
3. Remove any remaining fat from the pan and add the butter and garlic. Sauté garlic for 30 seconds. Add the wine, chicken stock, mustard, and Herb Salt. As the mixture cooks, scrape the bottom of the pan with a wooden or plastic spatula to blend all ingredients. Return the veal and any liquid to the pan, sprinkle with parsley, and heat for about 1 minute.

6 servings of 3 ounces (80 g) each (cooked weight; about 3 slices).

Per Serving: 228 calories, 114 mg cholesterol, no dietary fibre, 14 g fat, 851 mg sodium.

Pork

Pork, like lamb, is not a regular part of our diet. We have a few favourite recipes for pork as a main course that we occasionally make, and we include three others that illustrate how you can use pork in combination with vegetables.

Contrary to what most people believe, pork can be a lean meat! If you serve the lean meat from the shoulder or loin, it runs to only about 55 calories an ounce (28 g), and the percentage of fat calories is 30 to 35. But be sure to trim the meat well, because the fat content will more than double the calories if you don't.

We calculate the calories in the roast recipes for serving sizes of 4½ ounces (125 g). We slice our meat thinly, averaging three slices of meat per serving of that size. A good-size rib or loin chop, about 1 inch (2 cm) thick before cooking, will have about 2 to 3 ounces of lean meat and contain fewer than 200 calories (eat the fat, and it's more than double).

Normally, the price of pork makes it a bargain compared to other meats and it's as full of the B vitamins and iron as beef. Trim it well and it's just as lean.

You will rarely see bacon in our recipes. Bacon, grilled or fried *crisp*, contains about 160 calories an ounce, and of those calories, over 80 per cent come from fat!

Whenever bacon is called for in your own recipes, try using lean ham (about 55 calories an ounce (28 g) and about 33 per cent fat).

PORK LOIN STIR-FRY

PREPARATION TIME: 12 TO 15 MINUTES.   COOKING TIME:
                                                15 TO 20 MINUTES.

This stir-fry is mild and very good. Serve it over cooked grain or whole-wheat pasta.

2 pounds (900 g) lean
  boneless pork loin or
  shoulder
1 dessertspoon peanut oil
1 clove garlic, minced or
  crushed
½ inch (1 cm) fresh ginger
  root, minced, OR 1 scant
  teaspoon ground ginger
1 medium onion, cut in
  chunks

1 medium apple, chopped
1 medium green pepper,
  sliced in thin strips
4 medium carrots, cut in
  thin strips, 1 inch (2 cm)
  long
4 fluid ounces (110 ml)
  water OR stock

1. Trim all visible fat from pork, and cut into strips about 2 inches by ½ inch (5 cm by 1 cm).
2. Heat the oil in a wok or large frying pan over medium-high heat. Add the pork and brown it, stirring constantly. Remove pork and drain on paper towels.
3. Add the garlic, ginger if using fresh, and onion to the wok, cover, and sauté/steam until onions are translucent.
4. Add the apple, green pepper, carrots and water. Stir, cover, and reduce the heat to medium-low. Cook for about 3 minutes, and return the pork to the pan.
5. If you're using ground ginger, add it to the stir-fry when the apple is just tender. Let sauté/steam for a few more minutes, until pork is cooked through.

6 servings of 4½ ounces (125 g) each (cooked weight), plus vegetables.

Per Serving: 354 calories, 115 mg cholesterol, 2 g dietary fibre, 20 g fat, 108 mg sodium.

PORK CHOPS PARMESAN

PREPARATION TIME: 8 TO 10 MINUTES.　　　　COOKING TIME: 30 MINUTES.

2 tablespoons maize meal, whole-wheat flour or breadcrumbs
1 dessertspoon grated Parmesan cheese
½ teaspoon fresh-ground black pepper
½ teaspoon salt
½ teaspoon basil

4 pork loin chops, about ½ inch (1 cm) thick
1 dessertspoon vegetable oil
3 spring onions, chopped
1 clove garlic, minced
¼ teaspoon fennel seeds, crushed

1. Combine the maize meal, Parmesan cheese, pepper, salt and basil.
2. Trim the pork chops of all visible fat, pat them dry, and dredge in the meal mixture.
3. Heat a pan over medium heat, and add the oil. When the oil is hot, place the chops in the pan and reduce the heat to low.
4. Fry the chops for 10 minutes on each side. Then add the onions, garlic and fennel, and continue frying for another 10 minutes, turning as necessary to keep from sticking.

4 servings of 2½ ounces (70 g) each (lean meat only, cooked weight).

Per Serving: 198 calories, 56 mg cholesterol, 1 g dietary fibre, 12 g fat, 340 mg sodium.

ROAST PORK WITH VEGETABLES

PREPARATION TIME: 10 MINUTES.　COOKING TIME: 2 TO 2½ HOURS.

1 pork roast, about 3 pounds (1 kilo 350 g) with bone

1 teaspoon garlic powder
1 teaspoon fresh ginger root, minced

1 teaspoon sage
2 large potatoes, sliced ½
inch (1 cm) thick
1 large onion, sliced
4 ounces (110 g) fresh
mushrooms

4 fluid ounces (110 ml)
beef OR vegetable stock
2 teaspoons tamari OR soy
sauce

1. Trim the roast of all visible fat. Place the roast in a baking pan, and rub all sides with the garlic powder, ginger and sage.
2. Arrange the vegetables around the roast. Combine the stock and the tamari sauce, and pour over the roast and vegetables.
3. Bake at 375°F (Gas Mark 5/190°C) for 30 minutes then reduce the heat to 350, and bake an additional 1½ to 2 hours, or until pork is cooked, and appears grey throughout. Baste every 40 minutes.

6 servings of 4½ ounces (125 g) each (cooked weight), plus vegetables.

Per Serving: 397 calories, 115 mg cholesterol, 3 g dietary fibre, 18 g fat, 283 mg sodium.

BAKED PORK CHOPS

PREPARATION TIME: 5 TO 10 MINUTES.   COOKING TIME: 1 HOUR.

4 pork chops, 4–6 ounces
(110–175 g) each
⅛ teaspoon garlic powder
¼ teaspoon Traditional
Italian Herb Blend
(p. 245)
Dash of salt and black
pepper

1 16-ounce (450-g) tin of
unsalted tomatoes
4 ounces (110 g) fresh
mushrooms, sliced
2 ounces (56 g) grated
cheese

1. Trim the chops of all visible fat and place them in a roasting pan. Sprinkle with the herbs.
2. Drain the juice from the tomatoes into the pan, over the pork chops. Reserve the tomatoes.
3. Bake the chops at 375°F (Gas Mark 5/190°C) for 30 minutes.

4. Cover the chops with the mushrooms, the reserved tomatoes and the cheese, and bake an additional 30 minutes.

4 servings of 2½ ounces (70 g) each (lean meat only, cooked weight), plus vegetables.

Per Serving: 229 calories, 61 mg cholesterol, 2 g dietary fibre, 11 g fat, 324 mg sodium.

ORIENTAL PORK CHOPS

PREPARATION TIME: 5 MINUTES.   COOKING TIME: 35 MINUTES.

Serve this with a cooked grain or a baked potato, and a vegetable stir-fry, such as Chinese Cabbage Stir-Fry (pp. 197–8).

4 lean pork chops, 4–6 ounces (110–175 g) each
1 dessertspoon tamari OR soy sauce
½ teaspoon salt
½ teaspoon black pepper
1 slice fresh ginger root, about ¼ inch (5 mm) thick, minced
2 tablespoons white wine
4 tablespoons beef stock

1. Trim the chops of all visible fat and place them in a baking pan.
2. Combine the remaining ingredients, except for the stock, in a small bowl. Brush the sauce mixture over each chop, reserving any remaining sauce.
3. Bake the chops at 350°F (Gas Mark 4/180°C) for 20 minutes.
4. Pour the stock over the chops, along with any remaining sauce. Bake an additional 10 to 15 minutes, basting occasionally, until chops are cooked (grey all the way through the centre).

4 servings of 2½ ounces (70 g) each (lean meat only, cooked weight), plus sauce.

Per Serving: 177 calories, 55 mg cholesterol, no dietary fibre, 9 g fat, 629 mg sodium.

PORK CHOPS À LA GRECQUE

PREPARATION TIME: 15 MINUTES.   COOKING TIME: 35 MINUTES.

4 lean pork chops, 4–6
ounces (110–175 g) each
½ teaspoon salt
2 medium onions, sliced
1 dessertspoon olive OR
vegetable oil
4 ounces (110 g) fresh
mushrooms, sliced
4 tablespoons
unsweetened orange
juice

4 tablespoons water or
beef stock
2 ounces (56 g) Greek OR
other black olives, diced
1 dessertspoon lemon
juice
¼ teaspoon black pepper

1. Trim all visible fat from the chops. Place the chops in a baking pan and sprinkle with the salt.
2. Bake at 350°F (Gas Mark 4/180°C) for 20 minutes.
3. While the chops are baking, prepare the sauce by sautéing the onions in the oil. When onions are translucent, add the mushrooms, cover, and cook two to three minutes more. Add the remaining ingredients, and heat through.
4. Spoon the sauce over the chops. Bake another 10 to 15 minutes or longer, depending on the thickness of the chops. Baste occasionally, until the chops are cooked through.

4 servings of 2½ ounces (70 g) each (lean only, cooked weight), plus sauce.

Per Serving: 255 calories, 55 mg cholesterol, 2 g dietary fibre, 16 g fat, 435 mg sodium.

STIR-FRY PORK WITH MANGE-TOUT PEAS

PREPARATION TIME: 10 MINUTES.   COOKING TIME: 30 MINUTES.

4 pork chops, 4–6 ounces
(110–175 g) each
1 dessertspoon peanut OR
vegetable oil

¼ teaspoon black pepper
1 dessertspoon tamari OR
soy sauce
1 clove garlic, crushed

*1 slice fresh ginger root,
about ½ inch (1 cm)
thick, minced*
2 teaspoons sesame seeds
5 tablespoons water

½ pint (275 ml) water
4 spring onions OR *2 small
leeks, diced*
*6 ounces (175 g) mange-
tout peas*

1. Trim all visible fat from the chops, and slice the meat into thin strips, about ¼ inch (5 mm) thick, and ½ to 1 inch (1 to 2 cm) wide.
2. Heat the oil in a wok or large pan over medium heat, then add the pork and brown, stirring often.
3. Mix together the pepper, tamari sauce, garlic, ginger, sesame seeds and the 5 tablespoons of water, and add to the browned meat. Add the onions.
4. Cover, reduce heat, and let simmer for about 30 minutes, until the pork is cooked through, stirring occasionally. Add more water if necessary to prevent sticking.
5. Meanwhile, cook the mange-tout peas. Add to fast-boiling water, no salt, and let boil for about 5 minutes until just tender. Drain and stir into the pork. Serve.

4 servings of 2½ ounces (70 g) each (lean meat only, cooked weight), plus vegetables.

Per Serving: 237 calories, 55 mg cholesterol, 2 g dietary fibre, 14 g fat, 316 mg sodium.

Lamb

Although I have never had much of a preference for fatty meats in general and have never regretted the close trimming of any other meat, lamb is an exception. I can remember, as a child, gnawing and sucking every gram of meat, fat and marrow from my serving of two little grilled lamb chops. I could never get enough of them, nor could the rest of the family.

But, yes, lamb is truly a fat meat. The chops that I trimmed to the bone with my teeth as an overweight child averaged 423 calories for just 3½ ounces (125 g)! But lamb doesn't have to be that fatty. If you thoroughly trim your roast or chops before eating, you can still enjoy the wonderful flavours in our recipes, and end up with lamb at 55 to 65 calories per ounce. So, don't pass by the recipes in this chapter.

Most of them, such as Moroccan Stew, one of our most special entrées, have their origin in Middle Eastern cooking, where lamb is a preferred meat. We guarantee both Sesame-Ginger Lamb Chops and Surprise Lamb Chops are two dishes worth keeping in your 'special dinner' category.

LAMB POTROAST WITH SAVORY TOMATO SAUCE

PREPARATION TIME: 10 MINUTES.   COOKING TIME: 2 HOURS.

*1 boned leg of lamb,
about 3 pounds (1 kilo
350 g)
1 medium white onion,
chopped in chunks
2 medium tomatoes, cut in
quarters
1 medium pepper, cut in
chunks
2 cloves garlic, crushed*

*5 tablespoons dry red
wine
1 6-ounce (175-g) tin
tomato paste
Fresh-ground black
pepper to taste
1 teaspoon dried thyme
½ teaspoon dried
summer savory
1 bay leaf*

1. Trim all visible fat from the leg of lamb. Place it in a large roasting pan or Dutch oven. Arrange the cut-up vegetables around the lamb. Spread the crushed garlic on top of the meat.
2. Pour the wine over the lamb, then top with tomato paste, black pepper, thyme and summer savory. Float the bay leaf in the bottom of the pan.
3. Cover and bake at 325°F (Gas Mark 3/170°C) for about 2 hours, basting occasionally.

8 servings of 4½ ounces (125 g) each (cooked weight).

Per Serving: 390 calories, 156 mg cholesterol, 1 g dietary fibre, 19 g fat, 114 mg sodium.

SWEET PEPPER LAMB

PREPARATION TIME: 10 MINUTES.   COOKING TIME: 1¼ HOURS.

If you can't find the red peppers that make this dish so attractive, try the yellow variety. Green peppers are fine, too.

*2½ pounds (1 kilo 150 g)
lean lamb meat – (leg
roast preferred)
8 fluid ounces (225 ml)
beef OR vegetable stock*

*2 large cloves garlic,
minced or crushed
1 tablespoon dried parsley
1½ teaspoons rosemary
1 teaspoon sage*

Salt and fresh-ground   *2 whole fresh red peppers,*
  black pepper to taste   *cut into strips*

1. Preheat oven to 350°F (Gas Mark 4/180°C).
2. Trim the visible fat from the lamb, and place the lamb in a roasting pan. Pour the stock over the lamb and add the spices. Arrange the strips of red pepper on top of the meat.
3. Cover and bake for 1 hour and 15 minutes.

8 servings of 4 ounces (110 g) each (cooked weight), plus peppers.

Per Serving: 309 calories, 130 mg cholesterol, no dietary fibre, 16 g fat, 487 mg sodium.

CUBED LAMB

PREPARATION TIME: 8 TO 10 MINUTES.   COOKING TIME: 1½ HOURS.

This goes well with a side dish of pasta and fresh cooked spinach or other greens, such as kale, broccoli, cabbage or turnip greens.

1 pound (450 g) lean lamb,   *1 teaspoon oregano*
  cubed   *2 to 3 spring onions or*
1 dessertspoon vegetable   *shallots, diced*
  OR *olive oil*   *1 dessertspoon lemon*
1 medium tomato, diced   *juice*
1 tablespoon parsley   *1 teaspoon salt*

1. Trim the lamb of all visible fat and brown in the oil in a large saucepan.
2. Add the remaining ingredients, stirring well. Cover, and reduce heat to low. Simmer for at least 1½ hours, stirring occasionally.

4 servings of 3 ounces (80 g) each (cooked weight), plus sauce.

Per Serving: 230 calories, 80 mg cholesterol, 1 g dietary fibre, 12 g fat, 609 mg sodium.

CURRIED LAMB WITH VEGETABLES

PREPARATION TIME: 20 MINUTES.   COOKING TIME: 40 MINUTES.

In countries where curries are popular, every great cook creates a curry powder out of a variety of spices such as the ones in this recipe. Even if you've never liked curry, you'll probably like this – it's quite mild.

4 lamb loin OR *shoulder chops, about ¾-inch (1.5-cm) thick (4–6 ounces/110–175 g each)*
2 cloves garlic, minced
1 dessertspoon vegetable oil
8 fluid ounces (225 ml) water OR *stock*
1 teaspoon cumin
½ teaspoon ground ginger
¼ teaspoon ground coriander
¼ teaspoon cayenne pepper
½ teaspoon turmeric
1 medium courgette, cut in chunks
2 medium carrots, sliced
1 medium onion, cut in chunks
Fresh-ground black pepper to taste
1 10-ounce (300-g) pack frozen peas

1. Trim any visible fat from the chops, and brown them with the garlic in the vegetable oil in a large frying pan.
2. Remove the lamb, and add the remaining ingredients except the peas. Cover and bring to a boil. Reduce heat to simmer, and put the lamb back in the pan. Cover, and simmer for 30 minutes.
3. Add the peas, and simmer another 10 minutes, until the vegetables are tender and the lamb is cooked.

4 servings of 2½ ounces (70 g) each (lean only, cooked weight), plus vegetables.

Per Serving: 223 calories, 60 mg cholesterol, 10 g dietary fibre, 10 g fat, 120 mg sodium.

MOROCCAN STEW

PREPARATION TIME: 20 MINUTES.   COOKING TIME: 2½ HOURS.

Serve this stew over Moroccan couscous or any other favourite cooked grains.

1¼ pints (700 ml) water
1 leg of lamb, about 3
   pounds (1 kilo 350 g)
1 16-ounce (450-g) tin
   tomatoes, with juice
2 medium onions, sliced
   or quartered
12 carrots, sliced
1 piece fresh ginger root,
   about ½ inch (1 cm)
   thick
2 cinnamon sticks
3 whole cloves
½ teaspoon saffron
1 teaspoon salt
½ teaspoon black pepper
½ teaspoon ground
   coriander
6 ounces (175 g) cooked
   chickpeas (2½ ounces/
   70 g) raw
1 medium courgette,
   diced
1 ounce (28 g) sultanas

1. Bring the water to a boil in a large pot. Meanwhile, trim the lamb of any visible fat. Add the lamb to the boiling water, along with the tomatoes and their juice, the onions and the carrots. Bring to a boil again. Reduce the heat to low, cover, and let simmer, turning the meat and basting it occasionally to cook evenly.
2. Put the ginger, cinnamon sticks and cloves in a muslin bag and add to the stew. (You can add these without the bag, but the bag makes them easier to remove.)
3. Combine the saffron, salt, pepper and coriander, and add to the stew after it has been simmering for about 1½ hours.
4. Add the chickpeas, courgette and sultanas and continue cooking for another hour.
5. Remove the spice bag or individual spices, and serve.

8 servings of 4½ ounces (125 g) of meat (cooked weight), plus vegetables.

Per Serving: 337 calories, 114 mg cholesterol, 4 g dietary fibre, 11 g fat, 476 mg sodium.

SESAME-GINGER LAMB CHOPS

PREPARATION TIME: 5 TO 10 MINUTES.   COOKING TIME:
                                             23 TO 26 MINUTES.

Prepare the marinade early in the morning (before work, for example) or the night before. Then almost all that remains to be done to prepare this main dish for dinner is to grill it. See pages 159–60 for instructions on how to toast seeds.

4 lamb chops, 4–6 ounces (110–175 g) each
2 tablespoons tamari OR soy sauce
2 fluid ounces (55 ml) water
1 teaspoon lemon juice

1 teaspoon honey
1 slice fresh ginger root, ½ inch (1 cm) thick, minced
3 teaspoons toasted sesame seeds, crushed with mortar and pestle

1. Trim the chops of all visible fat. Arrange the chops in a shallow pan.
2. In a small bowl, combine the tamari, water, lemon juice, honey and ginger. Pour this mixture over the lamb and cover. Marinate in the refrigerator overnight or for about 8 hours.
3. When you're ready to cook the meal, remove the chops from the marinade and arrange on a grill pan. Grill about 5 inches (12 cm) from the heat at your grill's lowest setting for 10 minutes. Turn and grill another 8 minutes.
4. Sprinkle the chops with the sesame seeds, and grill 5 to 8 minutes more.

4 servings of 2½ ounces (70 g) each (lean meat only, cooked weight).

Per Serving: 175 calories, 60 mg cholesterol, no dietary fibre, 8 g fat, 827 mg sodium.

SURPRISE LAMB CHOPS

PREPARATION TIME: 12 TO 15 MINUTES.   COOKING TIME: 1 HOUR.

This recipe is so named because each serving comes wrapped in its own foil 'surprise package'.

4 lamb chops, 4–6 ounces (110–175 g) each

1 teaspoon salt
½ teaspoon pepper

1 teaspoon oregano
3 small potatoes, sliced ¼ inch (5 mm) thick
1 large carrot, sliced ¼ inch (5 mm) thick
1 courgette, sliced
4 fresh mushrooms, sliced
1½ ounces (40 g) crumbled feta cheese (or other cheese of choice)
2 teaspoons lemon juice
Aluminium foil

1. Trim the chops of all visible fat. Place each chop on a *doubled over* piece of foil (or use heavy-duty foil) large enough to fold over the chop and vegetables.
2. Combine the salt, pepper and oregano, and sprinkle each chop with one-quarter of the mixture. Then cover each chop with a layer of each different vegetable, a scant teaspoon of cheese and a sprinkling of lemon juice.
3. Bring the longest edges of the foil together and roll down until it fits well across the top of the chop and vegetables, sealing them. Roll up the ends securely so that you have a neat package.
4. Place the 4 packages in a baking pan, in order to catch any juices. Bake at 350°F (Gas Mark 4/180°C) for 1 hour.
5. Serve in the package if you like; just be careful when unwrapping – it will be hot!

4 servings of 2½ ounces (70 g) each (lean only, cooked weight), plus vegetables.

Per Serving: 261 calories, 66 mg cholesterol, 5 g dietary fibre, 8 g fat, 728 mg sodium.

Poultry

Chicken in one form or another is about the most frequent main course for dinner in my home and in Terri's. One reason is that it is so simple to prepare. Buy extra and freeze it, if you like. If you forget to defrost the evening meal before you leave the house in the morning, and you have a microwave oven, chicken joints will defrost in just a few minutes in the microwave when you get home. Then you can pop it in the oven with very little fuss. Look, for example, at the variations of Baked Chicken (pp. 111–12) or, for a spicy treat, our Oven-Fried Chicken (pp. 114–15). Talk about ease of preparation!

In comparison with red meats, chicken is a low-fat source of protein. We knew there was a difference between the fat levels of beef and chicken, but it was not until we had to look up some information about the relative nutrient content of both that we became fully aware of some incredible differences. A half breast of chicken – about 3 ounces (80 g) of white meat without skin – might contain 140 or so calories, with only about 20 per cent of its nutrient weight, or 27 calories, in fat. A *small* fillet steak – about 3½ ounces (95 g) cooked, and not well trimmed – might contain 440 calories, with about 80 per cent, or 360 calories, in fat!

While we still like our chicken prepared as a main

course according to the recipes we include in this chapter, we have also begun using chicken as a condiment in combination with other foods. Try our various chicken combination dishes, such as Chicken with Broccoli and Carrot (pp. 115–16), with Cashew nuts and Broccoli (pp. 121–2), and with Leeks and Mushrooms (p. 118). Remember to save the carcass from roasted chicken to make soups and stock.

Our nutritional analyses assume half white meat, half dark, when whole chickens are called for. White meat contains about 25 per cent less fat and calories than dark meat. When our recipes call for chicken breasts, we mean split breasts; that is, '4 chicken breasts' means 4 half breasts unless otherwise specified.

Neither Terri nor I has ever cooked a duck! The thought of all the fat is a turn off. So you can imagine our surprise when Chef Sylvain Le Coguic at Julian's, which is one of Nashville's most noted restaurants, responded to our request to illustrate a dish that he might serve to someone interested in keeping fat and calories low, with a recipe for duck! It isn't, of course, possible to prepare duck so that it ends up containing as few calories as the white meat of chicken, but Julian's Grilled Breast of Duck ends up at only 60 calories an ounce. The entire main course, prepared as directed, is only 400 calories. If you like duck and thought you might have to deprive yourself because it's so high in fat, try preparing it this way. It's a pleasure to look at, as well as to eat.

BAKED CHICKEN

PREPARATION TIME: 5 TO 10 MINUTES.   COOKING TIME:
                                                  25 MINUTES.

For days when you really want a low-calorie entree or need something quick to throw in the oven, baked chicken is a simple yet delicious solution.

Try the following seasoning combinations for variety:

VARIATION 1: Sprinkle liberally with onion or garlic powder and Herb Salt (pp. 244–5). Or make your own selection of herbs, using one or more of the following: marjoram, oregano, rosemary leaves, tarragon or thyme. Add fresh-ground black pepper.

VARIATION 2: Sprinkle liberally with chilli powder, paprika and a dash of cayenne pepper. Add salt at the table after tasting.

VARIATION 3: Calories are significantly reduced if the chicken is skinned *before* baking. But skinning prior to cooking creates a problem since the meat is likely to dry out. You can prevent this by coating the skinned chicken with a basting sauce made from 4 fluid ounces (110 ml) tomato ketchup, 1½ tablespoons of tamari or low-sodium soy sauce, and 2 fluid ounces (55 ml) of sherry. Then sprinkle with herbs of your choice. (Additional salt is not needed because of the soy sauce.) Loosely cover the chicken with a piece of aluminium foil for about half the cooking time and it will stay moist.

Here are the basic directions for baking chicken.

1 small frying chicken,   *Your favourite seasonings*
   about 3 to 3½ pounds   *Aluminium foil*
   (1 kilo 350 g to
   1 kilo 575 g), cut-up

1. Line a baking pan with foil and lay out the pieces of chicken. Season as desired and bake at 400°F (Gas Mark 6/200°C) for approximately 25 minutes. Skin before eating. (Much of the flavour of the seasonings will have penetrated to the flesh of the chicken during baking; however, add more at the table, if desired.)

6 servings of about 3 ounces (80 g) each (cooked weight).

Per Serving (half dark meat): 155 calories, 72 mg cholesterol, no dietary fibre, 3 g fat, 63 mg sodium.

White meat without skin is about 45 calories an ounce, while dark meat is almost 60 because it contains more fat. Simply multiply the number of ounces per serving times the number of calories per ounce, and you will get the total calories per serving. On 600/900 rotations, serving size is 3 ounces (80 g) cooked (135 and 150 calories for white and dark meat). On 1200-calorie rotations, serving size is 4½ ounces (125 g) (208 and 270 calories for white and dark meat). On 1500 and 1800 rotations, serving size is 6 ounces (175 g) (270 and 360 calories for white and dark meat). Basting sauce will add between 15 and 30 calories per serving, depending on size.

BARBECUED CHICKEN

PREPARATION TIME: 5 MINUTES.   COOKING TIME:
               45 TO 50 MINUTES.

You can use this recipe with your own barbecue sauce, or a shop-bought brand low in sugar and salt.

2½ pounds (1 kilo 110 g) *8 fluid ounces (225 ml)*
 chicken pieces   *barbecue sauce*

1. Preheat oven to 350°F (Gas Mark 4/180°C).
2. Skin the chicken. Place the pieces 'skin' side down in a large, shallow baking pan. (You may wish to line the pan with foil for easy cleaning.)
3. Baste the chicken liberally with barbecue sauce, and place in the oven.
4. Bake 20 minutes, basting halfway through. Then turn the chicken over and bake another 25 to 30 minutes, or until chicken is tender, basting occasionally.

6 servings of about 3½ ounces (80 g) each (cooked weight), plus sauce.

Per Serving: 174 calories, 78 mg cholesterol, 1 g dietary fibre, 5 g fat, 86 mg sodium.

PATTI'S ROAST CHICKEN

PREPARATION TIME: 10 MINUTES.   COOKING TIME:
          1 HOUR AND 20 MINUTES.

Patti Bereyso is one of the video producers and writers at Scene Three, Inc. of Nashville, who helped produce The

Rotation Diet Home Companion video. Ever energetic, she cheerfully handed us this recipe as soon as she heard we were writing a cookbook.

Prepare this a day in advance, then discard the fat, reheat, and serve with its own rich-tasting gravy over cooked grain.

4 chicken breasts, skinned
  OR *4 turkey steaks*
  (about 6 ounces/175 g
  each)
6 fluid ounces (180 ml)
  water

2 fluid ounces (55 ml)
  tamari OR *soy sauce*
1 teaspoon garlic powder
1 teaspoon dried rosemary
1 bay leaf

1. Preheat the oven to 375°F (Gas Mark 5/190°C). Wash the chicken with cold water and pat dry with paper towels.
2. Place the chicken in a roasting pan. Pour ¾ of the water into the bottom of the pan. Pour the tamari or soy sauce over the chicken, then sprinkle with garlic and rosemary. Float the bay leaf in water in the bottom of the pan.
3. Bake for about 1 hour, basting frequently, until chicken is tender and well-browned. Add more water (and soy sauce, if you like) as needed.
4. Cool and refrigerate overnight. The fat will harden when chilled. Carefully spoon out the fat, leaving the jelled water-soy mixture in the pan. Place the pan in an oven heated to 325°F (Gas Mark 3/170°C) for 20 to 30 minutes, or until thoroughly heated.

4 servings of 3½ ounces (95 g) each (cooked weight).

Per Serving (using chicken): 157 calories, 73 mg cholesterol, no dietary fibre, 3 g fat, 1093 mg sodium.

OVEN-FRIED CHICKEN

PREPARATION TIME: 15 MINUTES.   COOKING TIME: 1 HOUR.

1 dessertspoon vegetable
  oil
1 teaspoon lemon juice

3 pounds (1 kilo 350 g)
  chicken pieces, skinned

About 3 fluid ounces
  (80 ml) skim OR low-fat
  milk OR buttermilk
2 ounces (56 g) flour
  (preferably wholemeal)
1½ teaspoons paprika
¼ teaspoon salt

¼ teaspoon black pepper
¼ teaspoon onion powder
¼ teaspoon garlic powder
¼ teaspoon cayenne
  pepper
¼ teaspoon marjoram
¼ teaspoon oregano

1. Combine the oil and lemon juice, and brush each piece of skinned chicken with the mixture.
2. Place the milk in a shallow bowl, and set aside. Combine the flour and seasonings in another bowl, mixing well.
3. Dip the chicken into the milk, coating all sides. Then coat with the flour mixture.
4. Place the chicken 'skin'-side-down in a foil-covered baking pan. Cover loosely with foil, and bake at 350°F (Gas Mark 4/180°C) for 30 minutes. Turn the chicken pieces over, and bake 30 minutes more, or until cooked through.

6 servings of 3½ ounces (95 g) each (cooked weight).

Per Serving: 221 calories, 78 mg cholesterol, no dietary fibre, 7 g fat, 168 mg sodium.

CHICKEN WITH BROCCOLI AND CARROT

PREPARATION TIME: 12 MINUTES.   COOKING TIME: 10 MINUTES.

Here we try to reproduce one of Chef Wang Chia Hsin's creations from Nashville's Peking Garden restaurant. It was the first dish in which we ever used the Chinese technique of dipping the cut-up chicken in egg white and sprinkling with cornflour before stir-frying. It's a technique worth using.

2 chicken breasts,
  skinned, boned, and cut
  into 1-inch (2-cm)
  pieces, 9 to 10 ounces
  (275–300 g) in all

1 egg white, lightly
  beaten
½ teaspoon cornflour
1 large stalk fresh broccoli
1 small carrot

1½ teaspoons vegetable
  oil
4 fluid ounces (110 ml)
  chicken stock

¼ teaspoon cornflour,
  dissolved in a small
  amount of water

1. Dip the chicken pieces in the egg white and place them on a dish. Sprinkle with the ½ teaspoon of cornflour.
2. Cut the broccoli and carrot into bite-size pieces and steam over hot water until tender.
3. While the vegetables are cooking, heat a wok or large frying pan until hot, add the oil and the chicken. Cook for about 3 minutes on high heat, or until nearly done, stirring frequently. Reduce heat to medium.
4. Remove the broccoli and carrot from the steamer and add to the wok.
5. Add the chicken stock and the dissolved cornflour. Bring to a boil, stirring constantly. Reduce heat and continue to stir, cooking only until sauce is just slightly thickened. Then immediately remove from the heat and serve.

2 servings of 1 cut up breast each, plus vegetables.

Per Serving: 176 calories, 42 mg cholesterol, 3 g dietary fibre, 9 g fat, 84 mg sodium.

HAPPY HEART CHICKEN

PREPARATION TIME: 10 MINUTES.   COOKING TIME: 1 HOUR.

The layer of vegetables in this recipe helps keep the skinned chicken moist. Notice that no oil is necessary!

3 pounds (1 kilo 350 g)
  chicken pieces, skinned
1½ teaspoons dried basil
2 tablespoons lemon juice
4 spring onions, chopped

1 14-ounce (400-g) tin
  artichoke hearts
1 large courgette
2 medium carrots

1. Arrange the chicken in a large casserole dish. Sprinkle with the basil and lemon juice. Chop the onions and spread over the chicken.

2. Scrub the carrots clean – do not peel – then cut each in half. Quarter them lengthwise to make 8 pieces out of each vegetable. Wipe the courgette and cut it up the same way. Arrange the vegetables in an alternating pattern on top of the chicken, along with the artichoke hearts.
3. Cover and bake at 350°F (Gas Mark 4/180°C) for 1 hour, or until the carrots are just tender.

8 servings of 3½ ounces (95 g) each (cooked weight), plus vegetables.

Per Serving: 191 calories, 59 mg cholesterol, 4 g dietary fibre, 8 g fat, 334 mg sodium.

GREEK CHICKEN

PREPARATION TIME: 4 MINUTES.   COOKING TIME: 35 MINUTES.

Try serving this with warmed whole-grain pita bread, rice or Tabbouli (p. 63) and Greek Salad (p. 60).

*4 chicken breasts OR 8
  thighs, skinned
Juice of 2 lemons
1 dessertspoon olive oil*

*3 cloves garlic, crushed
1 teaspoon oregano
Salt and pepper to taste*

1. Place the chicken in a shallow pan. Combine all remaining ingredients, and pour over the chicken. Cover and refrigerate at least 3 hours, preferably overnight.
2. Place the chicken on a grill pan, a barbecue grill, or on a rack in a baking pan in an oven heated to 450°F (Gas Mark 8/230°C) and cook for about 35 minutes.

4 servings of 3½ ounces (95 g) of meat (cooked weight).

Per Serving: 180 calories, 73 mg cholesterol, no dietary fibre, 6 g fat, 198 mg sodium. (Analysis is for chicken breasts. Thighs will contain about 50 calories more than breasts, with a total of about 11 grams of fat.)

CHICKEN WITH LEEKS AND MUSHROOMS

PREPARATION TIME: 10 MINUTES.   COOKING TIME: 1½ HOURS.

Mild, tasty and easy to prepare.

*16 fluid ounces (450 ml)
  stock
6 ounces (175 g) brown
  rice
4 chicken breasts,
  skinned, about 6 ounces
  (175 g) each*

*6 ounces (175 g) fresh
  mushrooms, quartered
2 whole leeks
Salt and pepper to taste*

1. Put the stock and the rice in a large casserole dish, and place the chicken breasts on top. Spread the mushrooms over the chicken.
2. Wash the leeks thoroughly, separating the leaves to get all the dirt out. Then slice the leeks in 1-inch (2-cm) pieces, and place on top of the chicken and mushrooms. Sprinkle with salt and fresh-ground black pepper.
3. Bake at 325°F (Gas Mark 3/170°C) for 1½ hours.

4 servings of 3½ ounces (95 g) meat (cooked weight), plus vegetables and rice.

Per Serving: 341 calories, 74 mg cholesterol, 5 g dietary fibre, 5 g fat, 808 mg sodium.

BAKED LEMON CHICKEN WITH VEGETABLES

PREPARATION TIME: 8 MINUTES.   COOKING TIME: 30 MINUTES.

It seems every low-fat cookbook has a recipe for lemon-baked chicken and *The Rotation Diet* is no exception. So this time we were going to leave it out, and substitute our Lime-Light Chicken (facing page). But this variation is so good, we gave in to tradition. It is excellent served with brown rice or any other cooked whole grain.

4 chicken breasts, skinned
   and boned, about 4½–5
   ounces (125 to 145 g)
   each
1 clove garlic, crushed
½ teaspoon oregano
Dash of salt (optional)
Fresh-ground black
   pepper to taste

2 medium courgettes,
   sliced
1 medium green pepper,
   sliced in strips
4 fluid ounces (110 ml)
   chicken stock
2 tablespoons lemon juice
1 dessertspoon white wine

1. Place the chicken in a casserole dish. Top with the garlic, the other seasonings and the vegetables. Pour in the stock, lemon juice and wine.
2. Cover tightly and bake at 350°F (Gas Mark 4/180°C) for 30 minutes or until chicken is cooked through.

4 servings of about 3½ ounces (95 g) meat (cooked weight), plus vegetables.

Per Serving: 164 calories, 73 mg cholesterol, 1 g dietary fibre, 3 g fat, 162 mg sodium.

LIME-LIGHT CHICKEN

PREPARATION TIME: 5 MINUTES.   COOKING TIME:
50 TO 55 MINUTES.

This is good hot, and for some reason even better cold. Make it ahead for a picnic lunch: chill it in the refrigerator for several hours or overnight, then skim off any fat that has risen to the top. Add a small amount of salt at the table if you like.

4 chicken breasts, skinned
   (about 6 ounces/175 g
   each)
1 bay leaf
1 dessertspoon vegetable
   oil
1 dessertspoon white wine
   vinegar

1 dessertspoon lime juice
1 teaspoon dried thyme
¼ teaspoon ground
   coriander
Fresh-ground black
   pepper to taste
1 lime, cut into thin
   rounds

1. Preheat the oven to 325°F (Gas Mark 3/170°C). Place

119

the chicken breasts and the bay leaf in a casserole dish. Pour the vegetable oil, vinegar and lime juice over the top.
2. Sprinkle with the seasonings, cover, and bake in the oven for 45 minutes.
3. Remove the chicken from the oven, and arrange the lime slices on top of the chicken. Return the chicken to the oven and bake uncovered for another 5 to 10 minutes or until chicken is cooked through.

4 servings of 3½ ounces (95 g) each (cooked weight).

Per Serving: 180 calories, 73 mg cholesterol, no dietary fibre, 6 g fat, 64 mg sodium.

EASY INDIAN CHICKEN STIR-FRY

PREPARATION TIME: 12 MINUTES.   COOKING TIME: 20 MINUTES.

We tried this with chicken, but it would do just as well with any leftover cooked meat, or even as a vegetarian stir-fry. It's also a great way to use up any extra raw or cooked vegetables you may have on hand. Use any vegetables you like, enough to fill a 16-fluid ounce (450-ml) measure, and always remember to start cooking the ones which take the most time first, adding the others as you go along. If you use cooked vegetables, they will need only a quick warming up.

For a 'make-ahead' dish, simply dice the meat and vegetables the night before or in the morning and store in the refrigerator.

Have ready:
1 dessertspoon peanut oil
1 clove garlic, crushed
2 spring onions, diced
1 medium courgette,
thinly sliced
8 ounces (225 g)
mushrooms, sliced

1 tomato, diced
Skinned, diced cooked
chicken to fill a 16-fluid-
ounce (450-ml) measure
(about 10 ounces/300 g)
1½ tablespoons tamari OR
soy sauce

Spices:

½ teaspoon cumin	½ teaspoon turmeric
½ teaspoon fresh ginger root, minced	¼ teaspoon fresh-ground black pepper
¼ teaspoon ground coriander	(Or substitute 2¼ teaspoons of Indian Spice Blend, p. 244 for these spices.)
¼ teaspoon cayenne pepper	

1. Heat the oil in a wok or large frying pan over medium heat. Add the garlic and onions, and cook for 2 to 3 minutes, stirring constantly. Add the courgette, and stir-fry for about 6 or 7 minutes. Add the mushrooms and tomato, and stir-fry until courgette is almost tender.
2. Add the chicken, and heat through, still stirring. Then add the tamari and the spices, mix well, and serve.

4 servings. Serving size is an 8-fluid-ounce (225-g) measure.

Per Serving: 255 calories, 96 mg cholesterol, 3 g dietary fibre, 8 g fat, 605 mg sodium.

CHICKEN WITH CASHEW NUTS AND BROCCOLI

PREPARATION TIME: 15 MINUTES.   COOKING TIME:
                                        10 TO 15 MINUTES.

Assemble all your ingredients ahead of time, so you can follow the steps of this Oriental dish quickly and easily. Serve with steaming-hot brown rice.

1 dessertspoon cornflour	3 whole chicken breasts, skinned, boned, and cut in 1-inch (2-cm) chunks
8 fluid ounces (225 ml) chicken stock	
2 tablespoons dry sherry	2 slices fresh ginger root, each ½ inch (5 mm) thick
1½ tablespoons tamari OR soy sauce	
½ teaspoon Tabasco sauce	3 heads of broccoli, broken into florets
1 dessertspoon peanut oil	

121

1 medium sweet red
  pepper, cut in 1-inch
  (2-cm) squares
8 ounces (225 g) fresh
  mushrooms, sliced
5–6 spring onions,
  chopped fine

1 clove garlic, crushed or
  minced
2 ounces (56 g) roasted
  unsalted cashews OR
  peanuts

1. Combine the cornflour, chicken stock, sherry, tamari sauce and Tabasco in a small bowl.
2. Heat the oil in a hot frying pan or wok. When the oil is very hot, add the chicken and ginger. Cook, stirring constantly, until chicken turns white. Remove the ginger and push the chicken aside.
3. Place the broccoli, red pepper, mushrooms, onions and garlic in the centre of the wok. Cook 3 minutes, stirring constantly.
4. Combine the broth mixture with the vegetables and continue stirring until the sauce thickens slightly. Stir in the chicken from the sides of the wok.
5. Sprinkle with nuts and serve immediately.

6 servings of ½ breast each (about 3½ ounces (95 g) of meat, cooked weight), plus vegetables.

Per Serving: 260 calories, 73 mg cholesterol, 5 g dietary fibre, 9 g fat, 548 mg sodium.

WORCESTERSHIRE CHICKEN

PREPARATION TIME: 15 MINUTES.   COOKING TIME:
                                              45 TO 60 MINUTES.

This very easy recipe uses Lea and Perrins Worcestershire sauce, along with a dry white wine, as seasoning.

3 pounds (1 kilo 350 g)
  chicken pieces, skinned
3 medium potatoes, cut in
  chunks
2 medium onions, cut in
  chunks

4 ounces (110 g)
  mushrooms, whole
12 ounces (350 g) cherry
  tomatoes, whole
4 fluid ounces (110 ml)
  white wine

1½ tablespoons   *1 bay leaf*
  Worcestershire sauce

1. Place the skinned chicken in a casserole dish and cover with the vegetables. Pour in the wine and the Worcestershire sauce, and float the bay leaf in the bottom of the dish.
2. Bake, covered, at 350°F (Gas Mark 4/180°C) for 45 minutes to 1 hour, until the chicken is cooked through and tender.

6 servings of 3½ ounces (95 g) each (cooked weight), plus vegetables and sauce.

Per Serving: 262 calories, 78 mg cholesterol, 5 g dietary fibre, 5 g fat, 176 mg sodium.

QUICK CHICKEN STIR-FRY WITH BULGUR WHEAT

PREPARATION TIME: 12 MINUTES.   COOKING TIME:
                                           10 TO 15 MINUTES.

4 ounces (110 g) bulgur   *½ teaspoon fresh-ground*
  wheat, uncooked   *black pepper*
Water to cover   *¼ teaspoon salt*
1 dessertspoon peanut oil   *2 ounces (56 g) unsalted,*
2 spring onions, minced   *dry roasted peanuts*
1 clove garlic, crushed or   *2 fluid ounces (55 ml)*
  minced   *plain low-fat yogurt*
¼ green pepper, diced   *1 dessertspoon tamari* OR
1 stalk celery, diced   *soy sauce*
6 fresh mushrooms, sliced
diced cooked chicken, to
  fill a 16-ounce (450-ml)
  measure (about 10
  ounces/300 g)

1. Soak the bulgur wheat in water to cover for 3 to 4 hours. When the bulgur is ready – puffy and chewable – drain off any remaining water.
2. Heat the oil in a large frying pan or wok over medium heat. Add the onions, garlic, pepper and celery, and

stir-fry for 2 minutes. Add the mushrooms, and stir-fry until vegetables are tender.
3. Add the chicken and seasonings, and stir-fry until chicken is heated through.
4. Stir in the peanuts, yogurt and tamari sauce, mixing well. Serve over the bulgur wheat.

8 servings of about 1 8-ounce (225-ml) measure each.

Per Serving: 204 calories, 49 mg cholesterol, 2 g dietary fibre, 6 g fat, 269 mg sodium.

NEW-STYLE CREAMED CHICKEN AND VEGETABLES

PREPARATION TIME: 20 MINUTES.   COOKING TIME:
                                            35 TO 40 MINUTES.

This recipe is based on an old Shaker recipe – a traditional American dish with a 'new-style' lower calorie twist that provides another complete meal-in-one when served with corn bread as suggested below.

1 large diced potato
3 ounces (80 g) peas OR
green beans
1 large diced carrot
Water
½ ounce (14 g) butter OR
margarine
1 large onion, chopped
2 stalks celery, chopped
*4 tablespoons wholemeal
flour*
½ teaspoon salt
2 teaspoons marjoram
*½ teaspoon fresh-ground
black pepper*

*Up to 8 fluid ounces
(225 ml) water* OR *stock*
*16 fluid ounces (450 ml)
low-fat milk*
*cooked chicken, chopped
and skinned to fill a 24-
fluid-ounce (700-ml)
measure (about 1
pound/450 g)*
*3 ounces (80 g) chopped
fresh parsley*
*½ teaspoon dried
rosemary*

1. Place the potato, peas, and carrot in a steamer over water and steam until just tender. Reserve the liquid used for steaming.

2. Meanwhile, melt the butter in a large saucepan and sauté the onion and celery in it until the onion is translucent. Remove from the heat and stir in the flour, 4 tablespoons of the reserved liquid, the salt, marjoram and pepper. Blend until smooth.
3. Return to the stove on medium heat. Add enough water or stock to the remaining reserved liquid to make 8 fluid ounces (225 ml) and gradually stir the liquid and the milk into the flour-onion mixture. Bring to a slow boil over medium heat, stirring frequently.
4. Add the chicken, steamed vegetables, parsley and rosemary. Heat through, and serve over warm Buttermilk Corn Bread (p. 223).

6 servings. Serving size is about a 14-fluid ounce (400-ml) measure.

Per Serving (not including corn bread): 380 calories, 109 mg cholesterol, 7 g dietary fibre, 8 g fat, 379 mg sodium.

CHICKEN ITALIAN-STYLE

PREPARATION TIME: 25 MINUTES.   COOKING TIME: 25 MINUTES.

1 dessertspoon olive oil
2 large tomatoes, diced
1 clove garlic, crushed
½ teaspoon salt
¼ teaspoon pepper
½ teaspoon dried parsley
½ teaspoon basil
1 egg, beaten
2 fluid ounces (55 ml) skim milk

4 chicken breasts, skinned and boned, about 4½ to 5 ounces (125 to 145 g) each
About 1 teaspoon olive oil
3 ounces (80 g) Wholemeal Breadcrumbs (p. 219)

1. Heat the dessertspoon of oil in a heavy pan over medium heat, then add the tomatoes, garlic and other seasonings. Simmer for 10 minutes, stirring occasionally. Set aside.
2. Beat together the egg and milk. Pound the chicken breasts between wax paper until thin.

3. Brush another pan with the 1 teaspoon of olive oil. Turn heat on to medium. Dip the chicken in the egg batter and then in the breadcrumbs. Sauté a couple of minutes on each side until lightly browned.
4. Place the chicken in a baking dish, and top with the tomato sauce. Bake at 350°F (Gas Mark 4/180°C) for 25 minutes.

4 servings of 1 breast each, plus sauce.

Per Serving: 336 calories, 143 mg cholesterol, 4 g dietary fibre, 11 g fat, 552 mg sodium.

INDIAN TANDOORI CHICKEN

PREPARATION TIME: 40 MINUTES.   COOKING TIME: 40 MINUTES.

This simple version of Tandoori Chicken should be prepared a day in advance, as it must marinate for twenty-four hours before cooking. Serve with cooked grain and curried vegetables.

4 chicken breasts, skinned (about 6 ounces (175 g) each)
1 teaspoon chilli powder
2 tablespoons lemon juice
8 fluid ounces (225 ml) plain low-fat yogurt
5 cloves garlic, roughly chopped
1 dessertspoon sultanas

1 slice ginger root, 1½ inches (3 cm) thick, roughly chopped
½ teaspoon ground cumin
1 teaspoon ground coriander
½ teaspoon crushed red pepper
¼ teaspoon salt

1. Place the chicken in a large shallow pan. Slash each chicken breast a few times. Mix together the chilli powder and lemon juice, and brush over the chicken breasts with a pastry brush. Let stand 30 minutes.
2. Combine all other ingredients in a blender or food processor, and purée until smooth. Pour over the chicken, cover, and refrigerate for 24 hours.
3. Bake the chicken at 450°F (Gas Mark 8/230°C) for about 40 minutes.

4 servings of about 3½ ounces (95 g) each (cooked weight).

Per Serving: 202 calories, 77 mg cholesterol, no dietary fibre, 4 g fat, 248 mg sodium.

BAKED HORSERADISH CHICKEN

PREPARATION TIME: 7 MINUTES.   COOKING TIME: 50 TO 60 MINUTES.

4 fluid ounces (110 ml) white wine
4 chicken breasts, skin removed, about 6 ounces (175 g) each
1 tablespoon vegetable oil
1½ tablespoons
horseradish sauce
1 teaspoon mustard seed
½ teaspoon onion powder
½ teaspoon garlic powder
¼ teaspoon dried thyme
2 tablespoons fresh parsley, chopped fine

1. Pour the wine into a casserole dish, then add the chicken breasts.
2. Using a pastry brush, baste each piece of chicken with the oil. Spread a teaspoonful of horseradish on each breast.
3. Bake covered at 350°F (Gas Mark 4/180°C) for about 30 minutes. While chicken is baking, grind the mustard seed and combine it with the remaining ingredients.
4. After 30 minutes, baste the chicken with the wine sauce in the pan. Then pour the mustard seed mixture over the chicken, and bake uncovered another 20 to 30 minutes, until chicken is tender.

4 servings of about 3½ ounces (95 g) each (cooked weight).

Per Serving: 178 calories, 73 mg cholesterol, no dietary fibre, 6 g fat, 72 mg sodium.

127

ALMOND CHICKEN

PREPARATION TIME: 10 MINUTES. 　　　　　COOKING TIME:
　　　　　　　　　　　　　　　　　　　　20 TO 25 MINUTES.

4 tablespoons tamari OR
　soy sauce
1 teaspoon ground ginger
1 teaspoon garlic powder
3 pounds (1 kilo 350 g)
　chicken, skinned and
　boned

2 ounces (56 g) wholemeal
　flour
3 ounces (80 g) ground
　almonds
½ teaspoon salt
½ teaspoon black pepper
2 dessertspoons peanut oil

1. In a large bowl, combine the tamari sauce, ginger and garlic powder. Cut the chicken into bite-size chunks, and marinate it in the tamari sauce mixture while preparing the other ingredients.
2. In another bowl, combine the flour, almonds, salt and pepper.
3. Heat the oil in a wok or large saucepan on high heat. When the oil is hot, coat the chicken pieces with the flour mixture and add to the wok. Reduce the heat to medium.
4. Cover and cook, stirring often, until the chicken is done, about 20 minutes.

8 Servings of 4½ ounces (125 g) each (cooked weight).

Per Serving: 325 calories, 108 mg cholesterol, 2 g dietary fibre, 12 g fat, 909 mg sodium.

GRILLED DUCK BREAST (JULIAN'S)

PREPARATION TIME: 10 MINUTES. 　　　　　COOKING TIME:
　　　　　　　　　　　　　　　　　　　　30 TO 40 MINUTES.

1 ounce (28 g) wild rice
Herbs to taste
1 duck breast
½ fresh tomato
2 ounces (56 g) fresh
　spinach

½ ounce (14 g) clarified
　unsalted butter
Pinch nutmeg
1 bunch watercress

1. Cook the wild rice in water with your favourite herb or herbs.
2. Grill the duck breast, skin side down, until medium-well done. At the same time, grill the half tomato. When cooked, peel the skin off the tomato if desired.
3. Just before the duck breast is ready to serve, thoroughly wash the spinach. Heat the butter in a sauté pan, add the spinach and nutmeg, and toss until tender.
4. Remove the skin from the duck breast, and slice the breast. Arrange the slices on a platter with the tomato and the rice. Garnish with watercress.

1 serving of 3½ ounces (95 g) meat (cooked weight).

Per Serving: 400 calories, 107 mg cholesterol, 6 g dietary fibre, 22 g fat, 118 mg sodium.

CHICKEN À L'ORANGE

PREPARATION TIME: 15 MINUTES.

COOKING TIME:
45 TO 50 MINUTES.

2½ pounds (1 kilo 100 g) chicken pieces, skinned
8 fluid ounces (225 ml) orange juice
4 fluid ounces (110 ml) white wine
Paprika to taste

Traditional Italian Herb Blend (p. 245) to taste
1 teaspoon peanut oil
1 medium onion, diced
1 large tomato, diced
4 ounces (110 g) fresh mushrooms, diced

1. Preheat oven to 375°F (Gas Mark 5/190°C). Place chicken pieces in a shallow baking pan. Combine the orange juice and white wine and pour them over the chicken.
2. Sprinkle seasonings over chicken.
3. Bake for 35 minutes.
4. While chicken is baking, prepare the sauce by brushing a pan with the peanut oil and heating over medium-high heat. Add the onions, tomato and mushrooms, and sauté, stirring constantly.

5. When onions are translucent, spoon the sauce over the chicken and bake an additional 10 to 15 minutes.

6 servings of 3½ ounces (95 g) each (cooked weight), plus sauce.

Per Serving: 190 calories, 78 mg cholesterol, 1 g dietary fibre, 6 g fat, 163 mg sodium.

TURKEY-APPLE STIR-FRY

PREPARATION TIME: 15 MINUTES.   COOKING TIME: 15 MINUTES.

This may sound like an odd combination at first, but the apple in this recipe won't taste too sweet, and it will blend well with the onion and celery. A great way to use up left over cooked turkey.

As always when stir-frying, be sure to have all your vegetables and the turkey chopped and ready to toss in the pan.

1 dessertspoon peanut OR
  vegetable oil
1 medium apple, chopped
1 small onion, chopped
1 clove garlic, minced or
  crushed
1 medium green pepper,
  diced
2 stalks celery, chopped
½ ounce (14 g) butter OR
  margarine
1 dessertspoon wholemeal
  flour

8 fluid ounces (225 ml)
  chicken stock
¼ teaspoon curry powder
  (try Indian Spice Blend,
  p. 244)
½ teaspoon lime juice
¼ teaspoon minced fresh
  ginger root
cooked turkey, diced to fill
  a 16-fluid-ounce
  (450-ml) measure (about
  10 ounces/300 g)
½ teaspoon salt

1. Heat the oil in a wok or medium-sized pan over medium heat. Add the apple, onion and garlic, and cook, stirring often, until tender.

130

2. Add the green pepper and celery and stir-fry 2 minutes more. Remove from the heat and set aside.
3. In another large pan, melt the butter or margarine, and stir in the flour. Cook, stirring, for a minute or two, until the flour is golden brown.
4. Slowly stir in the chicken stock, curry powder, lime juice and ginger. Then add the apple mixture and the turkey, and simmer until heated through. Stir in the salt, and serve.

4 servings. Serving size is about a 12-fluid-ounce (330-ml) measure.

Per Serving: 206 calories, 57 mg cholesterol, 2 g dietary fibre, 9 g fat, 554 mg sodium.

SOUTH AMERICAN TURKEY STEW

PREPARATION TIME: 15 MINUTES.

COOKING TIME: 1 HOUR AND 20 MINUTES.

4 tablespoons red wine vinegar
2 cloves garlic, crushed or minced
½ teaspoon salt
½ teaspoon black pepper
2 turkey drumsticks
1 dessertspoon olive OR corn oil
11 ounces (325 g) tomato purée

1 green pepper, sliced
Water
1½ tablespoons capers
3 medium potatoes, sliced
2 ounces (56 g) black olives, sliced
4 ounces (110 g) frozen peas

1. Combine the vinegar, garlic, salt and pepper. Marinate the turkey drumsticks in the mixture for 1 hour, turning once or twice.
2. Heat the oil in a heavy pan and brown the turkey. Add the tomato purée, pepper and water to cover. Simmer, covered, over medium-low heat for 1 hour.
3. Add the capers, potatoes and olives, and simmer for 20 more minutes. Add the peas and simmer another 15 minutes.

4. Remove the turkey and cut the meat off the bones. Chop into chunks, and return the meat to the stew. Heat thoroughly and serve.

4 servings of 3½ ounces (95 g) meat each (cooked weight), plus vegetables.

Per Serving: 363 calories, 74 mg cholesterol, 7 g dietary fibre, 10 g fat, 388 mg sodium.

TURKEY LOAF

PREPARATION TIME: 10 MINUTES.   COOKING TIME: 1 HOUR.

Minced turkey is a healthy substitute for minced beef in loaves and meatballs. Here we have used it alone, but you can blend it with other meats, such as veal. In this recipe we get a bit more elaborate than absolutely necessary by sautéing our mushrooms, onions and garlic before blending with the other ingredients, but you can whip up a quick version, with different herbs, such as we illustrate in Quick Turkey Loaf (opposite). If you are really in a hurry, do this one with tinned mushrooms, and use onion and garlic powder instead of the fresh onion and garlic cloves.

½ ounce (14 g) butter OR
  margarine
8 ounces (225 g)
  mushrooms, sliced
1 medium onion, chopped
2 garlic cloves, chopped
1½ pounds (675 g) lean
  turkey, minced
1 dessertspoon soy sauce
Fresh-ground black
  pepper to taste

3 ounces (80 g) dry
  breadcrumbs
4 tablespoons chicken OR
  turkey stock
4 tablespoons chopped
  fresh parsley OR *2*
  teaspoons dried
1 large egg, lightly beaten

1. Preheat the oven to 350°F (Gas Mark 4/180°C).
2. Melt the butter in a frying pan and sauté the mushrooms, onion and garlic until the onions are translucent.

132

3. Transfer the mixture to a bowl and combine with the turkey, soy sauce, pepper, breadcrumbs, stock, parsley and eggs. Blend thoroughly.
4. Bake uncovered in a 9 × 5 × 3-inch (23 × 12 × 8-cm) loaf tin for 1 hour. Let stand for 10 minutes before serving.

6 servings, 1½-inch (3-cm) slices each.

Per Serving: 288 calories, 124 mg cholesterol, 1 g dietary fibre, 15 g fat, 458 mg sodium.

QUICK TURKEY LOAF

PREPARATION TIME: 5 MINUTES.   COOKING TIME: 1 HOUR.

1½ pounds (675 g) lean
  turkey, minced
3 ounces (80 g) dry
  breadcrumbs
1 tablespoon soy sauce
4 tablespoons chicken OR
  turkey stock
1 scant teaspoon
  Worcestershire sauce

Fresh-ground black
  pepper to taste
½ teaspoon each thyme,
  marjoram and basil
1 teaspoon dried parsley
1 large egg, lightly beaten

1. Preheat the oven to 350°F (Gas Mark 4/180°C).
2. Blend all the ingredients thoroughly in a mixing bowl and bake uncovered in a 9 × 5 × 3-inch (23 × 12 × 8-cm) loaf tin for 1 hour. Let stand for 10 minutes before serving.

6 servings, 1½-inch (3-cm) thick slices.

Per Serving: 259 calories, 118 mg cholesterol, 1 g dietary fibre, 13 g fat, 436 mg sodium.

Fish

Fish is not only an excellent, low-calorie source of protein but there are certain fatty acids in fish, called Omega III fatty acids, that can reduce the risk of heart disease. One of these, eicosapentanoic acid (EPA), has been shown to lower serum cholesterol and triglycerides and to increase high-density lipoproteins (HDL). Higher HDL levels, like lower total cholesterol, are associated with a reduction in the risk of cardiovascular disease. EPA also brings about some changes in the red blood cells and the platelets in the blood stream that are responsible for clotting, so that the risk of blood clots and stroke is reduced.

The best sources of Omega III fatty acids are fatty fish such as salmon, mackerel, tuna and herring. Halibut, red snapper, swordfish and shellfish have medium amounts, cod and monkfish a little less.

I eat fish at least twice a week when I am in Nashville, and when I travel I tend to search out restaurants that feature seafood. I probably eat fish three or four times a week on the road, and much prefer it to meat.

I didn't always enjoy fish and my consumption went up from almost zero to the present high level when my wife, Enid, and I learned how to prepare it! Until about a dozen years ago, all of our efforts at cooking fish seemed to turn out badly. Then, on a trip to Miami, a relative introduced us to a former commodore of the New York Yacht Club, Jim Foster. As he drove us back to our relative's home after a sightseeing trip to the Everglades, the conversation turned to plans for dinner. I commented on our poor luck preparing fish. Jim snorted and said, 'Well, I think I can take care of that!' Without further comment, he made a heart-stopping U-turn in order to head for his favourite fish market. He bought three different varieties of fish, which he prepared by tossing together into a large covered baking dish and poaching to perfection in a broth containing sliced fresh tomatoes, onions and a fifty-fifty mixture of water and dry white wine. Along with one of the best dinners we had ever eaten, we had a lesson in how to prepare fish. Here are the rules we learned.

The first rule is: DO NOT OVERCOOK FISH. Follow cooking times closely.

Second, to keep your interest and appetite at a high level, learn to use many different ways of preparing fish: steam, bake and grill, as well as poach.

Third, learn to use herbs and spices appropriately, together with various sauces. Fish is mild flavoured and at its best when fresh. As with veal, this mildness permits a creative, delicate approach to seasoning. Fresh fish is firm to the touch, does not have a strong, unpleasant odour and, if you are buying the whole fish rather than fillets, has bulging eyes and reddish gills.

Of course, buy fresh fish whenever possible and cook it the same day. But if you happen to find a bargain, then purchase extra, wrap it well in freezer paper so it won't suffer 'freezer burn' and store it for special occasions. We have kept whole salmons frozen for six months or more, and they were still excellent when defrosted and either wrapped in foil and simmered in a court bouillon or grilled over a charcoal fire. Remember: if you want to freeze fresh fish and keep it in good condition your freezer *must* be kept at 0 degrees Fahrenheit (−17°C) or lower, and the fish must be wrapped in airtight freezer paper. (This applies to fresh meat, too.)

If we had to pick just a few recipes that we think can make you as enthusiastic about fish as we are, we advise starting with Royal Indian Salmon (pp. 141–2). I published this recipe of Terri's before, but it is SO good, and such a fine example of how to grill fish steaks in general, that we could not think of omitting it. Then, give Steamed Trout (see below) a try, using any other fish fillets if trout is not available or if you do not feel up to the difficult job of filleting a trout. This Oriental preparation method was demonstrated for us by Chef Wang Chia Hsin at the Peking Gardens in Nashville, and once you try it, we think you, too, will adopt this way of preparing fish as part of your stock in trade. Finally, there's Arthur's Court Bouillon, designed for poaching halibut steaks (p. 139) as part of a five-course, 600-calorie gourmet dinner. It can become your standard for poaching.

COURT BOUILLON (ARTHUR'S)

This is the Court Bouillon used at Arthur's, one of Nashville's finest restaurants, and recommended especially for the Poached Halibut (p. 139) as well other fish fillets and steaks.

1½ pints (850 ml) water
4 tablespoons wine
  vinegar OR *lemon juice*
1 small onion, sliced
1 stalk celery, sliced
1 medium carrot, sliced

1½ teaspoons salt
6 whole peppercorns,
  crushed
1 bay leaf
Pinch of thyme
3 to 4 fresh parsley sprigs

1. Combine all ingredients in a stock pot and bring to a boil. Reduce the heat and simmer 30 minutes. Strain and cool. (It is not possible to compute the caloric value of the strained bouillon, but it is very low.)

STEAMED TROUT

PREPARATION TIME: 10 TO 15 MINUTES.   COOKING TIME:
                                                 10 MINUTES.

You can steam just about any fish, and fillets of various kinds are perfect for the style of preparation we present here.

In order to preserve the sauce that develops as you

cook the fish, this recipe is served on the dish or platter that you have used for steaming, so prepare your dishes and pans in advance. You can invert one dish in the bottom of a pan, put enough water in it to just cover that dish, and place the fish platter on top. The pan or pot must be deep enough so that it can be covered. The first time I prepared fillets this way, I used a roasting pan with a rack inside, and fashioned a platter from heavy-duty aluminium foil by folding up the sides. I heated it on top of the stove over low heat, after bringing the water to a boil, and it worked perfectly.

1 ounce (28 g) dried black mushrooms (or white, if you cannot find black in the international or Oriental food section of your market

1 pound (450 g) rainbow trout, filleted as well as possible (it's quite impossible to bone a trout perfectly)

Dash of salt
2 spring onions
2 inches (5 cm) fresh ginger root
Fresh-ground black pepper to taste
1 teaspoon rice wine OR dry white wine
1 teaspoon vegetable oil

1. Soak the black mushrooms for about 30 minutes in warm water.
2. Score the trout with a sharp knife every inch (2 cm) or so on the back side. Sprinkle this side with salt and place the fish back-side down on the platter you will use for steaming and serving.
3. Use only the bottom 4 inches (10 cm) of the onions and cut these pieces in half. Peel the ginger. Remove the mushrooms from the water and pat dry with a paper towel. Remove the stems from the mushrooms and discard. Then, slice the onions and ginger lengthwise, julienne style, and do the same in the longest direction with the mushrooms. The closer you get to matchstick thinness the better, but it will taste fine even if your matchsticks are pretty thick.
4. Spread the onions, ginger and mushrooms evenly over the fish. Sprinkle the pepper, wine and oil evenly over the fish.

137

5. Place in the steamer and bring the water to a boil. Cover, reduce the heat, and steam for 10 minutes. Carefully remove the platter so as not to lose the sauce, and serve.

VARIATIONS: Add 1 carrot and/or 1 ounce (28 g) boiled ham, sliced julienne-style.

2 servings of about 6 ounces (175 g) each (cooked weight).

Per Serving: 144 calories, 67 mg cholesterol, no dietary fibre, 3 g fat, 155 mg sodium.

BAKED BASS WITH LEMON-WINE BOUILLON

PREPARATION TIME: 5 MINUTES.   COOKING TIME: 30 MINUTES.

4 fillets of bass or turbot, about 1½ pounds (675 g) in all, raw
½ teaspoon dried chives
¼ teaspoon dried chervil OR *parsley*
¼ teaspoon dried tarragon
1 tablespoon lemon juice (fresh is best!)

4 fluid ounces (110 ml) dry white wine
2 ounces (56 g) Wholemeal Breadcrumbs (p. 219)
1 dessertspoon butter OR *margarine*

1. Place the fillets in a shallow baking dish. Sprinkle with seasonings and lemon juice. Pour the wine over the fish.
2. Bake at 400°F (Gas Mark 6/200°C) for 15 minutes. Then sprinkle the breadcrumbs on top and dot with butter. Bake 15 minutes more, or until fish flakes easily with a fork.

4 servings of 4½ ounces (125 g) each (cooked weight).

Per Serving: 327 calories, 102 mg cholesterol, 1 g dietary fibre, 9 g fat, 201 mg sodium.

138

POACHED HALIBUT IN COURT BOUILLON
(ARTHUR'S)

PREPARATION TIME: 5 MINUTES.   COOKING TIME: 5 MINUTES.

Poaching the fish in the wonderful Court Bouillon is seasoning enough and no additional sauce is necessary. Serve the fish with Poached Vegetables with Shallots (pp. 195–6).

1 teaspoon butter   *Court Bouillon to cover*
1 or 2 chopped shallots   *(p. 136)*
6 ounces (176 g) halibut
  (or other fish fillets or
  steaks such as sole,
  turbot, haddock, cod,
  pike, perch or salmon)

1. Lightly butter the bottom of a pan with low sloping sides, such as a pie pan. Sprinkle with chopped shallots. Place fish on top in a single layer, and cover with boiling hot court bouillon.
2. Cover and place in an oven preheated to 350°F (Gas Mark 4/180°C). This takes just a few minutes to cook – no more than 5. Remove from the heat and place on a serving plate.

1 serving of 4½ ounces (125 g) (cooked weight).

Per Serving: 207 calories, 104 mg cholesterol, no dietary fibre, 9 g fat, 229 mg sodium.

VEGETABLE-SIMMERED FISH STEAKS

PREPARATION TIME: 10 MINUTES.   COOKING TIME:
                                        15 TO 20 MINUTES.

1 medium onion, chopped   *8 ounces (225 g) fresh*
1 clove garlic, chopped   *mushrooms, thickly*
½ ounce (14 g) butter OR   *sliced*
  margarine   *8 fresh basil leaves,*
4 small tomatoes, cut into   *coarsely shredded OR*
  eighths   *½ teaspoon dried basil*

139

¼ teaspoon salt
Fresh-ground black
   pepper to taste

1½ pounds (675 g) fish
   steaks, cut into 4
   servings

1. Sauté the onion and garlic in the butter, covered, over low heat, until golden. Add the tomatoes and simmer, covered, until the tomatoes soften. Add the mushrooms and seasonings, and simmer for about 3 minutes.
2. Add the fish, spoon some sauce over each portion, and simmer, covered, for 5 to 10 minutes, until fish flakes easily with a fork.

4 servings of 4½ ounces (125 g) each (cooked weight), plus vegetable sauce.

Per Serving: 331 calories, 98 mg cholesterol, 4 g dietary fibre, 12 g fat, 320 mg sodium.

SIMPLE SALMON

PREPARATION TIME: 5 MINUTES.   COOKING TIME:
                                            10 TO 12 MINUTES.

Most recipes for poached fish are simple to prepare and this one is no exception.

4 salmon steaks, 1 inch
   (2 cm) thick (about 6
   ounces (175 g) each)
4 fluid ounces (110 ml)
   white wine
4 fluid ounces (110 ml)
   lemon juice

1 bay leaf
1 medium onion, sliced
   into rounds
Fresh-ground black
   pepper to taste
Water

1. Place steaks in a large shallow enamel pan or glass or china dish. Add remaining ingredients, except the water, and marinate, covered, in the refrigerator, for 1 hour or more.
2. Remove from refrigerator, if necessary transfer to a cooking pan, and add enough water to cover the steaks. Heat on medium-high heat until just under a

boil, then turn to low and poach (simmer) for about 10 minutes, until fish flakes easily with a fork.

4 servings of about 4½ ounces (125 g) each (cooked weight).

Per Serving: 268 calories, 90 mg cholesterol, no dietary fibre, 8 g fat, 144 mg sodium.

TERIYAKI SALMON

PREPARATION TIME: 4 MINUTES.   COOKING TIME:
                                        14 TO 20 MINUTES.

This dish vies with Royal Indian Salmon for ease of preparation and exotic taste.

Nonstick vegetable cooking spray
4 salmon steaks, about 6 ounces (175 g) each
1 dessertspoon tamari OR soy sauce
1 dessertspoon honey
¼ teaspoon ground ginger
⅛ teaspoon mace (optional)

1. Spray a foil-lined grill pan with nonstick cooking spray.
2. Arrange the salmon on the pan. In a small bowl, combine the remaining ingredients to make a teriyaki sauce.
3. Brush the salmon with the teriyaki sauce. Grill about 7 to 10 minutes a side, basting frequently with the sauce.

4 servings of 4½ ounces (125 g) each (cooked weight).

Per Serving: 230 calories, 90 mg cholesterol, no dietary fibre, 8 g fat, 340 mg sodium.

ROYAL INDIAN SALMON

PREPARATION TIME: 5 MINUTES.   COOKING TIME:
                                        16 TO 20 MINUTES.

We couldn't resist including this recipe, which first appeared in the original *Rotation Diet* book. It is one of our all-time favourites, delicately flavoured and very easy to prepare.

4 salmon steaks, 1 inch (2 cm) thick (about 6 ounces/175 g each)	½ teaspoon fennel seeds, crushed
4 tablespoons chicken OR vegetable stock	¼ teaspoon cumin
2 dessertspoons lemon juice	¼ teaspoon ground coriander
	Dash of salt and fresh-ground black pepper

1. Place the steaks in a shallow dish. Pour the stock and the lemon juice over the steaks. Add the seasonings. Marinate, covered, in the refrigerator for at least two hours, turning the steaks occasionally.
2. To cook, place the steaks on a foil-covered grill pan. Spoon 2 teaspoons of the marinade on top of each steak. Place under the grill at low heat for 8 to 10 minutes, or until slighly brown on the edges. Turn steaks over, spoon on the remaining marinade, and grill for an additional 8 to 10 minutes.

4 servings of about 4½ ounces (125 g) each (cooked weight).

Per Serving: 215 calories, 90 mg cholesterol, no dietary fibre, 8 g fat, 198 mg sodium.

GRILLED COD WITH SHALLOTS

PREPARATION TIME: 10 MINUTES.   COOKING TIME: 10 MINUTES.

2 pounds (900 g) cod fillets	1 dessertspoon lemon juice
Nonstick vegetable spray	
Small knob of butter OR 2 teaspoons (10 ml) vegetable oil	1 teaspoon dried dillweed
	3 tablespoons fresh parsley, minced
3 shallots, chopped	Salt and fresh-ground black pepper to taste
1 clove garlic, minced	

1. Heat a small saucepan over medium heat, add butter or oil and shallots. Cover and let cook, stirring occa-

sionally, for about a minute, then add garlic, lemon juice, dillweed and parsley. Let cook until onions are translucent.
2. Place fillets on a foil-covered grill pan that has been sprayed lightly with vegetable spray.
3. Spread shallot mixture over fish. Add salt and pepper to taste.
4. Grill for about 5 minutes, turn, baste and grill for an additional 5 minutes, or until fish flakes easily with a fork.

6 servings of 4 ounces (110 g) each (cooked weight).

Per Serving: 185 calories, 80 mg cholesterol, no dietary fibre, 6 g fat, 243 mg sodium.

STEAMED FISH FILLETS ORIENTAL

PREPARATION TIME: 5 MINUTES.   COOKING TIME: 4 TO 5 MINUTES.

Remember one of the basic tricks to Oriental cooking: have everything chopped and ready to go, because the food cooks quickly.

1 pound (450 g) fish fillets
10 spring onions, chopped
  fine
1 small clove garlic,
  minced
1 slice ginger root, ¼ inch
  (5 mm) thick, minced
1½ tablespoons tamari OR
  soy sauce

1. Place the fish on a steamer rack over boiling water, and sprinkle with the onions.
2. Combine the garlic, ginger and tamari sauce in a small bowl, and spread all of the mixture over the fish.
3. Steam, covered, for about 4 to 5 minutes, or until fish flakes esily with a fork.

4 servings of 3 ounces (80 g) each (cooked weight).

Per Serving: 90 calories, 45 mg cholesterol, no dietary fibre, 1 g fat, 618 mg sodium.

143

FISH FILLETS *VÉRONIQUE*

PREPARATION TIME: 15 TO 20 MINUTES. COOKING TIME: 7 MINUTES.

8 ounces (225 g) seedless grapes

1½ tablespoons white wine

1 tablespoon lemon juice

2 pounds (900 g) white fish fillets (sole is best)

1 teaspoon grated lemon peel

1 dessertspoon lime juice

1 dessertspoon fresh ginger root, julienned in small strips

½ medium pepper, julienned

¼ teaspoon salt

Fresh-ground black pepper to taste

Fresh parsley OR coriander for garnish

Lemon and/or lime wedges for garnish

1. Slice the grapes in half and place them in a bowl with the wine and the lemon juice, tossing gently.
2. Line a grill pan with foil and arrange the fish in the pan. Sprinkle the lemon peel and lime juice over the fish. Top with the ginger, pepper and seasoning, except for the garnish.
3. Grill the fish for about 5 minutes, until the fillets begin to turn golden. Pour the grape-wine mixture over the fish, arranging the grapes cut-side down. Grill a couple more minutes, until fish flakes easily with a fork. Serve with garnishes.

6 servings of 4 ounces (110 ml) each (cooked weight), plus grapes and vegetables.

Per Serving: 160 calories, 103 mg cholesterol, 1 g dietary fibre, 2 g fat, 272 mg sodium.

FISH FLORENTINE

PREPARATION TIME: 8 MINUTES. COOKING TIME: 15 TO 20 MINUTES.

This Italian style of cooking (with spinach) works as well with fish as it does with veal and chicken.

1 pound (450 g) white fish
  fillets
8 ounces (225 g) frozen
  chopped spinach,
  thawed and drained
10 whole-wheat

crispbread, crushed
1½ tablespoons
  wheatgerm
2 tablespoons Parmesan
  cheese

1. Arrange the fillets in the bottom of a shallow baking dish.
2. Cover the fish with the well-drained spinach.
3. Combine the crispbread crumbs, wheatgerm and cheese, and pour over the fish and spinach.
4. Bake, uncovered, at 400°F (Gas Mark 6/200°C) for 15 to 20 minutes.

4 servings of 3 ounces (80 g) each (cooked weight), plus spinach.

Per Serving: 165 calories, 62 mg cholesterol, 2 g dietary fibre, 4 g fat, 296 mg sodium.

LIME-STEAMED FISH FILLETS

PREPARATION TIME: 3 TO 5 MINUTES.   COOKING TIME: 5 MINUTES.

If you have a wok, you may have a metal or bamboo steamer rack that came with it. If not, use any other steamer or rack you have on hand, or use the 'plate' method, as described in the recipe for Steamed Trout (pp. 136–8).

1½ pounds (675 g) white
  fish fillets
Juice of 1 lime

4 shallots, minced
Fresh-ground black
  pepper to taste.

1. Arrange fillets in foil or on a plate, and place on a steamer rack over boiling water.
2. Squeeze the lime juice over the fish, and top with shallots and pepper.
3. Cover and steam for about 5 minutes, until fish flakes easily with a fork.

4 servings of 4½ ounces (125 g) each (cooked weight).

Per Serving: 124 calories, 66 mg cholesterol, no dietary fibre, 2 g fat, 155 mg sodium.

BLACKENED FISH

PREPARATION TIME: 5 MINUTES.   COOKING TIME: 5 MINUTES.

The recent rise in popularity of this spicy, Cajun-style dish in restaurants is a testimonial to what spices can do to disguise the flavour of cheaper varieties of fish. At home, you can use any kind of firm-fleshed fish you like. Monkfish is ideal.

1 teaspoon salt
1 dessertspoon garlic powder
1½ teaspoons thyme
1 dessertspoon dried parsley flakes
1 dessertspoon basil

1 to 1½ teaspoons cayenne pepper
¼ teaspoon black pepper
4 fillets of firm fish, about 1½ pounds (675 g) raw
1 dessertspoon olive OR corn oil

1. Combine the spices on a flat plate. Press the fish fillets firmly into the spices, coating both sides.
2. Heat the oil to almost smoking in a heavy pan. Cook the fish about 2½ minutes on each side. Serve immediately.

4 servings of 4½ ounces (125 g) each (cooked weight).

Per Serving: 199 calories, 77 mg cholesterol, 1 g dietary fibre, 7 g fat, 602 mg sodium.

HALIBUT STEAKS

PREPARATION TIME: 15 MINUTES.   COOKING TIME:
                                       15 TO 20 MINUTES.

This dish is good hot or cold.

1 dessertspoon olive oil
1 small onion, diced
½ medium pepper (green, red or yellow), diced

8 fresh mushrooms, chopped fine
2 pounds (900 g) halibut steaks, 1 inch (2 cm) thick

146

½ teaspoon salt
½ teaspoon fresh-ground
  black pepper
½ teaspoon dried
  marjoram

1 medium tomato, sliced
  as thinly as possible

1. Preheat oven to 400°F (Gas Mark 6/200°C).
2. Heat oil in a pan on medium heat, and sauté onions, pepper and mushrooms, covered, stirring occasionally, until onions are translucent.
3. Place steaks in baking dish, and season with salt, pepper and marjoram. Spread sautéed vegetables over the top.
4. Bake for 10 minutes, then cover with a layer of tomato slices. Bake an additional 5 minutes, or until fish flakes easily with a fork.

6 servings of 4½ ounces (125 g) each (cooked weight).

Per Serving: 244 calories, 93 mg cholesterol, 2 g dietary fibre, 11 g fat, 337 mg sodium.

MONKFISH ITALIAN-STYLE

PREPARATION TIME: 8 MINUTES.

COOKING TIME:
15 TO 20 MINUTES.

1 medium onion, sliced
8 ounces (225 g)
  mushrooms, sliced
1 medium green pepper,
  diced
1 dessertspoon vegetable
  oil
4 fluid ounces (110 ml) dry
  white wine

2 cloves garlic, minced or
  crushed
11 ounces (325 g) tomato
  purée
1½ teaspoons dried basil
2 pounds (900 g) monkfish
  fillets

1. Sauté the onions, mushrooms and green pepper in the oil over medium-low heat, covered, until the onions are translucent.
2. Add the remaining ingredients, cover, and let simmer for about 12 to 15 minutes, or until fish flakes easily with a fork.

VARIATIONS: For a quick version of this recipe, you can use our Real Italian Tomato Sauce, (pp. 206–7), if you have any pre-made. Pour 1 pint (570 ml) of sauce into a saucepan on medium heat, add the fish, and cook until done.

6 servings of 4 ounces (110 g) each (cooked weight), plus sauce.

Per Serving: 246 calories, 82 mg cholesterol, 2 g dietary fibre, 11 g fat, 150 mg sodium.

Pasta

Pasta used to be considered fattening, along with bread and potatoes, but now that carbohydrates are getting a better press and people are realizing their healthful attributes, we find a surge of interest in new and attractive pasta dishes.

Pasta can be made from wheat, soy, rice, maize, buckwheat, other grains or a wide variety of other ingredients, including legumes and even seaweed. Pastas come in many colours: you can sometimes even find black or brown noodles; green noodles are coloured with spinach. Egg noodles are made from durum-wheat semolina that is often enriched to provide extra nutrients. One 8-fluid-ounce (225-ml) measure of cooked egg noodles contains about 50 milligrams of cholesterol; we normally use pasta made from enriched semolina that contains no eggs or cholesterol.

Look in health-food stores or international markets for more exotic noodles. Oriental noodles are especially delicate in texture and flavour. Whole-wheat pasta is higher in fibre but has a somewhat stronger flavour so you may want to combine it with other kinds of pasta until you get accustomed to it or use it to add colour to your dish.

An 8-fluid-ounce (225-ml) measure of cooked spaghetti

contains about 200 calories. With a low-calorie sauce, a fresh garden salad, a beverage and a fruit for dessert, you have a complete meal. Although spaghetti is mentioned here pasta comes in dozens of shapes and sizes, from shells and corkscrews (*fusilli*) to the wide noodles used in fettucine and lasagne. One of the delights of discovering pasta is determining by experiment which pasta forms go best with your favourite sauces.

In addition to serving our tomato sauces with pasta, be sure to try our delicious recipes using minced meat – Turkey Loaf for example. Also see our tofu section for several more pasta recipes that use tofu as a principal ingredient.

As you experiment with cooking different types of pasta, keep in mind the amount of time you'll need to cook your pasta *al dente* – that is, it should be slightly firm, not mushy, when you bite into it.

SPINACH ROLL-UPS

PREPARATION TIME: 30 MINUTES.   COOKING TIME: 30 MINUTES.

6 lasagne strips
10 ounces (300 g) frozen
  chopped spinach
4 ounces (110 g) fresh
  mushrooms, diced
2 dessertspoons water
2 eggs, slightly beaten
8 ounces (225 g) low-fat
  cottage cheese
⅛ teaspoon garlic powder
⅛ teaspoon onion powder
Fresh-ground black
  pepper to taste

½ ounce (14 g) butter OR
  margarine
2 dessertspoons
  wholemeal flour
8 fluid ounces (225 ml)
  low-fat milk
⅛ teaspoon salt
2 dessertspoons grated
  Parmesan cheese
Nonstick vegetable
  cooking spray

1. Cook the lasagne according to the package directions. Then place them in cool water until ready to use.
2. Cook the frozen spinach and mushrooms in the 2 dessertspoons of water until the spinach is completely defrosted and the mushrooms are just beginning to look cooked. Drain well.

3. In a medium to large bowl, combine the eggs, cottage cheese, garlic and onion powders, pepper and spinach and mushrooms, mixing well.
4. In a saucepan, melt the butter slowly over medium-low heat. Stir in the flour, mixing until it is thoroughly moistened. Add the milk slowly, stirring constantly. Add the salt and the Parmesan cheese, and cook over very low heat, stirring frequently, until the sauce just begins to thicken. Remove from the heat and cover.
5. Spray a casserole dish with the cooking spray or lightly grease. On a plate, cut each lasagne strip in half. Place about a dessertspoonful of the spinach mixture on each strip and fold the ends over, leaving the sides open. Place the roll-ups folded-side down in the casserole dish. Fill in the empty spaces in the dish with any leftover spinach mixture. Cover with the cheese sauce.
6. Bake at 350°F (Gas Mark 4/180°C) for about 30 minutes, or until bubbly.

4 servings of 3 roll-ups each.

Per Serving: 280 calories, 157 mg cholesterol, 4 g dietary fibre, 9 g fat, 497 mg sodium.

SPINACH LASAGNE

PREPARATION TIME: 30 MINUTES.   COOKING TIME: 30 MINUTES.

2 pounds (900 g) fresh spinach
3 tablespoons grated Parmesan cheese
8 ounces (225 g) low-fat ricotta cheese
¼ teaspoon nutmeg
⅛ teaspoon salt
Fresh-ground black pepper to taste
1 dessertspoon vegetable
OR *olive oil*
2 cloves garlic, crushed
1 large onion, chopped
1 pepper, chopped
16 fluid ounces (450 ml) Real Italian Tomato Sauce (see pp. 206–7)
¼ teaspoon basil
¼ teaspoon oregano
¼ teaspoon thyme
8 ounces (225 g) lasagne

1. Wash the spinach carefully to remove grit, then

    steam until just limp, about 1 or 2 minutes. Chop the spinach and mix with half the Parmesan, the ricotta, nutmeg, salt and pepper.

2. Heat the oil in a large saucepan, and sauté the garlic, onion, and pepper until the onion is translucent. Stir in the tomato sauce, basil, oregano and thyme. Cover and let simmer until ready to use.

3. Cook the lasagne according to the package directions, then place in cold water until ready to use.

4. Preheat the oven to 350°F (Gas Mark 4/180°C).

5. Layer the lasagne alternately with the cheese-spinach mixture and the tomato sauce in an 8 × 13-inch (20 × 33-cm) baking dish. Sprinkle the top with the remaining Parmesan.

6. Bake for 30 minutes, until bubbly.

8 servings. Serving size is about a 12-fluid-ounce (330-ml) measure.

Per Serving: 387 calories, 41 mg cholesterol, 6 g dietary fibre, 17 g fat, 871 mg sodium.

CAPELLINI DI ANGELO CON SALSA DI POMODORO (ANGEL-HAIR PASTA WITH BASIL-TOMATO SAUCE)

PREPARATION TIME: 15 MINUTES.   COOKING TIME: 15 TO 20 MINUTES.

The original recipe for this dish from the Villa Romano restaurant in Nashville calls for four times the amount of olive oil used here. Olive oil has about 135 calories per dessertspoon, so this version has 405 fewer calories.

    The recipe for the basil-tomato sauce given here appears also in the sauce section, on page 210. Though tomato skins contain fibre, vitamins, and minerals, more elegant recipes, such as this one, generally say to remove them. If you wish to remove the skins, drop the tomatoes in boiling water for about 1 minute. Remove them from the pot and run them under cold water; the skins should now peel off easily. Fresh basil will give the richest flavour, but the dried herb can be substituted.

Villa Romano's proprietor and chef, Kem Ramovic, suggests serving this delicate pasta as an appetizer or as a light main course.

*1 dessertspoon olive oil
(extra-virgin if available)
4 to 5 cloves garlic,
minced
1 large shallot, minced
1 28-ounce (800-g) tin
Italian plum tomatoes,
quartered, OR 6 large
ripe tomatoes, skinned,
seeded and chopped
Salt and coarse fresh-
ground black pepper to
taste*

*4 tablespoons fresh basil,
chopped OR 4 teaspoons
dried basil
8 ounces (225 g) angel-
hair pasta
3½ pints (2 litres) water
3 tablespoons grated
Parmesan cheese*

1. Heat the oil over medium heat. Add the garlic and shallot, and sauté until the garlic is golden and the shallot wilted. Add the tomatoes. Season with salt, pepper and basil.
2. Meanwhile, cook the pasta in an uncovered pot in rapidly boiling water for about 1 to 2 minutes. Test it after 1 minute for *al dente* ('firm to the bite') texture.
3. Drain the pasta, reserving 2 dessertspoons of the water it was cooked in. Add the pasta and the reserved water to the tomato sauce. Stir gently to coat the pasta with the sauce. Remove to a serving platter, sprinkle with the Parmesan cheese and serve immediately.

4 servings. Serving size is about an 8-fluid-ounce (225-ml) measure of pasta with half that amount of sauce.

Per Serving: 246 calories, 4 mg cholesterol, 4 g dietary fibre, 6 g fat, 240 mg sodium.

TUNA-PASTA SALAD

PREPARATION TIME: 20 TO 25 MINUTES.

Combine whole-wheat and regular egg macaroni for a

pleasing colour and taste combination, and do try the caraway seeds.

8 ounces (225 g) macaroni
10 ounces (300 g) frozen
  peas
2 small tins (6½ ounces/
  190 g each) water-
  packed tuna, drained
2 spring onions, minced
2 dessertspoons
  mayonnaise
6 fluid ounces (180 ml)
  plain low-fat yogurt

1 dessertspoon prepared
  mustard
1 teaspoon garlic powder
Fresh-ground black
  pepper to taste
1 teaspoon caraway seeds
  (optional)
½ teaspoon salt

1. Cook the macaroni according to the package directions, without added salt. Drain and reserve.
2. In another saucepan, cook peas according to directions.
3. In a large bowl, combine remaining ingredients. Add drained macaroni and drained peas, and mix lightly. Chill.

8 servings. Serving size is about an 8-fluid-ounce (225-ml) measure.

Per Serving: 239 calories, 29 mg cholesterol, 4 g dietary fibre, 4 g fat, 477 mg sodium.

Meatless Main Courses

For those of you who are used to centring every meal on a main course of meat, it may be a surprise to learn that many Westerners eat twice as much protein each day as necessary to meet the body's daily protein needs. Much of this protein comes from meat.

Yet there is a wide variety of protein sources in the plant world: beans and other legumes, grains and seeds provide endless possibilities for tasty, protein-filled dishes.

I recommend that you try at least one meatless day a week. Begin to think of meat as a seasoning or special condiment to your main recipe ingredients from the plant world, which are generally lower in fat, cholesterol, chemical additives, and cost, than meat.

If you think going a whole day without meat is next to impossible for you, try one meatless meal first. As you realize you won't go hungry or be bored by a vegetarian meal, you'll see how easy it is to go for a whole day, or several days if you like, without meat.

Most people in the Orient eat very little meat. They survive primarily on what is known as 'complementary protein' from combinations of legumes, grains and seeds. This provides the same nutritional benefit as protein from meat.

To help you understand what protein is, think of mechanical gears meshing: one gear can't turn without at least one other. Likewise with complete proteins, which are made up of 'gears' called amino acids. We need twenty-two amino acids and our bodies can manufacture fourteen of them. The other eight must come from the foods we eat.

In order to utilize the protein effectively we need larger amounts of some amino acids than of others. You might think of amino acids, then, as *different-sized* gears, all moving together to keep our bodies moving.

Fish, poultry, meat, eggs and dairy products provide essentially complete, *usable* protein: all the amino acids are present in these foods in levels our bodies can use.

But did you know that soy flour has twice as much protein in it as some meat products? And that legumes, such as dried beans and peas, lentils and peanuts, have about the same amount of protein as meat? Yet these foods are limited in their protein *usability* because one or more of those eight essential amino acids are missing, or present only in limited amounts.

So we come to the concept of 'complementary protein'. To complement means 'to make complete or perfect'. To enable the amino acid 'gears' from plant foods to mesh and be completely usable, we must combine two or more different kinds of plant foods.

Here is one simplified example: wheat flour is low in lysine, while beans are high in lysine. Put them together in a bean burrito and you have complementary protein because the beans supply what the wheat flour lacks.

You can also use small amounts of dairy products and/or meat products to boost the usability of your plant proteins. To make it easy for you to experiment on your own with complementary protein combinations, here are the basic guidelines. Use:

—grains with legumes (for example, rice and beans)
—seeds with legumes (sesame with beans)
—grains with dairy products (macaroni and cheese)
—grains with sesame or sunflower seeds (breads with seeds)

—dairy products with seeds (sprinkle sesame on cheesy casseroles)

—dairy products with some legumes (cheese on chilli with beans)

LEGUMES, SPROUTS, GRAINS, NUTS AND SEEDS

These are the basic non-animal sources for protein and they are valuable sources of other nutrients including dietary fibre. We'd like to provide a few tips for combining and cooking these healthful foods so that you will use them more frequently.

LEGUMES

First, all beans are legumes, but not all legumes are beans. Any plant that has seeds growing in a pod is considered a legume; these include peas, french, broad and runner beans, dried beans and even pea-nuts, which are usually mistakenly thought of as nuts.

Among the many varieties of legumes in the world are the flavourful black bean, black-eyed peas, chickpeas, kidney beans, navy or haricot beans, lentils, pinto beans and, split peas. Soya beans, highest in protein of all the beans, are the most bland in flavour, but you can use them in any recipe calling for beans.

Beans seem to require more salt to bring out their flavour than many foods, and you will find our bean recipes contain more salt than our other recipes. However, as always, we combine salt with herbs, stock and other seasoning agents.

Before cooking, rinse dried beans and discard any small stones that may have got mixed in with them.

Different-sized beans require different cooking

cooking times, as we illustrate in recipes calling for several varieties of beans. They also expand in size, as do grains, when cooked. On average, any quantity of dried beans will bulk out two or three times when cooked.

Though we generally use the slow method of bean cookery, which involves soaking them overnight first, there is a quick method if you forget to soak them the night before.

Cover the beans well with water or stock, bring to a boil, and cook for 2 minutes. Remove from heat, cover, and let stand for 1 hour. Add more liquid if necessary. Then cook as you would if you had soaked them overnight.

Tinned beans are fine, but not so tasty or pleasant in texture as those cooked from raw.

SPROUTS

Sprouts from beans and seeds are high in nutrients and low in calories. You can grow your own fairly easily (there are many books that can tell you how), or look for them 'ready-made' in the vegetable section of your local supermarket. They are especially suitable for use in salads and sandwiches, or as a garnish.

GRAINS

Generally, when cooking grains, you'll need almost twice as much liquid (stock or water) as grain. Some of the larger grains need more water, the smaller ones, less.

Stirring is not necesary when cooking grains, and in fact seems to interfere with the even cooking and the final texture of the grain.

The best combination for brown rice seems to be about 1¾ times the amount of liquid to rice. Bring the liquid to a boil, add the grain, and bring back to a boil. Then cover, reduce heat, and let simmer until tender and fluffy. Long-grain brown rice takes about 40 to 45 minutes. Long-grain brown rice stays separated better and is fluffier than medium- or short-grain; experiment until you find the one you like the best. Short-grain brown rice is good for casseroles and stuffings, since it does tend to stick together.

The tiny kernels of millet take less cooking time, while larger grains, such as whole wheat and barley, take about the same time as rice or a few minutes longer.

Millet and brown rice cooked together in vegetable or chicken stock make a delicious combination. Experiment with combining one or more grains: long-, medium-, or short-grain brown rice; wild rice, which isn't a rice at all but the seed of an aquatic grass; barley; millet; oats; wheat; bulgur wheat; buckwheat; wheat berries; rye and so on.

Though some purists say that when combining grains for a dish you should cook them separately, Terri often throws them in a pot together, sacrificing perhaps a small amount of delicate consistency for ease of preparation and less mess.

NUTS AND SEEDS

Nuts and seeds are good sources of protein, but unfortunately they contain a high proportion of fat as well. We use them sparingly as a protein booster in meatless cooking and as a garnish (for example, Thai Stir-Fry, p. 83, uses sesame seeds in this way).

Toasting your own seeds and nuts means you can control the amount of fat and salt added – you don't really need to add any, especially when the final product will be used in another recipe. You can sometimes find dry-roasted, unsalted nuts and seeds in a supermarket; a better bet for finding raw nuts and seeds is a health-food store.

To toast your own, use one of the following methods:
Oven-Toasting – Spread the nuts or seeds in a single layer on a baking sheet and place in an oven heated to 400°F (Gas Mark 6/200°C). Let bake, stirring occasionally, until golden brown, which could take anywhere from 3 to 10 minutes depending on the type of nut or seed. A general rule of thumb is the smaller the nut or seed, the shorter the roasting time. Try a small amount first so you can monitor the time and heat.
Pan-Toasting – Place the nuts or seeds in a hot, dry heavy frying pan and toast over medium heat, stirring often, until golden brown.
By the way, toasted pumpkin seeds are delicious. We do them in the oven and they are among our favourite snacks.

Now we are ready to go on to some of our favourite meatless main dish recipes, and we hope to get you started on the road to at least one meatless day each week.

CLASSIC STEAMED VEGGIES AND RICE

PREPARATION TIME: 10 MINUTES.   COOKING TIME: 40 MINUTES.

This is a standard vegetarian recipe, easy to prepare, with complementary protein provided by the brown rice and the cheese. Our favourite vegetable combination for this recipe is broccoli, carrots, onions and mushrooms. We start cooking the broccoli and carrots first, because they take longer. Then we add the other veggies as we go along.

We also like chunks of red cabbage, courgette, tomatoes, green beans, cauliflower – well, just put in your favourite vegetables, and enjoy!

12 fluid ounces (330 ml)
water OR *Vegetable Stock*
(p. 37)
6 ounces (175 g) brown rice

a 16-fluid-ounce (450-ml)
measure of mixed
vegetables, cut in chunks
Water for steaming

160

4 ounces (110 g) grated	Dash tamari OR soy sauce
Cheddar cheese	(optional)

1. Pour the water or vegetable stock into a saucepan, cover and bring to a boil. Pour in the brown rice, cover and reduce heat to simmer. Do not stir.
2. After rice has been cooking for about 20 minutes, start steaming your vegetables (see directions for steaming, p. 185).
3. When all veggies are just tender, ladle them over the rice and top with the cheese. Let everyone add their own tamari sauce if they desire.

4 servings. Serving size is a 4-fluid-ounce (110-ml) measure of rice with the same amount of vegetables, plus 1 ounce (28 g) of cheese.

Per Serving: 251 calories, 30 mg cholesterol, 4 g dietary fibre, 10 g fat, 180 mg sodium.

AUBERGINE PARMESAN

PREPARATION TIME: 35 MINUTES.   COOKING TIME: 40 MINUTES.

Aubergine is known for its ability to absorb huge quantities of oil. This 'no-fry' version of a delectable Italian dish eliminates almost all of the oil and, therefore, several hundred calories. Protein in this recipe comes from the egg, milk and cheese, along with the wheatgerm and wholemeal breadcrumbs.

1 large aubergine (about 1	*Nonstick vegetable*
pound/450 g)	*cooking spray*
1 egg OR 2 egg whites	*16 fluid ounces (450 ml)*
2 dessertspoons skim milk	*Real Italian Tomato*
3 tablespoons wheatgerm	*Sauce (pp. 206–7)*
3 ounces (80 g) Whole-	*3 ounces (80 g) low-fat*
meal Breadcrumbs	*mozzarella*
(p. 219)	
1 dessertspoon Parmesan	
cheese	

1. Slice the aubergine into 8 slices, ½ inch (1 cm) thick.

161

2. Beat together the egg and milk in a small, shallow bowl.
3. In another bowl, combine the wheatgerm, bread-crumbs and Parmesan cheese.
4. Heat oven to 350°F (Gas Mark 4/180°C).
5. Spray a foil-lined baking sheet with cooking spray. Dip the aubergine slices into the egg mixture, coating well. Then dip them into the breadcrumb mixture. Place the slices on the baking sheet, and bake for 15 minutes. Turn the slices over, and bake for 10 more minutes. Remove from oven.
6. Make a layer of aubergine in a casserole dish, top with tomato sauce, then mozzarella cheese. Repeat the layers until no ingredients remain.
7. Bake covered for 25 minutes, then uncover and bake 15 minutes more.

4 servings. Serving size is 2 slices each, plus sauce.

Per Serving: 256 calories, 81 mg cholesterol, 9 g dietary fibre, 8 g fat, 438 mg sodium.

BASIC BEANS

PREPARATION TIME: 15 MINUTES.   COOKING TIME: 4½ HOURS.

Here's a basic bean recipe that you can use with virtually any dried bean. Serve over grain to provide complementary protein for your main course or as a side dish. Add the optional crushed red pepper if you like spicy food.

1 pound (450 g) dried
  beans
Water
½ bulb garlic (about 4 to 5
  cloves), minced
2 teaspoons salt

1 dessertspoon olive oil
2 medium onions, cut in
  chunks
½ to 1 teaspoon crushed
  red pepper (optional)

1. Rinse the beans thoroughly in water to remove dirt. Pick over to remove any small stones. Soak the beans overnight in a large pan, in 2 pints (1 litre 150 ml) of water. (Before cooking the beans, some people will

162

change the water. Since we are more likely to use the recipe for Basic Better Beans (below), which calls for soaking beans in stock, we don't discard the liquid.)
2. The next day, bring the beans to a boil. Turn to simmer, and add the remaining ingredients. Let simmer about 4 hours, until most or all of the water is gone, stirring occasionally.

8 servings. Serving size is about a 4-fluid-ounce (110-ml) measure.

Per Serving: 133 calories, no cholesterol, 7 g dietary fibre, 2 g fat, 542 mg sodium.

BASIC BETTER BEANS

PREPARATION TIME: 15 MINUTES.   COOKING TIME: 1 HOUR.

The use of stock – along with a whole onion stuck with whole cloves – makes beans even more flavourful.

1 pound (450 g) dried | *2 large onions*
beans OR *lentils* | *6 whole cloves*
1¾ pints (1 litre) chicken | *2 dessertspoons olive oil*
stock | *Dash of salt and pepper*

1. Wash the beans thoroughly then place in a pot with the stock. Peel the onions, stick the whole cloves in them, and place with the beans. Soak beans overnight; lentils may be cooked immediately.
2. Remove the onions and cloves, bring the beans to a boil, then reduce heat and cook, covered, until just tender: about 3 hours for beans; ¾ to 1 hour for lentils.
3. Discard the cloves, chop the onions, and sauté in the oil until translucent.
4. Place all ingredients in a large casserole dish and bake for 1 hour at 325°F (Gas Mark 3/170°C).

8 servings. Serving size is about a 4-fluid-ounce (110-ml) measure.

Per Serving: 181 calories, no cholesterol, 6 g dietary fibre, 5 g fat, 438 mg sodium.

SWISS-MOZZARELLA BAKE

PREPARATION TIME: 10 MINUTES,
PLUS 30 TO 40 MINUTES STANDING TIME.   COOKING TIME: 1 HOUR.

This is a very good and simple dish that's especially handy if you have some leftover bread that's beginning to get stale. Fresh bread works wonderfully too. The dish is like a soufflé or pudding, and is baked by setting the pan in a larger pan of hot water in the oven. This helps keep the consistency moist and light.

We like to use whole mustard seed and crush it ourselves with a mortar and pestle, but if you prefer you can substitute ground dry mustard. As always, you can leave out the tamari sauce if you wish to cut back on salt.

*4 ounces (110 g)
Emmenthal or Gruyère
cheese, grated
8 ounces (225 g) mozzarella
cheese, grated
5 slices whole-grain bread
12 fluid ounces (330 ml)
low-fat milk
2 eggs
4 fluid ounces (110 ml)
plain low-fat yogurt*

*½ teaspoon dried thyme
¼ teaspoon crushed
mustard seed OR ground
dry mustard
¼ teaspoon fresh-ground
black pepper
¾ teaspoon dried parsley
½ teaspoon tamari OR soy
sauce (optional)*

1. Combine the two cheeses. Then, in an 8-inch (20-cm) square baking dish, alternate layers of bread and cheese until used up.
2. Combine the remaining ingredients and pour over the bread and cheese. Let stand for 30 to 45 minutes, until the bread soaks up the liquid.
3. Place the casserole in a larger pan of hot water, and bake at 350°F (Gas Mark 4/180°C) for 1 hour.

6 servings. Serving size is about a 8-fluid-ounce (225-ml) measure.

Per Serving: 309 calories, 137 mg cholesterol, 3 g dietary fibre, 16 g fat, 477 mg sodium.

TERRIFIC TATER TOPPERS

A hot, freshly baked potato can be the foundation for a complete, delicious meal. We hope the following ideas and recipes will tantalize your tastebuds, and trigger your imagination to create your own delectable, low-calorie tater-topping alternatives to sour cream and butter. Here are some ideas for toppings; use them singly or in combination. The majority are meatless, but we include a few that do have meat in order to show you the wide variety that is possible.

(*Notes:* Tater Toppers cooking times do not include time for baking the potatoes. A medium potato weighs 5–6 ounces (125–175 g) or roughly 3 to the pound.)

Mix-and-Match Tater Topper ideas:

Low-fat cottage cheese
Parmesan cheese
Cheddar cheese
Neufchatel cheese
Imitation bacon bits (made from soy)
Chunks of lean meat or poultry
Shrimps
Steamed vegetables (mushrooms, broccoli, carrots, spinach, courgette, tomatoes or onions)
Meatless tomato sauce
Meatless chilli (see below)
Beans and legumes
Tofu (see p. 177)
Chives
Herbs and spices

Mexican Tater Topper

PREPARATION TIME: 5 MINUTES. COOKING TIME (USING JUST-BAKED POTATOES): 10 TO 15 MINUTES.

Here's another 'meal-in-one' that's high in protein and has no meat. The protein is provided by the beans, cheese and potato.

16-fluid-ounce (450-ml)
measure of cooked
kidney beans
½ onion, minced
¼ teaspoon cayenne
pepper
1 scant teaspoon chilli
powder

1 teaspoon garlic powder
2 dessertspoons water
4 medium baked potatoes,
hot
Shredded lettuce
4 tomatoes, diced
4 ounces (110 g) cheese,
grated

1. In a hot pan combine the beans, onion, seasonings and
water. Mash with a fork as the mixture heats, for a
chunky-smooth texture.
2. Spoon the 'refried beans' into the hot, split potatoes.
Top with as much shredded lettuce as you like, and a
quarter of the tomatoes and cheese for each potato.

*4 servings. Serving size is about a 4-fluid-ounce (110-ml)
measure of the sauce, plus 1 potato and the condiments.*

Per Serving: 330 calories, 15 mg cholesterol, 15 g dietary
fibre, 6 g fat, 108 mg sodium.

Broccoli and Chicken (or Lean Beef) Tater Topper

PREPARATION TIME: 5 MINUTES.   COOKING TIME
(USING JUST-BAKED POTATOES): 15 MINUTES.

1 small onion, chopped
4 ounces (110 g)
mushrooms, sliced
1 dessertspoon vegetable
oil
2 dessertspoons water
3 tablespoons wholemeal
flour
12 fluid ounces (330 ml)
skim OR low-fat milk
Herb blend and/or fresh-
ground black pepper to
taste

16-fluid-ounce (450-ml)
measure of cooked
chicken OR lean beef,
cubed (about 10 ounces/
300 g)
1 large head of broccoli,
steamed and chopped
4 medium baked potatoes,
hot

1. Sauté the onion and mushrooms in the oil in a large
pan. Stir in the water and flour.

2. Gradually add the milk, stirring until slightly thickened.
3. Add the seasonings, chicken or beef, and the broccoli. Cook uncovered, stirring occasionally, for 2 to 3 minutes.
4. Slice open the baked potatoes, and pour the broccoli mixture on top.

4 servings. Serving size is about a 12-fluid-ounce (330-ml) measure over 1 potato.

Per Serving: 462 calories, 98 mg cholesterol, 10 g dietary fibre, 8 g fat, 153 mg sodium.

Twice-Baked Stuffed Potatoes

PREPARATION TIME: 12 MINUTES.   COOKING TIME
                (USING JUST-BAKED POTATOES): 10 MINUTES.

4 medium baked potatoes
8 ounces (225 g) low-fat cottage cheese OR 4 ounces (110 g) low-fat shredded cheese, such as mozzarella or Emmenthal
1 egg white
¼ teaspoon salt

1½ teaspoons prepared mustard
1 dessertspoon minced onion
Dash fresh-ground black pepper
Dried parsley OR paprika (optional)

1. Cut the potatoes in half, lengthwise. Scoop out the insides into a mixing bowl, leaving the skins intact.
2. Add the remaining ingredients to the bowl, and beat with a wire whisk or electric mixer until smooth and fluffy.
3. Arrange the potato skins on an ungreased baking sheet. Spoon the potato mixture into the skins. Sprinkle with dried parsley or paprika if desired.
4. Bake at 375°F (Gas Mark 5/190°C) for about 10 minutes, or until lightly browned.

4 servings.

Per Serving: 203 calories, 5 mg cholesterol, 4 g dietary fibre, 1 g fat, 416 mg sodium.

COURGETTE SOUFFLÉ

PREPARATION TIME: 20 MINUTES.   COOKING TIME: 45 MINUTES.

1 medium courgette,
coarsely grated
2 tablespoons onion,
minced
4 ounces (110 g) fresh
mushrooms, sliced
1½ teaspoons cornflour
6 fluid ounces (180 ml)
skim milk

2 eggs
½ teaspoon salt
¼ teaspoon fresh-ground
black pepper
¼ teaspoon nutmeg
2 ounces (56 g) mozzarella
cheese, diced

1. In a large bowl, combine the courgette, onion and mushrooms.
2. In a medium bowl, mix together the cornflour and 1 dessertspoon of milk, then stir in the remaining milk. Beat in the eggs and seasonings.
3. Stir the egg mixture into the vegetables, then stir in the cheese.
4. Pour into a 9-inch (23-cm) pie plate, and bake at 350°F (Gas Mark 4/180°C) for 45 minutes.

4 servings.

Per Serving: 151 calories, 151 mg cholesterol, 4 g dietary fibre, 9 g fat, 423 mg sodium.

THREE-WAY BEANS AND RICE

PREPARATION TIME: 5 MINUTES.   COOKING TIME:
                                    4 HOURS AND 15 MINUTES.

You may substitute chicken or beef stock for the water if you are not concerned about whether this meal is totally meatless.

8 ounces (225 g) black or
pinto beans
8 ounces (225 g) white
beans
2 ounces (56 g) lentils

2½ pints (1 litre 330 ml)
water OR vegetable stock
2 medium onions
½ bulb (about 4 to 5
cloves) garlic, minced

2 teaspoons salt   8 ounces (225 g) brown rice
1 dessertspoon olive oil

1. Wash and drain the beans and lentils, picking over to be sure there are no stones. Reserve the lentils.
2. Place the beans in a large soup pot with the water or stock, and bring to a boil.
3. Turn the heat down to simmer. Add the onions, garlic, salt and oil. Let simmer for about 3½ hours, stirring occasionally.
4. Add the lentils and the rice. Bring to a boil again, then reduce heat and let simmer for 40 minutes, until rice and lentils are tender and the broth is like a thick gravy.

12 servings each of about an 8-fluid-ounce (225-ml) measure.

Per Serving: 152 calories, no cholesterol, 7 g dietary fibre, 2 g fat, 373 mg sodium.

STIR-FRY VEGETABLES

PREPARATION TIME: 5 MINUTES.   COOKING TIME: 15 TO 20 MINUTES.

Finely chopped fresh vegetables to fill a 16-fluid-ounce (450-ml) measure
1 dessertspoon peanut oil
1 clove garlic, minced
¼ teaspoon ginger

1 ounce (28 g) hard cheese, grated
Tamari OR soy sauce to taste
A portion or portions of cooked grain

1. Have your vegetables ready; use any combination you like. In a large frying pan or wok, heat the oil. Add the garlic and ginger, then add the vegetables requiring the most cooking, such as carrots, broccoli, green pepper and so on.
2. Stir constantly, adding the vegetables that require less cooking as you go along. If necessary, add a tablespoon or two of water to prevent sticking. Cook until tender-crisp.

169

3. Spoon over cooked grain, sprinkle with cheese and tamari sauce if desired, and serve.

Serves 1 as a main course, 4 as a side dish.

Per Complete Recipe (using equal quantities of carrots, onions, celery and broccoli): 257 calories, 8 mg cholesterol, 7 g dietary fibre, 17 g fat, 314 mg sodium.

Per Serving (as a side dish, quarter of mixed stir-fry vegetables recipe, with a 4-fluid-ounce (110-ml) measure of brown rice): 180 calories, 2 mg cholesterol, 4 g dietary fibre, 5 g fat, 78 mg sodium.

Note: a 4-fluid-ounce (110-ml) measure of brown rice (cooked) contains 118 calories, no cholesterol, 2 g dietary fibre, 1 g fat, no sodium.

WHITE BEAN CASSEROLE

PREPARATION TIME: 10 MINUTES.   COOKING TIME: 1 HOUR.

1 pound (450 g) dried white beans
Small knob butter OR margarine
2 dessertspoons olive oil
10 ounces (300 g) tomato purée
4 ounces (110 g) Cheddar cheese, shredded
4 ounces (110 g) mozzarella cheese, shredded
2 tablespoons wholemeal flour
2 dessertspoons dried oregano

1. Cook the beans according to the Basic Bean recipe (pp. 162–3), cooking off as much liquid as possible.
2. Lightly butter an 8½ × 11-inch (21 × 28-cm) casserole dish. Mix the cooked beans with the olive oil and tomato purée, and pour into the dish.
3. Combine the cheeses, flour and oregano, and spread on top of the beans.
4. Bake uncovered at 275°F (Gas Mark 1/140°C) for 1 hour.

8 servings. Serving size is about an 8-fluid-ounce (225-ml) measure.

Per Serving: 267 calories, 27 mg cholesterol, 8 g dietary fibre, 12 g fat, 159 mg sodium.

SPINACH PIZZA

PREPARATION TIME: 50 MINUTES.   COOKING TIME: 30 MINUTES.

If you like spinach and pizza, you will love this combination! You can use the same crust as in the Courgette Pizza (pp. 172–3), or you can use this rapid-rise version. The water needs to be a little warmer than usual (but never hot!) for the rapid-rise version, since you are combining the yeast with so many ingredients at once.

Serve with a salad on the side.

The crust:
3 ounces (80 g) wholemeal flour
1 ounce (28 g) strong white flour
1½ ounces (40 g) soy flour
½ teaspoon salt
1 package easy-blend dry yeast

4 fluid ounces (110 ml) lukewarm water (120° to 130°F/49° to 54°C)
Nonstick vegetable cooking spray

The filling:
½ medium onion, minced
4 ounces (110 g) fresh mushrooms, sliced
10 ounces (300 g) frozen chopped spinach, thawed
5 ounces (140 g) low-fat mozzarella cheese, shredded

4 ounces (110 g) low-fat ricotta OR 6 ounces (175 g) low-fat cottage cheese
1 egg OR 2 egg whites
1 clove garlic, crushed
1 tablespoon Traditional Italian Herb Blend (p. 245)

1. To prepare the crust, combine the flours, salt and yeast in a large bowl. Add the water. Mix well. If necessary, add a little more white flour to make the dough the right consistency. Knead the dough for 5 minutes on a floured board or other flat surface.
2. Replace the dough in the bowl and cover with a damp

cloth to let rise in a draught-free place. Let double (about 30 minutes), then punch down. Let the dough rest for 5 minutes, then gently pat it out to fit a baking tray approximately 7 × 11 inches (18 × 28 cm).

3. Steam the onions and mushrooms over a small amount of water until tender. Meanwhile, drain the thawed spinach in a colander, pressing out as much liquid as possible. (You can save the liquid for stock, if you wish.)

4. Combine cooked onions and mushrooms with the spinach and all remaining ingredients in a large bowl, mixing well. Pour into the crust, and bake at 375°F (Gas Mark 5/190°C) for 30 minutes.

4 servings. Serving size is ¼ pizza.

Per Serving: 307 calories, 102 mg cholesterol, 6 g dietary fibre, 12 g fat, 594 mg sodium.

COURGETTE PIZZA

PREPARATION TIME: 1 HOUR AND 10 MINUTES.   COOKING TIME: 30 MINUTES.

The original recipe calls for half courgettes, half yellow crookneck squash. You may be able to obtain squash in a first-class supermarket or greengrocer. If not, the pizza is good made with courgettes only, tasting like a 'real' pizza even though it has no meat or tomato sauce. Serve it hot or cold as a main dish with a salad on the side, or cut it up in small pieces and serve as an hors d'oeuvre.

The crust:
1 package active dry yeast
4 fluid ounces (110 ml)
  lukewarm water (105° to
  115°F/41° to 46°C)
⅛ teaspoon sugar
2½ ounces (70 g)
  wholemeal flour

1½ ounces (40 g) strong
  white flour
1½ ounces (40 g) soy flour
½ teaspoon salt
2 additional tablespoons
  white flour

The filling:

1 dessertspoon olive oil	2 tablespoons fresh
1 medium onion, chopped	parsley, chopped
1 clove garlic, minced or	1 teaspoon Traditional
crushed	Italian Herb Blend
1 pound (450 g) courgettes	(p. 245)
OR half courgettes, half	½ teaspoon fresh-ground
squash, sliced thin	black pepper
2 eggs	
8 ounces (225 g) low-fat	
mozzarella cheese,	
grated	

1. Dissolve the yeast in half the warm water, along with the sugar. In another bowl, combine the flours and the salt, reserving the 2 tablespoons white flour.
2. Stir the rest of the warm water into the yeast mixture, then stir the mixture into the dry ingredients. Turn out on a lightly floured board or flat surface and knead for about 5 minutes, or until smooth and elastic, adding a little more strong white flour as needed. Return the dough to the bowl, cover with a damp cloth and set in a warm, draught-free place to rise for 45 minutes.
3. Meanwhile, heat the oil in a large pan over medium heat and add the onion and garlic. Cover, and sauté/steam until onions are translucent.
4. Add the courgettes or half courgettes and squash, cover, and reduce heat to low. Cook for 10 minutes, or until vegetables are tender.
5. Preheat the oven to 375°F (Gas Mark 5/190°C).
6. Combine the eggs, the cheese and the seasonings in a large bowl. When the vegetables are cooked, drain them thoroughly and stir them into the egg mixture.
7. Punch down the dough after it doubles, and let it rest for 5 minutes on the board. Then gently pat it out to fit a baking tray approximately 7 × 11 inches (18 × 28 cm). Place the dough into the lightly greased dish and press into the sides. (If it cracks in places, pat it with lightly floured fingers to smooth it out.) Pour the vegetable mixture on top and spread evenly. Let prove above the warm oven for 10 minutes.

8. Bake for about 30 minutes, or until a knife or toothpick inserted in the centre comes out clean. Let cool for 10 minutes before slicing.

4 servings. Serving size is ¼ pizza.

Per Serving: 377 calories, 169 mg cholesterol, 7 g dietary fibre, 17 g fat, 572 mg sodium.

PEAS AND RICE

PREPARATION TIME: 10 MINUTES.   COOKING TIME:
                                                45 TO 50 MINUTES.

Here's a special-tasting vegetable-and-grain dish that cooks in one pan.

1 dessertspoon vegetable oil
1 small onion, chopped
1 clove garlic, crushed
1 teaspoon dried basil
8 ounces (225 g) brown rice
12 fluid ounces (330 ml) vegetable OR chicken stock
1 bay leaf
Salt and fresh-ground black pepper to taste
8 ounces (225 g) fresh or frozen peas

1. Heat the oil in a large saucepan over medium heat. Add the onion, garlic and basil. Cover and sauté, stirring occasionally, until onions are translucent. Add the rice, and stir.
2. Add the stock, the bay leaf, salt and pepper, and bring to a boil.
3. Cover, and reduce heat to simmer. Let cook about 20 to 25 minutes.
4. Pour the peas on top. Do not stir.
5. Cover and let cook until the peas are just tender and the liquid has boiled away.

4 servings. Serving size is about a 6-fluid-ounce (180-ml) measure.

Per Serving: 258 calories, no cholesterol, 5 g dietary fibre, 5 g fat, 427 mg sodium.

ITALIAN COURGETTE CASSEROLE

PREPARATION TIME: 10 MINUTES. COOKING TIME: 1 HOUR.

2½ pounds (1 kilo 150 g)
  courgettes
Small knob butter OR
  margarine
4 ounces (110 g) Cheddar
  cheese, coarsely grated
4 ounces (110 g) mozzarella
  cheese, coarsely grated

10 ounces (300 g) tomato
  purée
3 tablespoons wholemeal
  flour
1 dessertspoon olive oil
1 teaspoon basil
½ teaspoon salt
½ teaspoon garlic powder

1. Wash the courgettes and chop into chunks.
2. Lightly butter an 8 × 11½-inch (20 × 30-cm) casserole. Put in the courgettes. Spread the cheeses over the courgettes, then the tomato purée. Sprinkle the flour over the top, then the oil and then the spices, spreading all the ingredients as evenly as possible.
3. Cover and bake at 350°F (Gas Mark 4/180°C) for 1 hour.

6 servings. Serving size is about an 8-fluid-ounce (225-ml) measure.

Per Serving: 221 calories, 38 mg cholesterol, 4 g dietary fibre, 4 g fat, 392 mg sodium.

WELSH RAREBIT

PREPARATION TIME: 7 MINUTES. COOKING TIME: 12 MINUTES.

4 ounces (110 g)
  Emmenthal or Gruyère
  cheese, diced
1 egg
4 fluid ounces (110 ml)
  skim milk
1 scant teaspoon dry
  mustard

⅛ teaspoon Tabasco sauce
¼ teaspoon salt
¼ teaspoon fresh-ground
  black pepper
1 teaspoon cornflour
4 slices whole-grain toast

1. Melt the cheese in a double boiler or a bowl set over a saucepan of boiling water. While the cheese is melting,

175

beat together the remaining ingredients except for the
cornflour and toast.

2. When cheese is melted, add the cornflour, stirring
   constantly until it is absorbed.
3. Add the egg mixture and stir constantly (a wire whisk
   is best for this) until the sauce thickens. Serve
   immediately over whole-grain toast.

*4 servings. Serving size is about a 3-fluid-ounce (80-ml)
measure.*

Per Serving: 221 calories, 95 mg cholesterol, 4 g dietary
fibre, 11 g fat, 449 mg sodium.

Tofu

Tofu, soybean curd, soy cheese – these terms all refer to the same thing. At best, they may sound unusual to most of us. At worst, they sound downright unappetizing!

Yet this light, mild-tasting and versatile meat substitute is extremely high in protein and extremely low in calories, saturated fat and salt. It has no cholesterol to speak of, and is a staple ingredient in many Oriental countries where meat is not as readily available as it is in the Western world. Also it's high in calcium, iron and other valuable minerals and vitamins.

Due to its delicate flavour, tofu blends well with practically everything. It can be grilled, sautéed, stir-fried, added to soups or mashed or blended to resemble cottage cheese and then used as a base for desserts, dips, salads, sandwiches and main courses.

Tofu is available in an array of textures – regular, firm, silken, wine-fermented, and so on – but the recipes in this book use the kind you are likely to find refrigerated in the dairy section of your local supermarket or health food shop. Firm tofu may be more easily obtained in an ethnic shop but you can make ordinary supermarket tofu into the 'firm' variety by placing the rinsed tofu on several paper towels with a light weight on top such as a plate or two. After 10 to 20 minutes the tofu will be dry and easy to crumble. Be sure

177

to follow any other directions in the recipes for draining or pressing the tofu before using it in order to get the right consistency.

Although we had used tofu occasionally before writing this cookbook, we learned a great deal more about this versatile and healthful food as we tested the following recipes, many of which were created especially for us by Margaret Nofziger Dotzler.

SHRIMP AND TOFU

PREPARATION TIME: 7 MINUTES.   COOKING TIME: 10 MINUTES.

Another of Chef Wang Chai Hsin's creations from the Peking Garden restaurant. If you're not already a fan of tofu, this will do the trick.

2 teaspoons vegetable oil
1/2-inch (1-cm) piece of
  ginger root, peeled and
  chopped
1 or 2 spring onions,
  chopped
8 ounces (225 g) shelled
  shrimps
6 ounces (175 g) firm tofu,
  cut into 1-inch (2-cm)
  pieces

Dash of salt
Fresh-ground black pepper
  to taste
Dash of sugar
4 fluid ounces (110 ml)
  chicken stock
1/4 teaspoon cornflour,
  dissolved in a bit of water

1. In a wok or frying pan, heat the oil, add the ginger root and onions and stir for 10 seconds, then add the shrimps and tofu and cook half to 1 minute more.
2. Add the salt, pepper, sugar, chicken stock and dis-solved cornflour. Bring to a boil, stirring frequently. Reduce heat and simmer for about another minute or until sauce is at desired consistency.

2 servings of about an 8-fluid-ounce (225-ml) measure each.

Per Serving: 245 calories, 168 mg cholesterol, 2 g dietary fibre, 10 g fat, 534 mg sodium.

TOFU MANICOTTI

PREPARATION TIME: 30 MINUTES.   COOKING TIME:
1 HOUR AND 5 MINUTES.

1 pound (450 g) firm tofu
½ teaspoon salt
8 ounces (225 g) low-fat
  mozzarella cheese,
  grated
3 tablespoons fresh
  parsley, finely chopped
1 28-ounce (800-g) tin
  whole tomatoes

1 6-ounce (175-g) tin
  tomato paste
1 dessertspoon leaf
  oregano
1½ teaspoons basil leaf
¼ teaspoon garlic powder
16 fluid ounces (450 ml)
  water
8 ounces (225 g) canelloni

1. Rinse the tofu and crumble finely into a mixing bowl. Add the salt, mozzarella and parsley. Mix well, and set aside.
2. Place the tomatoes with their juice, the tomato paste, oregano, basil, garlic powder and water in a blender. Blend briefly, for a chunky consistency.
3. Place 16 fluid ounces (450 ml) of this tomato sauce in the bottom of a 9 × 12-inch (23 × 30-cm) glass or stainless steel baking pan (*not* aluminium).
4. Boil the cannelloni in a large saucepan until just tender, then drain.
5. Fill the cooked cannelloni with the tofu mixture. Using your hands, pack them firmly. You should have exactly enough filling for all of the cannelloni.
6. Place the cannelloni side by side in the baking pan. Pour the remaining sauce over the top. Make sure the cannelloni are completely covered. Cover the pan with foil.
7. Bake at 400°F (Gas Mark 6/200°C) for 45 minutes. Then remove the foil, being careful not to let the hot steam burn your hands. Turn the cannelloni with tongs. Cover again, and bake another 20 minutes. Remove from the oven and let stand for 10 minutes before serving.

6 servings. Serving size is 1 filled cannelloni each, plus sauce.

Per Serving: 217 calories, 10 mg cholesterol, 4 g dietary fibre, 7 g fat, 518 mg sodium.

ORIENTAL TOFU SOUP

PREPARATION TIME: 15 MINUTES.   COOKING TIME: 30 MINUTES.

*2 pints (1 litre 150 ml)
vegetable OR chicken
stock (see Onion Stock,
pp. 37–8)
1 medium carrot, sliced
thinly on the diagonal
6 to 8 leaves Chinese
cabbage, chopped
1 small stalk celery, with
leaves, sliced thinly
2½ ounces (70 g) sliced
bamboo shoots, drained*

*1 dessertspoon tamari OR
soy sauce
4 large mushrooms, sliced
1 tablespoon cornflour
3 tablespoons water
8 ounces (225 g) tofu
¼ teaspoon crushed red
pepper
3 slices fresh ginger root,
¼ inch (5 mm) thick
1 whole black peppercorn*

1. Bring the stock to a boil in a large pot. Add the carrot, cabbage and celery, and bring back to a boil. Then reduce the heat to medium or medium low, and simmer, covered, for 10 minutes.
2. Add the bamboo shoots, tamari or soy sauce, and the mushrooms.
3. Put the cornflour in a small bowl and stir in the water to make a smooth paste. Add this to the soup.
4. Bring the soup back to a gentle boil. Meanwhile, handling the tofu carefully, cut it into julienne strips and add to the soup. The tofu will become firmer after it simmers for a short time.
5. Put the red pepper, ginger root and black pepper into a stainless steel teaball or a cheesecloth bag. Add to the soup and let simmer for 10 minutes.
6. Remove the teaball or bag, and serve the soup at once, ladling the tofu carefully.

6 servings. Serving size is about a 12-fluid-ounce (330-ml) measure.

Per Serving: 84 calories, 1 mg cholesterol, 2 g dietary fibre, 3 g fat, 835 mg sodium.

POTATO-TOFU SALAD

PREPARATION TIME: 20 MINUTES.

As a complete lunch, this recipe will serve four. It is also good served on a bed of your favourite lettuce and garnished with sliced hard-boiled eggs.

(*Note:* No cooking time if potatoes have been previously cooked.)

6 *medium red potatoes*	*¹⁄₂ to 1 teaspoon salt*
4 *tablespoons water*	*¹⁄₈ teaspoon garlic powder*
4 *tablespoons vegetable oil*	1 *pound (450 g) firm tofu,*
1 *dessertspoon lemon juice*	*crumbled*
2 *dessertspoons vinegar*	2 *stalks celery, sliced thinly*
1¹⁄₂ *teaspoons prepared*	4 *radishes, sliced thinly*
mustard	*¹⁄₂ medium onion, minced*

1. Steam, microwave, or boil the potatoes until tender. Drain (if boiled) and let cool. (You can set the pan of potatoes over ice cubes to hurry this process, or put the potatoes in the refrigerator or freezer. Don't let them freeze though!) Trim any blemishes.
2. Meanwhile, place the water, oil, lemon juice, vinegar, mustard, sugar if desired, salt and garlic powder in a blender or food processor and blend briefly to mix. Add the crumbled tofu and blend until smooth.
3. When the potatoes are cool, dice them. Add the celery, radishes and onions, tossing gently. Add the tofu mixture and mix gently. Adjust the salt if necessary.

4 servings. Serving size is about a 16-fluid-ounce (450-ml) measure.

Per Serving: 309 calories, no cholesterol, 5 g dietary fibre, 19 g fat, 327 mg sodium.

TOFU STIR-FRY

PREPARATION TIME: 6 MINUTES.   COOKING TIME: 20 MINUTES.

Serve this over cooked grain, with a dark green or yellow

vegetable on the side. See the introduction to this section for directions on how to make your tofu firmer, if desired.

8 ounces (225 g) tofu, regular or firm

1 dessertspoon peanut OR *vegetable oil*

1 teaspoon tamari OR *soy sauce*

2 stalks celery, sliced thinly

Wedge white cabbage, coarsely shredded

1 pound (450 g) fresh bean sprouts

2½ ounces (70 g) water chestnuts, drained

1 dessertspoon cornflour

2 dessertspoons water

1 tablespoon tamari OR *soy sauce*

1. Cut the tofu into pieces about ¼ by ½ by 1-inch (5 mm by 1 by 2 cm).
2. Heat the oil in a large frying pan or wok. Carefully place the pieces of tofu in the pan, side by side. Sprinkle with the 1 teaspoon of tamari sauce. Fry over medium heat until the bottom of the tofu starts to brown. Carefully turn over, and cook the other side until it starts to brown. Remove the tofu and set aside.
3. Add the celery and cabbage, and stir-fry for 3 minutes. Add the bean sprouts and water chestnuts and stir-fry for 3 more minutes.
4. Mix the cornflour with the water and the 1 tablespoon of tamari sauce. Pour the mixture over the vegetables and stir well. Add the tofu, mix gently, and cover. Steam for a few minutes, until the liquid has thickened and the tofu is hot. Serve immediately.

4 servings. Serving size is about a 12-fluid ounce (330-ml) measure.

Per Serving: 117 calories, no cholesterol, 3 g dietary fibre, 6 g fat, 26 mg sodium.

CRÊPES WITH TOFU FILLING

PREPARATION TIME: 20 MINUTES.   COOKING TIME: 10 MINUTES.

2½ pints (1 litre 330 ml) water

1 pound (450 g) tofu

Dash or two of lemon juice

Dash of salt
2 ounces (56 g) wholemeal
*   flour*
2 ounces (56 g) plain white
*   flour*
1 teaspoon baking powder
1 dessertspoon sugar
1 large egg
10 fluid ounces (275 ml)
*   low-fat milk*
¼ teaspoon vanilla extract

1 to 2 tablespoons
*   vegetable oil*
10 ounces (300 g) fresh or
*   frozen raspberries* OR
*   strawberries, thrawed if*
*   necessary*
4 fluid ounces (110 ml)
*   plain low-fat yogurt*
*   (optional)*
4 fluid ounces (110 ml) sour
*   cream (optional)*

1. In a large saucepan, bring the water to a boil. Gently crumble the tofu and add to the boiling water. Reduce heat and let simmer for 1 minute. Drain in a mesh strainer until fairly dry, and stir in the lemon juice and salt. Set aside.
2. Combine the flours, baking powder and sugar in a medium bowl.
3. In another bowl, beat the egg. Beat in the milk and vanilla and add to the flour mixture. Stir until smooth.
4. Heat a small (5-inch/12-cm) nonstick pan on medium heat. Place the oil in a small bowl, and brush the pan with a small amount of oil. Pour in 3 tablespoons of the batter, tipping the pan around to spread the batter thinly and evenly. Cook over medium-high heat until the top is dry and the bottom is browned. Turn over and cook for about 10 seconds.
5. Fill the crêpe with 2 dessertspoons of tofu, roll up and set in a warm oven as the others are cooked. When the crêpes are all cooked and assembed, top with about 2 dessertspoons of berries. If you are using the yogurt and sour cream, blend them together in a small bowl and top each serving with 2 dessertspoons of the mixture.

8 crêpes. Serving size is 1 crêpe.

Per Serving: 211 calories, 42 mg cholesterol, 5 g dietary fibre, 10 g fat, 96 mg sodium.

TOFU 'CHEESECAKE'

PREPARATION TIME: 20 MINUTES.   COOKING TIME: 40 MINUTES.

9 digestive biscuits,
  crushed
1 teaspoon brown sugar
½ ounce (14 g) melted
  butter OR margarine
1 pound (450 g) tofu
2 eggs
1 dessertspoon vegetable
  oil

4 ounces (110 g) sugar
¼ teaspoon salt
½ teaspoon vanilla essence
1 ounce (28 g) flour
8 ounces (225 g)
  strawberries OR other
  berries, thawed if frozen

1. Preheat the oven to 350°F (Gas Mark 4/180°C).
   Combine the crumbs, the brown sugar and the melted
   butter or margarine in a small bowl. Press firmly into
   the bottom of an 8-inch (20-cm) pie plate. Bake for 10
   minutes, then set aside and let cool.
2. Crumble the tofu into a blender or food processor. Add
   all the other ingredients except the fruit and blend for
   about 3 minutes or until very smooth.
3. Pour the mixture into the cooled crust, and bake at
   350°F (Gas Mark 4/180°C) for 40 minutes.
4. Turn off the oven, open the oven door, and let the pie
   stand in the open oven for 20 minutes. Then chill in the
   refrigerator overnight or at least 4 hours. Keep chilled
   until serving time. Just before serving, top with the
   fruit.

8 servings.

Per Serving: a little more than 196 calories, 74 mg cholesterol, 2 g dietary fibre, 8 g fat, 159 mg sodium.*

* The calorie count for this recipe is not exact because there is no
British equivalent for the graham cracker crumbs in the original
formula.

Vegetable Side Dishes

Almost any cooked vegetable tastes fantastic simply steamed over hot water. You can eat them plain, or add a touch of salt and pepper if you wish. The naturally sweet flavour of fresh vegetables needs no other enhancement.

Here's how to steam vegetables: Put about an inch of water in a pan. Place a stainless steel, bamboo or ceramic steamer in the water. (The stainless steel steamers are cheap, conduct heat quickly, and are readily available.) Put the vegetables that need the longest cooking time in the steamer. Cover, and bring to a boil. Then reduce the heat to medium low, allowing the steam to cook the vegetables. After about 3 to 5 minutes, add the vegetables that need less cooking time.

Hard vegetables, such as carrots, broccoli, cauliflower, peppers and so on, need about 10 to 20 minutes of cooking time, depending on how thinly you've sliced them and how tender you like your vegetables to be. The less cooked they are, the more vitamins and minerals are retained, so getting them just barely tender is best. Onions, courgettes, mushrooms and similarly textured vegetables take less time, while spinach and other greens take only a minute or two.

Of course, it's also fun to doctor up the taste of fresh vegetables with seasonings and spices. We hope you enjoy

185

the 'fancier' recipes we have here. Most of them are really quite simple – fast yet festive. But if you're ever in such a rush that you don't want to bother with a recipe, plain steamed vegetables are the answer.

You can also use a microwave oven to good advantage with vegetables. If you have a microwave, check the instruction manual that came with it. Vegetables cooked in a microwave retain the nutrients better perhaps than through any other way of cooking.

To prepare vegetables for *any* cooking method, leave edible skins on most vegetables and fruits (such as potatoes, carrots, apples, tomatoes); the skins contain healthy fibre and nutrients. If your produce has been waxed for longer shelf-life, as is often the case these days with apples, try scraping the wax off with a paring knife or washing the produce under hot, soapy water using a brush. The wax is *supposed* to be harmless and quite edible (there is some controversy about that), but in any case it seems to give an off-flavour to the peel.

Frozen vegetables are good to have on hand in case you run out of fresh ones. In terms of time, however, it really doesn't take longer to rinse a couple of courgettes, slice them, and toss them in the steamer, than it does to unwrap a freezer package, take the vegetables out of the box and put them in a pan of boiling water.

Tinned vegetables are usually overcooked, over-salted or preserved with other ingredients you may wish to avoid, so check labels carefully.

Nutritionists used to suggest that we have green or yellow vegetables every other day for their vitamin A content, but many are now increasing that recommendation to a leafy green every day because of the additional calcium contained in greens. Kale, for example, is about as good a source of calcium as milk products – and it contains no fat! For the record, a recent survey of research in the journal *Contemporary Nutrition* suggests that oxalic acid in spinach does not prevent the absorption of calcium from that green to any appreciable extent. So, go to it, spinach lovers!

SHADES OF GREEN

PREPARATION TIME: 8 MINUTES.   COOKING TIME: 15 TO 20 MINUTES.

2 stalks celery, sliced
½ green pepper, diced
3 spring onions, chopped
  (separate white part from
  green)
1 tablespoon water

3 ounces (80 g) runner or
  french beans, cut into
  1-inch (2-cm) pieces
1 stalk broccoli, chopped
  into florets
1 large courgette, sliced

1. In a covered pan, sauté/steam the celery, green pepper and the white part of the onions in the water until tender.
2. Add the beans and steam until the beans are tender. Then add the broccoli, courgette and the green parts of the onions. Steam until just tender, and serve.

4 servings. Serving size is about a 10-fluid-ounce (275-ml) measure.

Per Serving: 33 calories, no cholesterol, 3 g dietary fibre, no fat, 16 mg sodium.

CHERRY TOMATO BAKE

PREPARATION TIME: 7 MINUTES.   COOKING TIME: 6 MINUTES.

Serve hot or cold, as a side dish, an appetizer, or a salad.

12 ounces (350 g) ripe
  cherry tomatoes
6 spring onions, diced
4 tablespoons fresh
  parsley, minced
1 medium clove garlic,
  crushed

¼ teaspoon thyme
½ teaspoon salt
⅛ teaspoon black pepper
2 dessertspoons grated
  Parmesan cheese

1. Heat oven to 375°F (Gas Mark 5/190°C).
2. Remove any stems from the tomatoes and place the tomatoes in a metal baking dish. Sprinkle the onions on top.
3. In a small bowl, combine the remaining ingredients. Sprinkle this mixture over the tomatoes.

187

4. Bake for 3 minutes. Stir, turning the tomatoes, and bake an additional 3 minutes. Mix, and serve.

4 servings. Serving size is about a 4-fluid-ounce (110-ml) measure.

Per Serving: 31 calories, 2 mg cholesterol, 2 g dietary fibre, 1 g fat, 322 mg sodium.

CHEESE-BAKED CAULIFLOWER

PREPARATION TIME: 15 MINUTES.   COOKING TIME: 10 MINUTES.

1 large head cauliflower
2 eggs
2 dessertspoons skim milk
1 teaspoon dried dillweed

2 dessertspoons grated
Emmenthal OR *Cheddar*
cheese

1. Trim the leaves and stem off the cauliflower, and steam the whole head for about 10 to 15 minutes, until just tender. (If you don't have a steamer big enough, cut the cauliflower into chunks.)
2. Meanwhile, beat together the eggs, milk, dillweed and cheese.
3. Heat oven to 375°F (Gas Mark 5/190°C).
4. Place the cooked cauliflower in a casserole dish, and pour the egg mixture on top. Cover and bake for about 10 minutes, until the egg has begun to set and the cheese has melted.

8 servings. Serving size is about a 4-fluid-ounce (110-ml) measure.

Per Serving: 56 calories, 70 mg cholesterol, 3 g dietary fibre, 2 g fat, 38 mg sodium.

BROCCOLI WITH WATER CHESTNUTS

PREPARATION TIME: 5 MINUTES.   COOKING TIME: 10 TO 15 MINUTES.

1 onion, chopped
2½ ounces (70 g) water
  chestnuts, drained and
  chopped
½ ounce (14 g) butter
1 small head fresh broccoli

OR *1 10-ounce (300-g)*
pack of frozen broccoli,
chopped
Salt and fresh-ground
black pepper to taste

188

1. Sauté onion and water chestnuts in butter until onion is translucent.
2. Add the broccoli. Cover and cook on low heat until the broccoli is tender. Add a small amount of water during cooking if necessary, to keep the vegetables from sticking to the pan.
3. Add salt and pepper to taste, or leave unseasoned so everyone can add their own at the table.

4 servings. Serving size is about a 4-fluid-ounce (110-ml) measure.

Per Serving: 61 calories, 8 mg cholesterol, 3 g dietary fibre, 3 g fat, 183 mg sodium.

COURGETTES WITH DILL

PREPARATION TIME: 5 MINUTES.   COOKING TIME: 15 MINUTES.

This attractive and easy dish, created by my wife, Enid, is also delightful made with yellow squash if you see some in the market.

4 to 6 courgettes
1 medium onion, diced
½ ounce (14g) butter OR
margarine
¼ teaspoon salt

Fresh-ground black pepper
to taste
Dried or fresh dillweed to
taste

1. Cut the larger courgettes in halves or quarters; leave the small ones whole. Place in a steamer over hot water, and let cook until tender.
2. Meanwhile, sauté the onion in the butter or margarine until translucent. Add the seasonings.
3. When the courgettes are done, place them in a serving bowl, top with the seasoned onion and serve.

4 servings. Serving size is about an 8-fluid-ounce (225-ml) measure.

Per Serving: 79 calories, 8 mg cholesterol, 5 g dietary fibre, 4 g fat, 167 mg sodium.

GINGER CARROTS

PREPARATION TIME: 10 MINUTES.   COOKING TIME: 30 MINUTES.

This is a mild recipe that goes well with just about any main course. However, if you like your carrots spicier, add more ginger to taste.

8 medium carrots
⅓ ounce (10 g) butter OR
  margarine

2 teaspoons lemon juice
1 teaspoon fresh ginger
  root, minced

1. Scrub the carrots well and slice into julienne strips. Heat a pan on medium heat, and add the butter. When the butter is melted, reduce the heat to low and add the remaining ingredients.
2. Cover the pan and sauté/steam about 25 minutes, stirring occasionally, until the carrots are tender. Add a little bit of water if necessary to prevent sticking.

8 servings. Serving size is about a 4-fluid-ounce (110-ml) measure.

Per Serving: 31 calories, 4 mg cholesterol, 1 g dietary fibre, 2 g fat, 41 mg sodium.

SAUTÉED COURGETTES VILLA ROMANO

PREPARATION TIME: 5 MINUTES.   COOKING TIME: 8 TO 10 MINUTES.

This recipe from the Villa Romano illustrates how a small amount of butter, when mixed with an oil and seasoning (in this case, olive oil and basil), can add flavour.

⅓ ounce (10 g) butter
1½ tablespoons minced
  shallots
2 teaspoons minced garlic
1 pound (450 g) courgettes,
  sliced into rounds
1 teaspoon dried basil OR *2*
  dessertspoons fresh,
  chopped

Coarse fresh-ground black
  pepper to taste
Pinch of salt
1 teaspoon olive oil (extra-
  virgin if available)

1. Melt the butter in a pan over medium heat. Add the shallots, garlic and courgettes. Sauté for 3 to 4 minutes.
2. Season with the basil, pepper and salt, and cook 3 to 4 additional minutes, until courgettes are cooked but still firm.
3. Sprinkle the olive oil over all, stir well, and serve.

4 servings. Serving size is about a 4-fluid-ounce (110-ml) measure.

Per Serving: 47 calories, 5 mg cholesterol, 1 g dietary fibre, 3 g fat, 75 mg sodium.

SUNSHINE VEGETABLE MEDLEY

PREPARATION TIME: 8 MINUTES.   COOKING TIME: 30 TO 35 MINUTES.

1 dessertspoon olive oil
1 medium onion, sliced (preferably yellow)
1 large tomato, chopped
1 pound (450 g) yellow squash, sliced (use yellow marrow OR *courgettes as alternatives)*

8 ounces (225 g) carrots, sliced
2 medium red or yellow peppers, cut into chunks
1 teaspoon Traditional Italian Herb Blend (p. 245)

1. Heat the oil in a large pan over medium heat. Add the onions, and sauté until onions are translucent.
2. Add the tomato, and reduce the heat to low. Cover, and sauté/steam for 3 minutes.
3. Add the remaining ingredients, and continue cooking until vegetables are just tender, about 20 to 25 minutes. Add a little water if necessary to prevent sticking.

6 servings. Serving size is about a 12-fluid-ounce (330-ml) measure.

Per Serving: 73 calories, no cholesterol, 4 g dietary fibre, 3 g fat, 32 mg sodium.

HONEY-NUT GLAZED CARROTS

PREPARATION TIME: 5 MINUTES.   COOKING TIME: 20 MINUTES.

8 to 12 carrots, sliced into   *Small knob of butter*
  rounds ¼ inch (5 mm)   *1½ teaspoons honey*
  thick   *Dash nutmeg*
Water
1½ teaspoons flaked
  almonds

1. Steam the carrots over a small amount of water until just tender.
2. Heat a small pan over medium heat. Measure the almonds into the pan and toast, stirring constantly, until golden brown. Remove the pan from the heat and remove the almonds, setting aside.
3. When the carrots are done, melt the butter in the pan you used for the almonds. Add 2 to 3 tablespoons of liquid from the steaming carrots, and add the carrots.
4. Stir in the honey and toasted almonds until the carrots are well coated. Sprinkle with nutmeg, and serve.

4 servings. Serving size is about a 4-fluid-ounce (110-ml) measure.

Per Serving: 63 calories, 3 mg cholesterol, 3 g dietary fibre, 2 g fat, 62 mg sodium.

AUBERGINE STOVE-TOP CASSEROLE

PREPARATION TIME: 5 MINUTES.   COOKING TIME: 20 MINUTES.

1 large aubergine (about 1   *1 small onion, diced*
  pound/450 g)   *½ teaspoon salt*
1 dessertspoon vegetable   *⅛ teaspoon cardamom*
  oil   *1 dessertspoon unsalted,*
1 beef bouillon cube   *dry-roasted peanuts,*
2 fluid ounces (55 ml) water   *chopped*
2 stalks celery, chopped

1. Cut the aubergine into ¾-inch (2-cm) cubes.

2. Heat the oil in a large pan, add the aubergine and toss to coat.
3. Crumble the bouillon cube into the water, and add to the pan. Cover and let cook over medium-low heat for 15 minutes, stirring every 5 minutes or so.
4. Stir in the remaining ingredients, cover and cook an additional 5 minutes.

6 servings. Serving size is about a 4-fluid-ounce (110-ml) measure.

Per Serving: 48 calories, no cholesterol, 3 g dietary fibre, 3 g fat, 193 mg sodium.

SPINACH BAKE

PREPARATION TIME: 15 MINUTES.   COOKING TIME: 30 MINUTES.

This recipe is easy to prepare.

2 pounds (900 g) fresh OR 1 10-ounce (300-g) pack of frozen spinach, cooked and drained
4 ounces (110 g) fresh mushrooms, sliced
4 ounces (110 g) mozzarella cheese, diced
½ teaspoon salt
¼ teaspoon fresh pepper
1 teaspoon basil

1. Mix all ingredients thoroughly and bake at 350°F (Gas Mark 4/180°C) for 30 minutes.

6 servings. Serving size is about a 3-fluid-ounce (80-ml) measure.

Per Serving: 47 calories, 8 mg cholesterol, 2 g dietary fibre, 3 g fat, 258 mg sodium.

FRESH BEETROOT

Many of us have never bothered to cook fresh beetroot for ourselves. Yet it's as easy as baking a potato. You can also boil beetroot, a slightly messier but quicker method. Try them either way, plain or with a dollop of plain low-fat yogurt and a dash of salt and pepper. Or use them in another beetroot recipe. Beware the juice, as it is a powerful staining agent!

To bake:

PREPARATION TIME: 5 MINUTES.   COOKING TIME: 1½ HOURS.

1 pound (450 g) fresh   *Aluminium foil*
  beetroot

1. Preheat the oven to 350°F (Gas Mark 4/180°C). Wash the fresh beetroot, trim off the stems and tightly wrap each beetroot in aluminium foil. Place them in the oven for about 1½ hours.
2. Remove the beetroot from the oven and unwrap the foil. Peel the beetroot with a knife or paring knife as soon as they're cool enough to handle, and enjoy!

To boil:

PREPARATION TIME: 5 MINUTES.   COOKING TIME: 35 MINUTES.

1. Place the washed, trimmed beetroot in a pan and cover with cold water. Bring to a boil and simmer, uncovered, for about 35 minutes or until the beetroot are tender.
2. Pour the beetroot into a colander and run cold water over them to stop the cooking process, drain, and peel.

4 servings. Serving size is about a 4-fluid-ounce (110-ml) measure.

Per Serving: 35 calories, no cholesterol, 3 g dietary fibre, no fat, 56 mg sodium.

SWEET SPICED BEETROOT

PREPARATION TIME: 30 MINUTES.   COOKING TIME: 10 MINUTES.

If you buy cooked beetroot for this recipe just dice them and skip the first two steps. Add the spices and sultanas later.

1 pound (450 g) small fresh   *Water to cover*
  beetroot, washed and   *3 whole cloves*
  trimmed   *2 ounces (56 g) sultanas*

Dash allspice
⅓ ounce (10 g) butter OR
  margarine
1 slice fresh ginger root, ¼
  inch (5 mm) thick, minced

1 teaspoon grated orange
  OR *lemon rind*
1 teaspoon red wine
  vinegar
1½ teaspoons honey

1. Place the beetroot in water to cover in a saucepan. Bring to a boil, add the cloves, and reduce the heat to simmer. Let cook, uncovered, for 20 minutes. Add the sultanas and allspice and cook 5 minutes more.
2. Drain, and rinse with cold water until the beetroot are cool enough to handle. Peel, and cut them into bite-size chunks.
3. Heat a large saucepan over medium heat. Add the butter. When the butter is melted, add the ginger, orange or lemon rind and vinegar, and cook, covered, about 5 minutes.
4. Add the beetroot and sultanas, and the honey. Stir, and cook until heated through.

4 servings. Serving size is about a 4-fluid-ounce (110-ml) measure.

Per Serving: 95 calories, 5 mg cholesterol, 3 g dietary fibre, 2 g fat, 77 mg sodium.

POACHED VEGETABLES WITH SHALLOTS (ARTHUR'S)

PREPARATION TIME: 3 MINUTES.   COOKING TIME: 5 MINUTES.

The chef at Arthur's restaurant suggests trying this with carrots or courgettes.

4 fluid ounces (110 ml)
  water
4 fluid ounces (110 ml)
  white wine
1 teaspoon chopped
  shallots

Vegetable of choice, sliced
  or chopped (enough to
  fill a 4-fluid-ounce
  (110-ml) measure)
Dash salt, pepper
Herbs to taste

1. Put the water, wine and shallots in a hot frying pan and simmer for 1 minute on medium heat.

2. Add the vegetables, cover, and simmer for 2 minutes. Add the seasonings, and serve at once.

1 serving.

Per Serving (with courgettes): about 14 calories, no cholesterol, 1 g dietary fibre, no fat, 100 mg sodium (with dash of salt). If you use carrots, the calories will be about 25.

KOHLRABI

PREPARATION TIME: 8 MINUTES.   COOKING TIME: 20 MINUTES.

Some say kohlrabi tastes like a cross between an artichoke and a mild turnip. Others compare it to cabbages, radishes and cucumbers (singly or combined). We have decided that kohlrabi tastes like kohlrabi; try expanding your vegetable repertoire to include it. For variety, you might occasionally substitute it in recipes that call for some of the other vegetables listed above. Buy the small knobs of kohlrabi, which are more tender than the larger ones. Here is the basic recipe for cooking them.

16 small kohlrabi   *Boiling water*

1. Wash the kohlrabi, cut off and reserve the tops and peel the knobs.
2. Slice and drop the knobs into a small amount of boiling water. Cook, uncovered, about 20 minutes. Drain.
3. Meanwhile, in another pot, boil the tops of the kohlrabi and drain when tender.
4. Finely chop the tops and add to the cooked knobs.

4 servings. Serving size is 4 kohlrabi.

Per Serving: 66 calories, no cholesterol, 3 g dietary fibre, no fat, 47 mg sodium.

BRUSSELS SPROUTS WITH WINE SAUCE

PREPARATION TIME: 7 MINUTES.   COOKING TIME: 20 MINUTES.

*12 ounces to 1 pound
(350–450 g) fresh Brussels
sprouts* OR *1 10-ounce
(300-g) pack of frozen
2 fluid ounces (55 ml) white
wine*

*1 teaspoon lemon juice
8 fresh mushrooms, sliced
¼ teaspoon salt
Fresh-ground black pepper
to taste
Dash oregano*

1. Place the trimmed sprouts, wine and lemon juice in a saucepan, cover, and cook over medium-low heat for 10 minutes.
2. Add the mushrooms and seasonings. Cover and let simmer for another 10 minutes, or until sprouts and mushrooms are tender.

4 servings. Serving size is about a 4-fluid-ounce (110-ml) measure.

Per Serving: 35 calories, no cholesterol, 3 g dietary fibre, no fat, 142 mg sodium.

CHINESE CABBAGE STIR-FRY

PREPARATION TIME: 12 MINUTES.   COOKING TIME: 10 MINUTES.

This vegetable combination is especially good with Oriental Pork Chops (p. 100).

1 small head fresh OR *1
10-ounce (300-g) pack
frozen cauliflower
4 fluid ounces (110 ml)
water
2 teaspoons peanut oil
Wedge of Chinese cabbage
(or other cabbage),
chopped (about 4
ounces/110 g)*

*¼ pepper, diced
1 ounce (28 g) mushrooms,
chopped
½ teaspoon salt
1 teaspoon tamari* OR *soy
sauce
1 dessertspoon dry-roasted,
unsalted peanuts,
chopped*

1. Partially cook the fresh cauliflower in the water, about 7 minutes.

2. Brush a wok or frying pan with the oil, and heat over medium to medium-high heat. Add the cauliflower and cabbage, and stir. Add the remaining ingredients and cook, stirring often, until tender.

4 servings. Serving size is about a 4-fluid-ounce (110-ml) measure.

Per Serving: 52 calories, no cholesterol, 2 g dietary fibre, 4 g fat, 375 mg sodium.

CARROT CRUNCH

PREPARATION TIME: 15 MINUTES.   COOKING TIME: 20 MINUTES.

The carrots in this recipe stay slightly crunchy – very satisfying for those who are cutting back on food intake and feel the urge to do a lot of chewing!

2 teaspoons olive oil
1 tablespoon onion, diced
1 egg
2 fluid ounces (55 ml) skim milk
½ teaspoon salt
½ teaspoon fresh-ground black pepper
1 teaspoon oregano
1 small clove garlic, crushed
1 teaspoon Traditional Italian Herb Blend (p. 245)
1 pound (450 g) carrots, grated
6 ounces (175 g) frozen peas

1. Heat oven to 350°F (Gas Mark 4/180°C).
2. Brush a pan with oil, heat over medium heat and add onions. Sauté, stirring constantly, until onions are translucent.
3. Beat together the egg and milk. Add the seasonings. Blend in the cooked onions and grated carrots. Pour the mixture into a casserole dish, and bake for 20 minutes.
4. While the casserole is baking, cook the peas according to package directions, but without added salt.
5. Stir the cooked peas into the carrots, mixing well.

6 servings. Serving size is about a 4-fluid-ounce (110-ml) measure.

Per Serving: 72 calories, 46 mg cholesterol, 4 g dietary fibre, 3 g fat, 247 mg sodium.

COURGETTES WITH OLIVES

PREPARATION TIME: 5 MINUTES.   COOKING TIME: 10 MINUTES.

This is another recipe that can be served hot or cold.

4 medium courgettes
1 dessertspoon olive oil
1 large clove garlic,
  crushed
6 black olives, diced

1 teaspoon dried parsley
¼ teaspoon salt
¼ teaspoon black pepper
½ teaspoon marjoram

1. Wash and dice the courgettes.
2. Heat the oil in a saucepan. Stir in all ingredients, and reduce the heat to low. Cook, covered, for about 10 minutes.

4 servings. Serving size is a 5–6-fluid-ounce (150–180-ml) measure.

Per Serving: 70 calories, no cholesterol, 3 g dietary fibre, 5 g fat, 188 mg sodium.

OVEN-FRIED POTATO STICKS

PREPARATION TIME: 8 MINUTES.   COOKING TIME: 35 MINUTES.

Potatoes are a powerhouse when it comes to nutritional value: they are good-to-excellent sources of protein, phosphorus, thiamine, niacin, vitamin C, potassium and a broad array of other vitamins and minerals. You could survive for months, possibly years, on potatoes alone, plus some green vegetables and a small amount of dairy products! We eat a lot of potatoes, usually just baked, but here is a recipe for people (like ourselves) who just can't do without something that resembles a chip occasionally.

4 medium potatoes
1 dessertspoon oil
⅛ teaspoon garlic powder
⅛ teaspoon onion powder

1½ teaspoons paprika
¼ teaspoon salt
¼ teaspoon black pepper

1. Wash the potatoes well and slice them lengthwise into strips, leaving the skins on.

199

2. Heat the oven to 425°F (Gas Mark 7/220°C).
3. Line a shallow baking pan with foil, and put all the ingredients into the pan, tossing well to coat the potatoes with the oil and seasonings.
4. Bake for about 35 minutes, stirring often, until the potatoes are tender. Adjust the seasoning if necessary.

4 servings of about an 8-fluid-ounce (225-ml) measure.

Per Serving: 178 calories, no cholesterol, 4 g dietary fibre, 4 g fat, 142 mg sodium.

CREAMY POTATOES WITH HERBS

PREPARATION TIME: 25 MINUTES.   COOKING TIME: 35 MINUTES.

4 medium potatoes,
unpeeled, boiled or
baked until tender
6 ounces (175 g) soft white
cheese
2 fluid ounces (55 ml) skim
or low-fat milk
1 egg

½ teaspoon basil
½ teaspoon thyme
½ teaspoon salt
½ teaspoon fresh-ground
black pepper
1 medium pepper, diced
Nonstick vegetable
cooking spray

1. Heat oven to 350°F (Gas Mark 4/180°C).
2. Mash potatoes in a large bowl. Blend in cheese, milk, egg and seasonings.
3. Stir in diced pepper.
4. Place mixture in a lightly greased 8-inch (20-cm) square baking dish. Bake uncovered for 35 minutes.

10 servings. Serving size is about a 4-fluid-ounce (110-ml) measure.

Per Serving: 114 calories, 41 mg cholesterol, 2 g dietary fibre, 5 g fat (with low-fat milk), 188 mg sodium.

SWEET POTATO STRUDEL

PREPARATION TIME: 15 MINUTES.   COOKING TIME: 50 MINUTES.

3 medium sweet potatoes
OR *yams*

1 dessertspoon vegetable
oil

3 tablespoons grated
  Parmesan cheese
1 dessertspoon toasted
  sesame seeds

1 teaspoon dried parsley
$\frac{1}{4}$ teaspoon black pepper
$\frac{1}{4}$ teaspoon salt

1. Peel and slice the raw sweet potatoes as thinly as possible.
2. Measure oil into a small bowl.
3. Combine the dry ingredients in another small bowl.
4. Heat oven to 425°F (Gas Mark 7/220°C).
5. Layer one-quarter of the potatoes in a casserole dish, brushing the tops of the potatoes lightly with oil as you go, using a pastry brush. Then sprinkle a scant table-spoon of the Parmesan cheese mixture on top.
6. Repeat step 5 until potatoes and cheese are used up.
7. Bake, covered, for 30 minutes. Uncover, and bake about 20 minutes more, until browned on top.

6 servings. Serving size is about a 4-fluid-ounce (110-ml) measure.

Per Serving: 125 calories, 3 mg cholesterol, 2 g dietary fibre, 5 g fat, 164 mg sodium.

DILL POTATOES

PREPARATION TIME: 5 MINUTES.   COOKING TIME: 20 MINUTES.

This recipe is simple, tasty and filling.

4 medium potatoes, cut
  into chunks
6 fluid ounces (180 ml)
  vegetable OR meat stock

1 teaspoon dried dillweed
$\frac{1}{4}$ teaspoon salt (optional)
Fresh-ground black pepper
  to taste

1. Place all ingredients except salt and pepper in a saucepan and bring to a boil. Then lower the heat to simmer and cook until the potatoes are tender and the broth has reduced somewhat.
2. Mash potatoes just a little with a fork, add the salt (if desired) and the pepper, and serve.

4 servings. Serving size is about an 8-fluid-ounce (225-ml) measure, plus broth.

Per Serving: 123 calories, no cholesterol, 3 g dietary fibre, no fat, 281 mg sodium.

BRUSSELS SPROUTS IN LIGHT BECHAMEL SAUCE

PREPARATION TIME: 5 MINUTES.   COOKING TIME: 10 MINUTES.

Small baby Brussels sprouts have a tender, more delicate flavour than the full grown ones, although you may use full-grown instead if they are all you can find.

1½–2 pounds (675–900 g)
 fresh Brussels sprouts
2 fluid ounces (55 ml) water
1 teaspoon basil
⅓ ounce (10 g) butter or
 margarine
1 dessertspoon plain or
 wholemeal flour

8 fluid ounces (225 ml)
 low-fat milk
2–4 cloves garlic, minced
 or crushed
Pinch of chervil (optional)

1. Wash the Brussels sprouts and pull off any yellowing leaves, then trim the ends, and make a small gash in the bottom of each one to help them cook to tenderness. Place them in a saucepan with the water and the basil, and bring to a boil. Then reduce heat and simmer for about 10 minutes.
2. Melt the butter or margarine in a large pan over medium-low heat. Add the flour and cook, stirring constantly, to form a *roux*. Stir in the milk and garlic, and cook until the sauce has thickened slightly. Serve over the cooked Brussel sprouts.

8 servings. Serving size is a 4-fluid ounce (110 ml) measure of sprouts with 2 dessertspoons of sauce.

Per Serving: 64 calories, 7 mg cholesterol, 3 g dietary fibre, 2 g fat, 37 mg sodium.

SPANISH RICE

PREPARATION TIME: 10 MINUTES.   COOKING TIME: 1 HOUR.

1 dessertspoon olive oil
4 ounces (110 g) brown
* rice, uncooked*
1 medium onion, chopped
1 medium green pepper,
* chopped fine*

10 ounces (300 g) tinned
* tomatoes*
1 clove garlic, minced or
* crushed*
¼ teaspoon salt
1 teaspoon paprika

1. Heat the oil in a large pan on medium heat. Add the rice and cook until browned, stirring constantly. Add the onions, and cook until golden, still stirring constantly. Add a little water if necessary to prevent sticking.
2. Place the rice and onions in the top part of a double boiler or a bowl set above a saucepan of boiling water. Add the remaining ingredients to the rice, cover, and steam for about 1 hour.

4 servings. Serving size is about a 6-fluid-ounce (180-ml) measure.

Per Serving: 141 calories, no cholesterol, 2 g dietary fibre, 4 g fat, 260 mg sodium.

YELLOW RICE

PREPARATION TIME: 5 MINUTES.   COOKING TIME: 15 MINUTES.

1 medium onion, diced
1 clove garlic, crushed
4 large mushrooms, diced
¼ teaspoon salt
¼ teaspoon pepper
¼ teaspoon turmeric
1 tablespoon fresh parsley,
* minced*
1 dessertspoon oil

Cooked brown rice to fill a
* 16-fluid-ounce (450-ml)*
* measure (4 ounces/110 g*
* raw)*
2 ounces (56 g) sultanas
1 ounce (28 g) chopped
* unsalted, dry-roasted*
* nuts*

1. Sauté the onions, garlic, mushrooms and seasonings in the oil in a large pan until onions are translucent.

2. Stir in the rice, sultanas and nuts. Heat through, and serve.

6 servings. Serving size is about an 8-fluid-ounce (225-ml) measure.

Per Serving: 164 calories, no cholesterol, 3 g dietary fibre, 5 g fat, 93 mg sodium.

COURGETTE-BROWN RICE PILAF

PREPARATION TIME: 15 MINUTES.   COOKING TIME: 20 MINUTES.

This dish is remarkably tasty. Try making it without the rice some time as a sauce for pasta. You may need to thicken it with up to a tablespoon of cornflour.

1 pound (450 g) courgettes
1 dessertspoon olive oil
2 cloves garlic, minced or crushed
8 ounces (225 g) brown rice, uncooked
12 fluid ounces (330 ml) stock
4 fluid ounces (110 ml) dry white wine
1 bay leaf
1 teaspoon dried basil

1. Wash and dice the courgettes. Sauté in the oil and garlic, then remove from the pan.
2. Add the rice to the pan, stirring to coat the grains with whatever oil is remaining. Add the stock, wine and bay leaf, and bring to a boil. Add the basil, and return the courgettes to the pan. Cover, and let simmer until rice is tender, about 20 minutes.

6 servings. Serving size is about a 4-fluid-ounce (110-ml) measure.

Per Serving: 173 calories, no cholesterol, 5 g dietary fibre, 4 g fat, 373 mg sodium.

Sauces

Looking through the sauce recipes in the average cookbook is almost like watching a contest to see how much butterfat a chef can squeeze into a sauce using, well, nothing but butter. Usually there are recipes for herb butters, garlic butters, and a host of cream sauces with a base of heavy cream and, you guessed it, butter.

We like butter as well as anyone, but find that small amounts mixed with a bit of olive oil, and with herbs and spices, do perfectly well for flavour, and are much easier on the arteries!

You will see that our sauces rely more on seasonings or wine than on butter and cream. As always, we substitute skim or low-fat milk for cream, sometimes in combination with yogurt. We also use yogurt alone, or in a mixture of part sour cream, part yogurt, which is higher in fat but milder in taste than plain yogurt (see especially Mushroom Sauce, pp. 209–10).

We also include a low-fat béchamel sauce in our vegetable side dishes section (see Brussels Sprouts in Light Béchamel Sauce, p. 202), which can be used with other vegetables or on fish.

REAL ITALIAN TOMATO SAUCE

PREPARATION TIME: 10 MINUTES.   COOKING TIME: 1 HOUR.

The Italians we have met tell us that the only *real* Italin tomato sauce uses for seasoning basil, garlic, a bit of salt and pepper and maybe a bay leaf. That's all. No or gano!

Here is our favourite basic sauce. It can be used for any recipe calling for tomato sauce, from pasta to aubergine to fish. It's wonderful with our Turkey Loaf (pp. 132–3). You can leave out the mushrooms if you prefer; we just happen to like mushrooms.

Look for no-salt-added varieties of tinned tomato products if you're trying to cut down on salt.

You can store this in a tightly sealed container in the refrigerator for up to a week, or freeze it indefinitely for later use.

1 dessertspoon olive oil
1 medium onion, cut in
 chunks
8 ounces (225 g) fresh
 mushrooms, sliced or
 quartered
1 to 2 tablespoons dried
 basil (even more if you
 use fresh!)
2 large cloves garlic,
 crushed or minced

1 large bay leaf
1 28-ounce (1-kilo-350-g)
 tin whole tomatoes
1 11-ounce (325-g) tin
 tomato purée
1 6-ounce (175-g) tin
 tomato paste
Salt and fresh-ground
 black pepper to taste

1. Heat a large pan on medium heat. Put in the oil, onion, mushrooms, basil and garlic. Cover, and reduce the heat to medium low. Stir frequently – you may need to add a tablespoon or two of water to keep it from sticking.
2. When the onions are translucent, add the remaining ingredients, except the salt and pepper. Bring to a boil on high heat, then reduce to simmer and let cook for an hour or so, stirring occasionally.
3. Add salt and pepper to taste.

Makes about 2½ pints (1½ litres). Serving size is an 8-fluid-ounce (225-ml) measure.

Per Serving: 110 calories, no cholesterol, 4 g dietary fibre,
3 g fat, 326 mg sodium.

ROUX

PREPARATION TIME: 1 MINUTES.   COOKING TIME: 5 TO 10 MINUTES.

This roux can be used to thicken soups, sauce or just about
any cooked item. It is also the basis for gravies.

1 dessertspoon vegetable   *2 dessertspoons flour*
  oil OR *butter*   *(plain, wholemeal or*
                       85%)

1. Heat the oil in a small pan over medium heat. Slowly
    add the flour, stirring constantly. Cook until golden
    brown, stirring constantly. Stir into the main recipe.

GRAVY

PREPARATION TIME: 1 MINUTES.   COOKING TIME:
                                        20 TO 30 MINUTES.

Add to the above roux 8 fluid ounces (225 ml) of stock, and
stir over medium-low to medium heat until thickened.
Season your gravy with a dash of salt and fresh-ground
black pepper if desired; we like to add a few pinches of
rosemary, sage, marjoram, and/or thyme to our Christmas
turkey gravy. Sodium content will vary with the stock you
use and the amount of salt. We use ¼ teaspoon salt and a
low-sodium, homemade stock.

*Makes about 8 fluid ounces (225 ml). Serving size is 2
tablespoons.*

Per Serving: 22 calories, no cholesterol, no dietary fibre, 2 g
fat, 63 mg sodium.

NUTTY PESTO

PREPARATION TIME: 10 MINUTES.

Many pesto recipes combine basil, huge amounts of oil and sometimes pine nuts. The resulting mixture is then tossed with cooked pasta. The recipe below is a lot lighter on the oil and goes well with cooked vermicelli, baked potatoes and other cooked vegetables or grains. (If you were to use butter or oil alone on a potato for flavouring instead of this sauce, it would have over twice the calories of this mixture.)

2 ounces (56 g) unsalted, raw nuts (almonds, walnuts, whatever you like)
4 tablespoons fresh parsley
8 tablespoons fresh basil
leaves OR 4 tablespoons dried basil
2 cloves garlic, chopped
2 dessertspoons olive oil
¼ teaspoon salt (optional)

1. Blend all ingredients in a food processor or blender.

Makes about 6 fluid ounces (180 ml). Serving size is 1 dessertspoon.

Per Serving: 58 calories, no cholesterol, 1 g dietary fibre, 6 g fat, 1 mg sodium.

SAVOURY SPOON-TOPPING

PREPARATION TIME: 5 MINUTES.   COOKING TIME: 12 TO 15 MINUTES.

Try sprinkling this on baked potatoes, hot cooked vegetables, salads or cottage cheese. Or mix it into dips or meat loaves for added flavour and fibre.

2 dessertspoons Worcestershire sauce
1 dessertspoon lemon juice
½ teaspoon Tabasco sauce
6 ounces (175 g) All-Bran

1. Mix together the Worcestershire sauce, lemon juice and Tabasco, blending thoroughly. Pour the cereal into a large bowl, and pour the sauce over it. Immediately toss to moisten evenly.
2. Spread evenly on a lightly greased baking sheet.

3. Bake at 325°F (Gas Mark 3/170°C) until dry and crisp, about 12 to 15 minutes. Cool completely, and store in an airtight container.

Serving size is 1 dessertspoon.

Per Serving: 15 calories, no cholesterol, 2 g dietary fibre, no fat, 60 mg sodium.

MUSHROOM SAUCE

PREPARATION TIME: 10 MINUTES.   COOKING TIME: 15 TO 20 MINUTES.

Though you may prepare this sauce with yogurt alone, the tartness of the yogurt is mellowed by the addition of a small amount of sour cream. If you are being especially careful about fat in your diet, replace the sour cream with 2 fluid ounces (55 ml) more yogurt and 2 fluid ounces (55 ml) skim milk. The milk also helps reduce the tart taste.

Serve the sauce over baked or boiled potatoes, cooked grain or pasta.

1 dessertspoon olive oil
12 ounces (350 g) fresh mushrooms, sliced
2 medium onions, sliced or diced
2 cloves garlic, minced or crushed
16 fluid ounces (450 ml) plain low-fat yogurt
1 dessertspoon cornflour

4 fluid ounces (110 ml) sour cream
1 dessertspoon tamari OR soy sauce
2 teaspoons dried basil
1 teaspoon dried thyme
Fresh-ground black pepper to taste
6 pimientos, chopped (optional)

1. Heat a pan over medium heat. Add the oil, mushrooms, onion and garlic, and turn the heat to medium low. Cover, and let cook until onions are translucent, stirring occasionally.
2. Meanwhile, mix 1 tablespoon of the yogurt with the cornflour then mix in the rest of the yogurt. Stir in the sour cream, and set aside.
3. When the onions are done, remove vegetables from

209

heat and turn heat to low. Add tamari sauce and seasonings to the pan, stir and add the yogurt-sour cream mixture.
4. Place the pan back on the burner, and heat through. Do not boil.

Makes 4 main course servings over an 8-fluid-ounce (225-ml) measure of cooked grain or pasta or 1 medium potato. Makes 16 servings as a sauce for a side dish.

Per Serving (4): 215 calories, 20 mg cholesterol, 3 g dietary fibre, 12 g fat, 359 mg sodium.

BASIL-TOMATO SAUCE

PREPARATION TIME: 5 MINUTES.   COOKING TIME: 10 TO 15 MINUTES.

Here is a basic, traditional Italian tomato sauce in the manner of Chef Ramovich, at Nashville's Villa Romano. We've reduced the fat content and use it with our version of Chef Ramovich's *Capellini di Angelo con Salsa di Pomodoro* (pp. 152–3). If you can't get to the Villa Romano, well, the next best thing is to make it yourself.

1 dessertspoon olive oil (extra-virgin if available)
4 to 5 cloves garlic, minced
1 large shallot, minced
1 28-ounce (1-kilo-350-g) tin of Italian plum tomatoes, quartered, OR 6 large ripe tomatoes,
skinned, seeded and chopped
Salt and coarse fresh-ground black pepper to taste
2 ounces (55 g) fresh basil, chopped

1. Heat the oil over medium heat. Add the garlic and shallot, and sauté until wilted and golden. Add the tomatoes. Season with salt, pepper and basil.

Per Recipe: 270 calories, no cholesterol, 11 g dietary fibre, 15 g fat, 578 mg sodium (assuming ¼ teaspoon of added salt and fresh tomatoes. The recipe will contain about 25 mg sodium if you add no salt, and about 1200 mg sodium if you use tinned tomatoes; ¼ teaspoon of salt contains about 550 mg sodium.)

SEAFOOD SAUCE

PREPARATION TIME: 5 MINUTES.

This versatile sauce needs no cooking, and can be used as a dipping sauce for seafood, vegetables, even meat. Usually served unheated, it can be served hot. Add it to an Oriental-style dish in the final stages of cooking, and heat through.

8 fluid ounces (225 ml)
  tomato ketchup
1½ tablespoons prepared
  mustard

1½ tablespoons tamari OR
  soy sauce
2 fluid ounces (55 ml) water
⅛ teaspoon Tabasco sauce

1. Combine all ingredients, blending well. Store in the refrigerator.

Serving size is 1 dessertspoon.

Per Serving: 14 calories, no cholesterol, no dietary fibre, no fat, 221 mg sodium.

DIJON DRESSING

PREPARATION TIME: 5 MINUTES.

For meats, especially lamb, this pungent sauce is fantastic. Try it with Sesame-Ginger Lamb Chops (pp. 107–8). The sauce is at its best when prepared a day ahead.

4 tablespoons Dijon
  mustard
4 tablespoons lemon juice
2 teaspoons tamari OR *soy*
  sauce

1 teaspoon salt
1 teaspoon pepper
2 large cloves garlic,
  crushed

1. Combine all ingredients, and chill. Serve cold.

Serving size is 1 dessertspoon.

Per Serving: 11 calories, no cholesterol, no dietary fibre, no fat, 450 mg sodium.

FRESH TOMATO SAUCE WITH WHITE WINE

PREPARATION TIME: 7 MINUTES.   COOKING TIME: 15 MINUTES.

This sauce is a good way to dress up leftovers of all kinds or as an accompaniment to simple baked chicken, fish or other entrées and vegetables. With only 1 teaspoon of oil in the entire recipe, it is very low in fat. The fresh tomatoes add enough liquid to the sauté to keep the ingredients from sticking to the pan.

1 teaspoon vegetable OR
  olive oil
1 medium onion, diced
2 large OR *6 ordinary*
  tomatoes, diced
1/4 greeen pepper, diced

4 ounces (110 g) fresh
  mushrooms, sliced
1/4 teaspoon salt
1/2 teaspoon pepper
1 tablespoon white wine

1. Brush a pan with the oil and heat over medium heat. Add the onions, stir and cover. Sauté, stirring often, until onions are translucent.
2. Stir in the remaining ingredients, and let cook, covered, stirring occasionally, until vegetables are tender. Drain if you want a more solid sauce, or leave as is.

Serving size is about a 4-fluid-ounce (110-ml) measure.

Per Serving: 51 calories, no cholesterol; 3 g dietary fibre, 3 g fat, 98 mg sodium.

HORSERADISH SAUCE

PREPARATION TIME: 5 MINUTES.

Use this versatile low-fat sauce for topping baked potatoes, beetroot or other cooked vegetables, as a sauce for meats, a dip for raw vegetables, or as a spread for sandwiches in place of or mixed with a little mayonnaise.

2 dessertspoons grated
  horseradish
8 fluid ounces (225 ml)
  plain low-fat yogurt

1 1/2 tablespoons skim milk
1/2 teaspoon dried dillweed
Salt and fresh-ground
  black pepper to taste

212

1. Combine all ingredients, chill, and serve.

VARIATION: Omit dill and horseradish; use 2 tablespoons of chives instead.

Serving size is 1 dessertspoon.

Per Serving: 8 calories, 1 mg cholesterol, no dietary fibre, no fat, 37 mg sodium.

ORANGE-CRANBERRY SAUCE

PREPARATION TIME: 15 MINUTES.   COOKING TIME:
                                           25 TO 30 MINUTES.

Fruit juice and rind replace much of the sugar that is normally called for in cranberry sauce recipes.

12 ounces (350 g) fresh cranberries
8 fluid ounces (225 ml) orange juice

4 ounces (110 g) sugar
Grated rind of 1 small orange

1. Rinse and drain the cranberries. Combine the orange juice, sugar and orange rind in a saucepan and bring to a boil.
2. Add the cranberries. Bring to a boil again. Reduce the heat and let cook for 10 minutes, stirring occasionally. Remove from the heat, cover, and let cool. Refrigerate after the sauce reaches room temperature.

Serving size is 3 tablespoons.

Per Serving: 83 calories, no cholesterol, 4 g dietary fibre, no fat, 1 mg sodium.

APRICOT SAUCE

PREPARATION TIME: 4 MINUTES.   COOKING TIME: 20 MINUTES.

This pungent, sweet sauce is good with lean pork. A small amount is enough; this is more like a relish than a sauce. You may substitute other nuts for the peanuts.

213

10 whole dried apricots,
   diced
Water
1 dessertspoon honey
4 tablespoons white wine
1 clove garlic, crushed

¼ teaspoon salt
¼ teaspoon pepper
1 dessertspoon chopped,
   unsalted, dry-roasted
   peanuts

1. Cook the apricots in a small amount of water until tender.
2. In a small saucepan, heat the honey until warm. Add the wine, stirring well to blend. Add the remaining ingredients, along with the cooked apricots, and heat through.

Serving size is 1 dessertspoon.

Per Serving: 28 calories, no cholesterol, 1 g dietary fibre, no fat, 72 mg sodium.

Breads, Muffins, Pancakes and Scones

BREADS

There is good reason to call bread the staff of life: when made with whole wheat it contains a very broad spectrum of vitamins and minerals. In fact, except for vitamin B_{12}, whole-wheat bread has much the same vitamin and mineral content as beef. When you eat bread with certain foods, such as legumes, nuts, seeds or a small amount of a dairy product, the combination makes the protein in bread more available to the human body. Thus, peanut butter sandwiches on wholemeal bread not only taste good to those of us who enjoy them (as we do), they are nourishing, especially when you use natural peanut butter without added sugar. (See our discussion of complementary protein on pp. 156–7).

Calorie for calorie, whole-grain foods are far less expensive to produce and yield far more nutritional value than animal foods. An acre of land devoted to grain production for human consumption can feed many more people than an acre devoted to grain production for livestock, especially cattle. In the future, this may prove to be very important as the world's population increases.

Bread in its earliest forms some eight thousand years ago, before the discovery of leavening, was not very appetizing. Produced in rock-hard slabs, it wore down the teeth of the ancient peoples who gnawed on it for nourishment. Perhaps by accident, as the story goes, an Egyptian baker let his flour-and-water mixture lie for a time in the sun, and it began to ferment. The bread rose as it baked and this was the beginning of bread in the form that we know it.

If you've never baked bread, you've missed out on one of the most satisfying creations of the kitchen. People are afraid to bake bread, thinking it's too difficult. However, many people who have become wonderful home bread-bakers will tell you that their first loaves were disappointing: hard, flat, and unappetizing, if not inedible.

Please don't be put off by the long directions included in some of our bread recipes. The steps are simple, and we want to take you through each one of them so you will have a perfect loaf.

It usually takes a couple of 'practice loaves' to get the hang of it. One essential step is to make sure your yeast is mixed with a liquid at the correct temperature. Mix it with lukewarm liquid, usually water, as listed in the recipes, and go on from there. The suggested temperature of the liquid is between 105° and 115° Fahrenheit (41° and 46°C) – i.e., lukewarm. (We call it 'baby-bottle warm'.) You may use a thermometer if you wish; you will probably soon learn to do it by 'feel'.

Yeast is actually made up of micro-organisms that feed on sugar and liquid, and that release carbon dioxide, which is one part of what makes your dough rise. So remember, yeast is alive – or should be. Prove it (make sure it's alive) by combining it with a small amount of water, sugar and maybe a pinch of ground ginger. Within 15 minutes, it should be bubbly. If not, throw it out and start a new batch. (If the water is the correct temperature, check the 'use-by' date on your yeast package for its expiration date.) Some of our recipes call for the new fast action or easy-blend dry yeast, which works very well and requires far less rising time. It must be mixed directly with dry ingredients, eliminating the proving step, but you can always substitute ordinary dry yeast. Remember, however, that easy-blend yeast can withstand slightly higher temperatures in liquids than regular yeast can.

216

As yeast feeds on sugars in the bread dough, it gives off alcohol and carbon dioxide which are what make the bread rise. When you put the dough in the oven, the high heat kills the yeast, the dough stops rising, the crust forms, and you have your bread.

HOW MUCH FLOUR?

You may need slighly more or less flour, depending on the flour itself, the humidity and temperature of the kitchen and other factors. This is why a bread recipe often calls for extra flour. Always add your flour slowly. You can add more as you go along, but you can't take any out! If you do find you've added too much, you can wet your hands a little while kneading and add moisture that way, but it's best to avoid this.

THE NEED TO KNEAD

Kneading is fun, burns a few calories, doesn't take long and gets you used to how the dough is supposed to feel. You can use kneading attachments on food processors and the like, but Terri and our bread-baking friends prefer getting in there with their hands.

Kneading, which develops the gluten in the dough, works with the yeast to help the dough to rise. Different flours have different protein contents, and since the gluten is formed when liquids are mixed with the protein in flour, flours with high protein levels produce the best breads. Bread flour or 'strong' flour made from hard wheat has a high protein level (over 10 per cent). It absorbs more water and, when kneaded, gives larger volume and lighter texture than soft flours. There are quick yeast breads that require no kneading and are still healthful and delicious, but it seems the best textured breads are kneaded. The following sequence will familiarize you with the basics of the bread-making process.

Rising: Some doughs need no rising time, including non-yeast and some batter breads. Others require several risings.

Usually, you will place the dough in a bowl, cover it with

217

a damp cloth and set it in a warm, draught-free place. We just put it in the oven so it's out of the way. In winter, if the house is cold, warm the oven on its lowest setting for a few minutes, turn it off and put the dough in. Or use a cupboard next to the oven if the oven is in use – the warmth from the oven will permeate the cupboard and keep the dough happy.

Punch down: This is just what it says. Punch the dough with your fist, and it will collapse so you can allow the dough to rise again.

The floured board: When you knead or roll out dough, do so on a large surface lightly dusted with flour. You can add more flour as you go along, if necessary. If you don't have a board, wipe an area of your kitchen worktop or table with a damp cloth, cover it with a large piece of wax paper and dust the wax paper with flour. The damp underneath keeps the paper from sliding.

How to knead: Press the heels of your hands into the dough, fold the dough over, turn it about one-quarter of the way round, and repeat the process. Dough is ready to rise when it appears smooth and elastic, and bounces back from a poke with a finger.

Greasing and dusting: Usually, baked bread will fall out of the pan easily if you follow this procedure: spray pans lightly with nonstick cooking spray, or lightly grease with some oil, lard or butter smeared on a paper towel. To dust the pans, add about 2 teaspoons whole-wheat flour or maizemeal to each pan, and tap it while holding it at different angles until flour coats all sides. Then tap out the excess flour. Your completed raw loaf will meet the corners of the pan and will usually fill a loaf pan about two-thirds full.

To test for doneness, tap on the top and *bottom* of the loaf with your knuckles. If it sounds hollow, and if the crust is nicely browned, it's done. If your knock *isn't* hollow, return the loaf to the pan and the oven, but be cautious about how long it stays in the oven.

It's easy to overeat fresh, hot, homemade bread that's just out of the oven. There really is no better food we can imagine. BUT – restrain yourself. Allow yourself one slice, if you must. Tell yourself it doesn't slice as well

218

when it's warm (it doesn't: it tears.) Let bread cool completely before serving, preferably on a wire rack, or your crust may get damp from the steam in the loaf. Joyce Weingartner, who created a number of the breads in this cookbook, never slices hers until it has cooled for 2 hours. How she can resist, we will never know, but we admire her for it.

After the bread cools, slice it with a long serrated knife. You can store the bread in airtight plastic bags and freeze a loaf for later use.

You can vary the type of crust on your breads in the following ways. Brushing the crust with 1 beaten egg mixed with 1 tablespoon of water results in a shiny crust. A soft, glazed crust is obtained by brushing with 1 egg white beaten with 1 tablespoon water. For a soft crust, brush a smidgen of melted butter or vegetable oil on top just before the last rising of the dough, or while baking. For a crisp crust, brush with cold water, a noncaloric alternative to a soft crust! Sweeteners and/or milk in the dough will make a darker crust.

WHOLEMEAL BREADCRUMBS

Take any wholemeal or whole-grain bread and whir in a blender or food processor. (Yes, at a pinch, you may use white bread.)

Use for casserole toppings, breading meats, etc. Commercial breads vary greatly in their nutritional value, so read the labels to determine calories, cholesterol, dietary fibre, fat and sodium.

ITALIAN WHOLE-WHEAT BREAD

PREPARATION TIME: 3 HOURS.   BAKING TIME: 40 MINUTES.

1 package active dry yeast
2 fluid ounces (55 ml)
  lukewarm water (105° to
  115°F/41° to 46°C)
¼ teaspoon sugar

¼ teaspoon ground
  ginger
12 fluid ounces (330 ml)
  lukewarm water
1 dessertspoon sugar

219

2 ounces (56 g) melted
  butter
2 teaspoons salt
10 ounces (300 g) whole-
  wheat flour
14 ounces (400 g) strong
  white flour
  (approximately)

Nonstick vegetable
  cooking spray
2 tablespoons maize meal
1 egg white
1 tablespoon water

1. Prove the yeast by pouring it into a small bowl with the two fluid ounces (55 ml) water, ¼ teaspoon sugar and the ginger. Wait about 5 to 15 minutes, or until bubbly.
2. In a large bowl, combine the remaining lukewarm water, the sugar, the butter and the salt. Add the proved yeast.
3. Add half the whole-wheat flour and one-third of the white flour. Mix 100 strokes. Add the rest of the brown flour and half the remaining white flour, mixing well. Then slowly add the remaining white flour, a little at a time, to make sure the dough is the correct consistency.
4. Knead for 8 to 10 minutes, adding up to 1 ounce (28 g) more strong white flour if necessary. Place in a lightly greased bowl, cover with a damp towel, and set in a draught-free place until doubled in bulk.
5. Punch down the dough with your fist. Knead on a lightly floured surface for about 2 minutes until smooth and elastic. Divide the dough into 2 equal balls. Cover with the damp towel and let stand for 10 minutes.
6. Spray a baking sheet with cooking spray, and dust with maize meal, pouring off the excess.
7. Shape each ball of dough into a long loaf – like a French loaf – about 14 inches (35 cm) in length, by holding each end and gently stretching the dough, shaking it gently at the same time. Pat into shape if necessary. Place loaves – not touching – on the baking sheet, cover with wax paper and let rise in a warm, draught-free place until doubled in bulk, about 1 hour.

8. Heat the oven to 425°F (Gas Mark 7/220°C).
9. Beat the egg white with the 1 tablespoon of water and brush the tops of the loaves with it. Make five shallow diagonal slashes in the tops of each loaf to let steam escape while baking.
10. Bake for 40 minutes, or until the loaves are a rich golden colour. If they begin getting too dark, you may cover them with a piece of foil; however, don't open the oven during the first 20 minutes or your bread may collapse. To test for doneness, tap the bread top and bottom; if it does not sound hollow, return it to the oven until it taps hollow. Cool on a wire rack.

Makes 2 loaves of 16 slices each. Serving size is 1 slice.

Per Serving: 86.5 calories, 4 mg cholesterol, 1.5 g dietary fibre, 1.5 g fat, 150 mg sodium.

HOMEMADE CROUTONS

PREPARATION TIME: 5 MINUTES.   COOKING TIME: 8 TO 10 MINUTES.

4 slices wholemeal or whole-grain bread
1/3 ounce (10 g) margarine OR *butter*
1 teaspoon basil
1/4 teaspoon oregano
1/4 teaspoon onion powder
1/8 teaspoon thyme
1/2 teaspoon garlic powder
Other herbs and spices of your choice (optional)

1. Cut the bread into ½-inch (1-cm) cubes. In a frying pan, melt the margarine, then add the seasonings.
2. Stir in the bread cubes and sauté until crisp.

Makes enough for 8. Serving size is 4 tablespoons.

Per Serving: 56 calories, 4 mg cholesterol, 2 g dietary fibre, 2 g fat, 133 mg sodium.

WHOLE-WHEAT FRENCH BREAD

PREPARATION TIME: 3 HOURS.   BAKING TIME: 25 TO 30 MINUTES.

If you enjoy French bread, which goes with just about any meal, you may want to invest in a French-bread pan,

221

a heavy pan made especially for its long shape. You can find one in most cookware shops but make sure it will fit into your oven. This bread freezes well wrapped in foil and placed in a sealed plastic bag.

1 package dry yeast	1½ teaspoons salt
2 fluid ounces (55 ml) warm water	8 ounces (225 g) strong white flour
¼ teaspoon sugar	4 ounces (110 g) whole-wheat flour
¼ teaspoon ground ginger	1 to 2 teaspoons vegetable oil
7 fluid ounces (200 ml) lukewarm water	2 tablespoons maize meal
1 dessertspoon sugar	1 egg white
1 ounce (28 g) unsalted butter OR margarine, melted	1 tablespoon water

1. Prove the yeast by putting it in a small bowl with the 2 fluid ounces (55 ml) warm water, the sugar and the ginger. In about 5 to 15 minutes, it should be bubbly. If not, throw it out and start with new yeast.
2. Meanwhile, in another bowl, combine the 7 fluid ounces (200 ml) warm water, the dessertspoon of sugar, the butter and the salt.
3. Add the proved yeast to the water mixture. Mix in two-thirds of the strong white flour and the whole-wheat flour. Stir 100 strokes.
4. Mix in half the remaining white flour, then slowly add the rest if it is needed. Knead the dough for 10 minutes.
5. Rub a small amount of vegetable oil over the surface of a bowl, place the dough in it, and cover with the damp towel until doubled, about 1 hour. Punch down the dough, knead 2 minutes more, then let rest with the towel over it for 10 minutes.
6. Divide the dough into 2 pieces. Shape into loaves by holding each end of a piece and gently stretching and shaking the bread into the shape of a long French loaf. Pat into shape if necessary.
7. Brush a baking sheet lightly with vegetable oil, and

evenly spread maize meal over it. Place the loaves on the baking sheet and cover with a damp cloth. Let double, about 30 to 45 minutes.

8. Heat the oven to 425°F (Gas Mark 7/220°C).

9. Brush each loaf with the egg white mixed with the 1 tablespoon of water. Put several diagonal slashes, ¼ inch (5 mm) deep, in the bread to let steam escape while it bakes. Bake for 25 to 30 minutes, until golden brown. Remove from the oven immediately and let cool on a rack.

10. If you serve the bread the same day you bake it, simply crisp it in the oven for 5 minutes before serving. This is the secret to getting traditional 'crusty' French bread. To thaw frozen bread and serve, warm in foil for 15 minutes at 350°F (Gas Mark 4/180°C). Then remove the foil, and leave in the oven for another 5 minutes.

VARIATION: For a pungent, East Indian-style loaf, add to the above recipe ½ teaspoon Indian Spice Blend (p. 244) or another curry powder, and 2 tablespoons of the green part of spring onions, minced. Reduce salt to 1 teaspoon.

Makes 2 loaves of 8 slices each. Serving size is 1 slice.

Per Serving: 91 calories, 4 mg cholesterol, 1 g dietary fibre, 2 g fat, 271 mg sodium.

BUTTERMILK CORN BREAD

PREPARATION TIME: 30 MINUTES.   BAKING TIME: ¾ TO 1 HOUR.

For several weeks, Enid tested revision after revision of this recipe until she triumphed with a light, tasty corn bread that rivals any other we have tasted. It is delicious toasted.

1 ounce (28 g) butter OR *margarine*

7 ounces (200 g) yellow maize meal, sifted

2 ounces (56 g) whole-wheat flour, sifted

12 fluid ounces (330 ml) cultured buttermilk

223

1 teaspoon bicarbonate   ¼ teaspoon salt
  of soda

1. Use a small amount of the butter to thoroughly coat a loaf pan. Melt the remainder in a small saucepan.
2. Combine all ingredients in a mixing bowl. Let stand for 20 minutes. Heat the oven to 375°F (Gas Mark 5/190°C).
3. Pour the mixture into the loaf pan, and bake for 45 minutes to 1 hour, until lighly brown on top.

Makes 1 loaf of 16 slices. Serving size is 1 slice.

Per Serving (16 slices): 94 calories, 9 mg cholesterol, 1 g dietary fibre, 3 g fat, 113 mg sodium.

GOOD BREAD

PREPARATION TIME: ¾ TO 1 HOUR.   BAKING TIME: 1 TO 1¼ HOURS.

Our longtime friend Denni Llovet says of her bread creation: 'Only 1½ hours from bowl to mouth!'
  We think she's more efficient than we are, because it usually takes us 2 hours to make this bread. Regardless of how long it takes to make, it is truly plain old-fashioned *good* bread.

Small knob of butter
Wholemeal flour – a little
4 fluid ounces (110 ml)
  lukewarm water (105° to
  115°F/41° to 46°C)
3 packages dry yeast
  (ordinary or easy-blend)
5 fluid ounces (140 ml)
  vegetable oil

5 fluid ounces (140 ml)
  honey
1 teaspoon salt
2 pints (1 litre 140 ml) hot
  water
About 3 pounds 2 ounces
  (1 kilo 450 g) whole-
  wheat flour

1. Lightly grease 3 large loaf pans with the butter, and dust with a little bit of flour.
2. Place the 4 fluid ounces (110 ml) of lukewarm water in a small bowl, and sprinkle the yeast on top. Do not stir.
3. Measure the oil into a measuring cup, then pour into

224

a small bowl. Measure the honey into the same measuring cup you used for the oil; this will keep the honey from sticking in the cup. Pour the honey into the bowl with the oil, and add the salt.

4. Mix the 2 pints (1 litre 140 ml) of hot water with 1 pound 12 ounces (800 g) of the flour in the largest mixing bowl you have – use a clean washing-up bowl. Keep the flour handy. Add the yeast-and-water mixture, then add the oil-honey-salt mixture, and blend. Keep mixing in flour, a little at a time, to make a pliant dough, firm but not stiff. Leave some of the flour if there seems to be too much. Turn the dough out onto a floured board and knead for 10 minutes with a folding-over, punching-down motion.

5. Divide the dough into three loaves and place in loaf pans. Cover with a damp cloth and let rise until half as big again.

6. Heat oven to 350°F (Gas Mark 4/180°C).

7. Bake until dark brown on top (about 1 hour to 1 hour and 15 minutes). Let cool on a wire rack 5 to 10 minutes before slicing if you want it to slice cleanly.

Makes 3 loaves of 16 slices each. Serving size is 1 slice.

Per Serving: 126 calories, no cholesterol, 3 g dietary fibre, 4 g fat, 47 mg sodium.

FOUR-GRAIN WHEATLESS BREAD

PREPARATION TIME: 45 MINUTES.   BAKING TIME: 1¼ TO 1⅓ HOURS.

We asked Joyce Weingartner, who helped us test many recipes, to create a wheatless bread for us. She delighted us with this, a batter bread that has a rich, nutty flavour, great in sandwiches or by itself. For those who are allergic to wheat, this bread is a suitable substitute, as buckwheat is actually not in the wheat family. This loaf will not rise as high as most kneaded wheat breads, because there is far less gluten in these flours. Store the loaf in the refrigerator, and slice thin to serve.

225

2 packages dry yeast
2 fluid ounces (55 ml)
lukewarm water (105° to
115°F/41° to 46°C)
¼ teaspoon sugar
⅛ teaspoon ground
ginger
8 fluid ounces (225 ml)
lukewarm water
3 tablespoons molasses or
black treacle

1 ounce (28 g) butter,
melted
1½ teaspoons salt
8 ounces (225 g) rye flour
3 tablespoons buckwheat
flour
3 tablespoons soy flour
3 ounces (80 g) oat flour
OR fine oatmeal
Nonstick vegetable
cooking spray

1. Prove the yeast in the 2 fluid ounces (55 ml) water, sugar and ginger. (The mixture should be bubbly after about 5 to 15 minutes.)
2. In a large bowl, combine the 8 fluid ounces (225 ml) water, molasses, butter and salt. Add the proved yeast, and mix well.
3. In another bowl, combine three-quarters of the rye flour, and all the remaining flours. Add the flours to the yeast mixture, and mix 100 strokes. Be sure to get all the flour at the bottom of the bowl mixed in with the dough.
4. Gradually add the remaining rye flour, stirring well.
5. Preheat the oven to 350°F (Gas Mark 4/180°C).
6. Spray a loaf pan with nonstick cooking spray and place the dough in the pan, spreading with a knife to meet the corners and smooth out the top of the loaf. Cover the loaf pan with buttered foil, and set in a warm draught-free place to rise. Place the loaf pan in a larger pan that has about 1 inch (2 cm) of hot water in it and place both pans in the centre of your oven.
7. Bake for 30 minutes, then remove the foil *and* the pan of water. Bake the loaf an additional 45 to 50 minutes. This loaf will not sound hollow when you tap it, but will have a rich, dark brown crust. Remove it from the pan and place on a rack to cool.

Makes 1 loaf of 20 thin slices. Serving size is 1 slice.

Per Serving: 78 calories, 3 mg cholesterol, 1 g dietary fibre, 1 g fat, 226 mg sodium.

SESAME-POPPY SEED LOAF

PREPARATION TIME: 10 MINUTES.   BAKING TIME: 40 MINUTES.

3 ounces (80 g) wholemeal
  flour
4 ounces (110 g) plain
  white flour
1 dessertspoon baking
  powder
½ teaspoon salt
2 dessertspoons sesame
  seeds

2 dessertspoons poppy
  seeds
6 fluid ounces (180 ml)
  orange juice
2 dessertspoons honey
1 egg
2 dessertspoons vegetable
  oil
1½ ounces (40 g) All-Bran

1. Heat oven to 350°F (Gas Mark 4/180°C).
2. In a medium bowl, stir together the flours, baking powder, salt and seeds. Set aside.
3. In a large mixing bowl, beat together the orange juice, honey, egg, oil and cereal until well combined. Let stand 2 minutes.
4. Add the flour mixture, stirring only until combined. Spread the batter evenly into a lightly greased 2-pound (1-kilo) loaf pan.
5. Bake about 40 minutes, or until a toothpick inserted near the centre comes out clean. Let cool 10 minutes before removing from the pan. Cool completely before slicing.

Makes 1 loaf of 16 slices. Serving size is 1 slice.

Per Serving: 100 calories, 20 mg cholesterol, 2 g dietary fibre, 3 g fat, 380 mg sodium.

WHOLE-WHEAT TORTILLAS

PREPARATION TIME: 1½ HOURS.   COOKING TIME: 1 HOUR.

Tortillas are the bread of Mexico. You can use them as you would bread, although we still think the traditional Mexican recipes are the best.

As for the use of vegetable *shortening*, which is often processed into a solid form that is similar to saturated fat, there is so little per serving in this recipe that we felt it was acceptable. You can substitute oil if you wish, although the resulting texture is not quite as good.

When cooking these, a little bit of cooking spray or fat on a wad of paper goes a long way. You can probably cook several tortillas before needing more.

These are great with *Fajitas* (pp. 78–9) or they can substitute for bread in Cheese Toast (p. 250); you can sprinkle them with grated cheese, chopped tomato, and/or onion, grill them and top with chopped lettuce.

You can also freeze them for later use.

10 ounces (300 g) whole-wheat flour
10 ounces (300 g) strong white or plain flour
1½ teaspoons salt
2½ ounces (80 g) vegetable shortening

8 fluid ounces (225 ml) warm water (or slightly more if needed)
Whole-wheat flour as needed
Nonstick cooking spray OR tiny knob of fat

1. Rub fat into flours and salt, then add warm water to make a light-textured dough. Form into 16 egg-sized balls, and place the balls in the bowl. Let stand for about 20 minutes.
2. Roll each ball of dough out on a lightly floured board to form a very thin circle, about ⅛ inch (2 mm) thick.
3. Spray a griddle or large frying pan with cooking spray, and fry each tortilla over medium-low heat for a minute on one side, and a minute on the other. NOTE: When one side is done, the tortilla will begin puffing up. Turn it over, and fry the other side. They will be slightly browned in spots, not all over. Serve warm.

Makes 16 tortillas. Serving size is 1 tortilla.

Per Serving: 140 calories, no cholesterol, 4 g dietary fibre, 5 g fat, 267 mg sodium.

CARAWAY-ONION-BRAN LOAF

PREPARATION TIME: 20 MINUTES. BAKING TIME: 30 TO 35 MINUTES.

2 ounces (56 g) margarine (regular, not light)

1 medium onion, finely chopped

Just under 8 fluid ounces
(225 ml) skim milk
1 dessertspoon lemon
juice
3 ounces (80 g) All-Bran
cereal
1 egg, slightly beaten
6 ounces (175 g) plain
flour

1 teaspoon baking powder
1 teaspoon bicarbonate of
soda
1 teaspoon salt
2 teaspoons caraway
seeds

1. In a medium saucepan, melt the margarine. Add the onion and cook over low heat until tender. Remove from the heat.
2. Combine the milk and the lemon juice to make sour milk. Stir the cereal and the milk into the onion. Let stand for 2 minutes, or until most of the liquid is absorbed. Add the egg and blend well.
3. Heat oven to 350°F (Gas Mark 4/180°C).
4. In a large mixing bowl, mix the flour, baking powder, soda, salt and caraway seeds. Add the cereal mixture to the flour. Stir just until moistened.
5. Spread in a lightly greased large loaf pan. Bake for 30 to 35 minutes, or until a knife inserted in the centre comes out clean. Let cool for 10 minutes. Remove from the pan, and let cool completely before slicing.

Makes 1 loaf of 16 slices. Serving size is 1 slice.

Per Serving: 90 calories, 20 mg cholesterol, 2 g dietary fibre, 4 g fat, 400 mg sodium.

SWEDISH LIMPA RYE

PREPARATION TIME: 3 HOURS.   BAKING TIME: 40 MINUTES.

2 packages dry yeast
2 fluid ounces (55 ml)
lukewarm water (105° to
115°F/41° to 46°C)

¼ teaspoon sugar
⅛ teaspoon ground
ginger

10 fluid ounces (275 ml)
lukewarm water
4 fluid ounces (110 ml)
unsweetened orange
juice
1 ounce (56 g) butter,
melted
5 tablespoons molasses OR
black treacle
2 teaspoons salt

2 dessertspoons orange
peel, finely grated
8 ounces (225 g) whole-
wheat flour
8 to 10 ounces (225 to
300 g) strong white flour
4 ounces (110 g) rye flour
1 egg white
1 tablespoon water

1. In a small bowl, prove the yeast by combining it with the 2 fluid ounces (55 ml) water, sugar and ginger.
2. In a large bowl, combine the 10 fluid ounces (275 ml) water with the orange juice, butter, molasses, salt and orange peel.
3. After the yeast has proved (about 5 to 15 minutes), add to the orange juice mixture. Stir in half of each of the flours, and mix 100 strokes. Add most of the remaining whole-wheat then the same amount of the white, stirring well after each addition. Slowly add the rest of the whole-wheat and the same amount of white. The dough will be sticky.
4. Dust your hands, the kneading board and the dough with flour, and knead for 8 to 10 minutes, adding more white flour a little at a time, if necessary.
5. Place the dough in a lighly greased mixing bowl and cover with a damp towel. Place in a warm, draught-free area, and let rise until it doubles, about 1 hour.
6. Punch down, and let rest for 10 minutes with the towel over it.
7. Form the dough into 2 round loaves, or use 2 1-pound (½-kilo) loaf pans. Let rise again until doubled, about 45 minutes.
8. Heat oven to 350°F (Gas Mark 4/180°C).
9. Mix the egg white with the tablespoon of water, and brush each loaf with the mixture. Put several diagonal slashes on the bread to let out steam while baking.
10. Bake for 40 minutes, or until the loaves sound hollow when tapped on the top and bottom. Cool on a wire rack for 2 hours before slicing.

Makes 2 loaves of 16 slices each. Serving size is 1 slice.

Per Serving: 76 calories, 2 mg cholesterol, 1 g dietary fibre, 1 g fat, 175 mg sodium.

BREADSTICKS

PREPARATION TIME: 50 MINUTES.   BAKING TIME: 15 MINUTES.

1 package active dry yeast
2 tablespoons sugar
Pinch ground ginger
8 fluid ounces (225 ml)
  lukewarm water
2 dessertspoons vegetable
  oil

1 teaspoon salt
1 pound (450 g) strong
  white flour OR *half white,*
  half whole-wheat flour

1. Combine the yeast, sugar, ginger and water in a large bowl. Let stand for 10 minutes.
2. Mix in the oil and salt, then slowly mix in the flour, adding just enough to get past the sticky stage and allow you to knead the dough. You may not need it all.
3. Knead for 5 minutes. Roll into long sticks, about ½ inch (1 cm) thick × 8 inches (20 cm) long. Place the sticks on a lightly oiled baking sheet. Leave about 30 minutes to double their size.
4. Bake at 375°F (Gas Mark 5/190°C) on the high rack of the oven for 15 minutes or until golden brown. Serve hot.

Makes about 2 dozen sticks. Serving size is 1 stick.

Per Serving: (with half white and half whole-wheat flour), 63 calories, no cholesterol, 1 g dietary fibre, 1 g fat, 90 mg sodium.

QUICK WHOLE-WHEAT BUTTERMILK BREAD

PREPARATION TIME: 1¼ HOURS.   BAKING TIME: 25 MINUTES.

This bread has a lovely even texture.

231

10 ounces (300 g) whole-
wheat flour
12 ounces (350 g) strong
white flour
2 packages easy-blend dry
yeast
2 ounces (56 g) wheatgerm
2 teaspoons baking
powder
2 teaspoons salt

10 fluid ounces (275 ml)
cultured buttermilk
6 fluid ounces (180 ml)
water
2 ounces (56 g) butter OR
margarine, melted
2 dessertspoons molasses
OR black treacle
Nonstick vegetable
cooking spray

1. In a large bowl, mix together three-quarters of the whole-wheat flour, the same quantity of strong white flour, the yeast, wheatgerm, baking powder and salt.
2. In a saucepan, heat the buttermilk and water on medium-low heat until lukewarm, not hot (105° to 115°F/41° to 46°C). Stir into the flour mixture.
3. Melt the butter or margarine and blend into the flour mixture. Blend in the molasses, and stir 100 strokes.
4. Slowly stir in the rest of the whole-wheat flour and 2 ounces (56 g) same quantity of white flour. When the flour is mixed into the batter, add half the remaining white flour, mix well, and add the rest of the white flour if necessary. Your dough will be a bit sticky, so dust your kneading board, your hands and the dough with flour.
5. Knead the dough for 8 to 10 minutes. Place in a lightly greased bowl and cover with a damp towel. Leave about 30 minutes, until doubled in size.
6. Spray 2 large pans with nonstick cooking spray, and preheat your oven to 425°F (Gas Mark 7/220°C).
7. Divide the dough into 2 pieces. Pat each piece into a square about 1 inch (2 cm) thick. Fold the square in thirds. Seal the seam, and place each loaf, seam down, in a loaf pan.
8. Cover the loaves with a damp towel and let rise again until doubled in bulk, about 30 minutes.
9. Place the loaves in the centre of the oven, evenly distanced and not touching each other. Bake for 25 minutes, or until the loaves sound hollow when tapped on the top and bottom. They should be nicely browned. Let them cool on a wire rack.

Makes 2 loaves of 16 slices each. Serving size is 1 slice.

Per Serving: 86 calories, 4 mg cholesterol, 1 g dietary fibre, 2 g fat, 182 mg sodium.

BRAN CHEESE TWISTS

PREPARATION TIME: 35 MINUTES.   BAKING TIME: 15 MINUTES.

This 'snack' bread is good with salads, instead of whole-grain crispbread, for example.

3 ounces (80 g) All-Bran
10 fluid ounces (275 ml)
  skim milk
1 dessertspoon lemon
  juice
10 ounces (300 g) plain
  flour
1 dessertspoon baking
  powder

1 teaspoon bicarbonate of
  soda
1 teaspoon salt
1 ounce (28 g) margarine,
  softened
2 ounces (56 g) Cheddar
  cheese, grated

1. In a small bowl, combine the cereal and the milk, which has been soured with the lemon juice. Set aside.
2. In a large mixing bowl, combine the flour, baking powder, soda and salt. Cut in the margarine to make a mixture like coarse breadcrumbs. Add the cereal mixture and blend well. Stir in the cheese.
3. Shape the dough into 20 ropes, ½ × 3 inches (1 × 8 cm) each, by rolling the dough between your hands. Fold each rope in half and twist each end. Place on a lightly greased baking sheet.
4. Bake at 425°F (Gas Mark 7/220°C) for 15 minutes or until golden brown.

Makes 20 twists. Serving size is 1 twist.

Per Serving: 80 calories, 3 mg cholesterol, 2 g dietary fibre, 2 g fat, 270 mg sodium.

233

MUFFINS

We are inveterate muffin-makers; nothing seems to give as much pleasure in the making and the eating for so little effort. An American muffin is really a 'quick bread' made, basically, from a batter that is baked in a high-sided individual muffin pan. For the British edition the instructions have been adapted to enable you to bake the 'muffins' in a conventional bun tin or paper baking case.

Our muffins blend a high-fibre source, such as a ceral product, with a flour. The batter is produced with the addition of low-fat milk, oil, an egg or two and the sweetener, which can be sugar, honey, molasses or a combination of the three. To this you can add an almost limitless combination of various dried fruits and nuts.

When it comes to satisfying a desire for something sweet or for something cake-like to go with a good cup of fresh-ground coffee, a muffin is a far healthier alternative than conventional biscuits or cakes. Also, it is *far* cheaper to bake your own than to buy and, because you select the ingredients, you know how fresh *and* healthy these muffins are.

Some of the recipes in this section were developed and tested for us in the Kellogg kitchens, so you will note that the recipes in question call for Kellogg products. You can, of course, try these recipes using your own favourite equivalent cereals, e.g., any 100% bran for All-Bran (but not 40% bran-content flakes).

MIXED RAISIN-OATMEAL MUFFINS

PREPARATION TIME: 10 MINUTES.   BAKING TIME: 15 MINUTES.

Whole-wheat pastry or cake flour is available in most health food stores and gives a slightly finer texture than whole-wheat bread flour. However, you may use wholemeal bread flour instead.

234

Nonstick vegetable
  cooking spray
4 ounces (110 g) Oat Bran
  OR 2 ounces (56 g) All-
  Bran AND 2 ounces (56 g)
  fine or medium oatmeal
4 ounces (110 g) whole-
  wheat pastry flour
2 ounces (56 g) brown
  sugar
3 ounces (80 g) seedless
  raisins

2 teaspoons baking
  powder
¼ teaspoon salt
8 fluid ounces (225 ml)
  low-fat milk
1 large egg, beaten
4 tablespoons molasses OR
  black treacle
2 dessertspoons vegetable
  oil

1. Heat oven to 425°F (Gas Mark 7/220°C). Spray 2 bun trays with nonstick cooking spray, or line with paper cups.
2. Combine dry ingredients in a large mixing bowl.
3. In separate bowl, mix milk, egg, molasses and oil.
4. Add the liquid mixture to the dry, and mix *only* until the dry ingredients are moistened (the mixture should be lumpy).
5. Fill cups until ¾ full and bake for 15 minutes, or until tops are golden brown.

Makes 24. Serving size is 2 buns.

Per Serving: 152 calories, 25 mg cholesterol, 2 g dietary fibre, 5 g fat, 238 mg sodium.

HONEY BRAN MUFFINS

PREPARATION TIME: 10 MINUTES.   BAKING TIME: 25 MINUTES.

6 ounces (175 g) All-Bran
4 tablespoons honey
10 fluid ounces (275 ml)
  skim milk
1 egg

4 ounces (110 g) plain
  flour
1 teaspoon bicarbonate of
  soda
½ teaspoon salt

1. Combine the cereal, honey and milk, and let stand for 2 minutes. Add the egg, beating well.
2. Heat oven to 400°F (Gas Mark 6/200°C).

3. Stir together the flour, soda and salt; add to the cereal mixture, stirring *only until combined*. Portion the batter evenly into lighly greased bun trays.
4. Bake for 20 to 25 minutes or until a toothpick inserted in the centre of a muffin comes out clean. Let stand about 5 minutes before removing from the pans. Serve immediately.

Makes 24. Serving size is 2 buns.

Per Serving: 115 calories, 25 mg cholesterol, 5 g dietary fibre, 1 g fat, 340 mg sodium.

APRICOT BRAN MUFFINS

PREPARATION TIME: 20 MINUTES.   BAKING TIME: 25 MINUTES.

6 ounces (175 g) plain flour
1½ tablespoons sugar
1 dessertspoon baking powder
½ teaspoon salt
4½ ounces (125 g) All-Bran

12 fluid ounces (330 ml) skim milk
1 egg
2 dessertspoons vegetable oil
3 ounces (80 g) dried apricots, chopped

1. In a small bowl, stir together the flour, sugar, baking powder and salt. Set aside.
2. In a large bowl, combine the cereal and the milk; let stand 2 minutes. Add the egg and oil, blending well. Add the flour mixture, stirring only until combined. Stir in the apricots.
3. Heat oven to 400°F (Gas Mark 6/200°C).
4. Portion the batter evenly into lighly greased bun trays. Bake for 20 to 25 minutes, or until a toothpick inserted in the centre of a muffin comes out clean. Serve warm.

Makes 24. Serving size is 2 buns.

Per Serving: 135 calories, 25 mg cholesterol, 4 g dietary fibre, 3 g fat, 580 mg sodium.

HERB BRAN MUFFINS

PREPARATION TIME: 12 TO 15 MINUTES. BAKING TIME:
18 TO 20 MINUTES.

*5 ounces (145 g) plain
  flour
1 dessertspoon baking
  powder
¼ teaspoon salt
2 dessertspoons sugar
2 dessertspoons toasted
  sesame seeds
¼ teaspoon dry mustard
½ teaspoon dried herb of
  your choice
(suggestions: sage,*

*dillweed, oregano, sweet
basil, chives, parsley,
marjoram, summer
savory, rosemary,
coriander or cardamom)
3 ounces (80 g) All-Bran
8 fluid ounces (225 ml)
  skim milk
1 egg
⅔ ounce (20 g) margarine,
  melted*

1. Stir together the flour, baking powder, salt, sugar, sesame seeds, dry mustard and herb of choice. Set aside. Heat oven to 400°F (Gas Mark 6/200°C).
2. In a large mixing bowl, combine the cereal and the milk. Let stand 2 minutes. Add the egg and margarine, blending well. Add the flour mixture, stirring only until combined.
3. Portion the batter evenly into lightly greased bun trays. Bake for 18 to 20 minutes, or until a toothpick inserted in the centre of a muffin comes out clean.

Makes 24. Serving size is 2 buns.

Per Serving: 110 calories, 25 mg cholesterol, 3 g dietary fibre, 3 g fat, 520 mg sodium.

PANCAKES AND SCONES

In America, thick pancakes, rather like Scottish tea or girdle pancakes, are eaten for breakfast, often with butter, honey, syrup or bacon. They are best warm but will keep in a tin and are good for elevenses or teatime snacks. The scone recipe also has a Scottish – or Welsh –

feel about it: very like the traditional girdle scone and conveniently cooked quickly on the top of the stove.

BRAN AND RAISIN PANCAKES

PREPARATION TIME: 10 MINUTES.

COOKING TIME:
25 TO 30 MINUTES.

3 ounces (80 g) plain white flour
2 dessertspoons sugar
1 dessertspoon baking powder
½ teaspoon salt
1 egg, slightly beaten

10 fluid ounces (275 ml) skim milk
3 ounces (80 g) All-Bran OR *Bran Buds*
1 ounce (28 g) margarine
2 ounces (56 g) seedless raisins OR *sultanas*

1. In a bowl, mix together the flour, sugar, baking powder and salt. Set aside.
2. In a large bowl, mix together the egg, milk, cereal, and two-thirds of the melted margarine. Let stand 1 to 2 minutes, or until the liquid is absorbed. Stir in the raisins.
3. Add the flour mixture all at once to the cereal mixture, and stir until moistened. The batter will be lumpy.
4. Heat the remaining margarine in a large frying pan over medium heat. Drop the batter in, using 1½ tablespoons of batter per pancake. Cook until golden brown, turning once, about 3 minutes on each side.

Makes 18 pancakes. 9 servings.

Per Serving, 2 pancakes: 160 calories, 30 mg cholesterol, 4 g dietary fibre, 5 g fat, 430 mg sodium.

BRANCAKES

PREPARATION TIME: 15 MINUTES.

COOKING TIME:
20 TO 25 MINUTES.

1 egg

16 fluid ounces (450 ml) skim milk

238

2 ounces (56 g) All-Bran
  OR Bran Buds
6 ounces (175 g) plain
  white flour

1 dessertspoon baking
  powder
¼ teaspoon salt
2 dessertspoons sugar

1. Beat the egg until foamy. Stir in the milk and the
   cereal. Let stand 4 minutes.
2. Stir together the flour, baking powder, salt and sugar
   in a medium mixing bowl. Add the cereal mixture,
   stirring to combine, and let stand 5 minutes.
3. Drop the batter, using 3 tablespoons for each pancake, onto a lightly greased, preheated griddle or
   heavy frying pan. Cook, turning once, until golden
   brown on both sides.

Makes 12 pancakes. 12 servings.

Per Serving: 95 calories, 24 mg cholesterol, 2 g dietary
fibre, 1 g fat, 220 mg sodium.

WHOLE-WHEAT CORN CAKES

PREPARATION TIME: 5 TO 6 MINUTES.   COOKING TIME:
                              20 TO 25 MINUTES.

5 tablespoons yellow
  maize meal
5 tablespoons whole-
  wheat flour
5 tablespoons plain white
  flour
1½ teaspoons sugar
1½ teaspoons baking
  powder

Dash of salt
1 egg
8 fluid ounces (225 ml)
  skim OR low-fat milk
2 dessertspoons vegetable
  oil
1 teaspoon honey
Nonstick vegetable
  cooking spray

1. Combine the dry ingredients in a medium-sized
   bowl.
2. In another bowl, beat the egg, then beat in the milk,
   oil and honey.
3. Make a well in the dry ingredients. Add the liquids
   and mix thoroughly.

239

4. Spray a griddle or frying pan with cooking spray or lightly oil and heat over medium heat. When hot, spoon batter into pan to make pancakes about 4 inches (10 cm) in diameter. Cook until they begin to bubble and are golden brown on the bottom. Turn them over and cook until done.

Makes 8 large pancakes. 4 servings.

Per Serving, 2 pancakes: 231 calories, 70 mg cholesterol, 2 g dietary fibre, 9 g fat, 297 mg sodium.

BRAN GIRDLE SCONES

PREPARATION TIME: 20 MINUTES.   COOKING TIME: 20 MINUTES.

*8 ounces (225 g) whole-
   wheat flour
3 ounces (80 g) All-Bran
   OR Bran Buds
1 dessertspoon baking
   powder*

*1 dessertspoon sugar
½ teaspoon salt
2 ounces (56 g) margarine
1 egg
4 fluid ounces (110 ml)
   skim milk*

1. In a large bowl, mix together the whole-wheat flour, cereal, baking powder, sugar and salt. Cut in the margarine until the mixture resembles breadcrumbs.
2. Beat together the egg and milk. Add to the flour mixture, and stir until well combined.
3. Knead on a lightly floured surface for 2 to 3 minutes, or until smooth. Roll out the dough ½ inch (1 cm) thick, and cut with a 2-inch (5-cm) biscuit cutter.
4. Place the scones in a heated, lightly greased or Teflon frying pan. Cook over low heat for 10 minutes, turn, and cook 10 minutes more.

Makes 14 scones. 14 servings.

Per Serving: 115 calories, 20 mg cholesterol, 3 g dietary fibre, 4 g fat, 500 mg sodium.

Seasonings

Human sensitivity to taste has certain peculiarities. It adapts to the use of salt and sugar, so that the more we use, the less sensitive to the flavour we become. This adaptation does not occur in our perception of bitter and sour.

Some people are 'salt-sensitive': their blood pressure rises when they consume salt. The effect is due to the sodium in salt. Table salt is 40 per cent sodium and 60 per cent chloride.

Although sodium is an essential nutrient, most people in the West consume 8 to 10 times more than our bodies need to stay alive and healthy. About 25 to 35 per cent of us are 'salt sensitive' and can develop high blood pressure if we consume too much salt. For this reason, most health professionals encourage us to cut back on salt. This is done by adding less salt in cooking and by reducing the consumption of certain processed foods, such as processed meats, soups and snack foods.

We agree with the suggestion to cut back on salt and have done it ourselves over the past few years. But we don't think you need to cut it out entirely from your cooking unless you are on a severely salt-restricted diet. The reason we include salt or other seasonings that contain some sodium in many of our recipes is that salt seems

241

to bring out the flavours in other ingredients, especially herbs and spices. Try it yourself: mix up a batch of herbs, taste them, and then add about one part salt to a mixture of six or seven parts herbs. You will agree, we're quite sure, that the flavour of the herbs fairly explodes to the taste with a little salt.

For this reason, our Herb Salt (pp. 244–5) is usually made with one part salt to six or seven parts herbs, yielding a mixture that has perhaps 285 milligrams of sodium per scant teaspoon, compared with 2200 milligrams in a scant teaspoon of salt.

We keep a wide assortment of herbs and spices on our shelves, including just about everything itemized on pages 17 to 18. We also keep a variety of our own blends, such as the recipes included here. In addition, we keep some commercial herb and salt mixtures on hand for the times we are in a hurry.

We also occasionally use Worcestershire sauce in small quantities, over steaks or in a meat loaf. Whenever possible, we use soy sauce in place of salt, since a scant teaspoon of soy sauce, in the usual commercial preparation, has about one-seventh the sodium content of salt.

And here's a hint for seasoning meat, chicken and turkey before roasting: place your selection of seasonings (a total of 4 to 6 teaspoons of crushed herbs and spices) in a small bowl, add 1 dessertspoon of oil and 1 dessertspoon of soy sauce. Mix it until it forms a paste, and then, before roasting, rub it well into the meat or poultry with your fingers. Since smoking food may increase the activity of certain carcinogenic substances we limit our consumption of smoked food to two or three times each year, but when we do smoke turkey for example, this soy-herb-spice paste is good rubbed into the flesh before smoking starts.

After they are emptied, save several of the spice jars you obtain when you purchase commercial spices. Wash and dry them well and use them to store your own blends. You can also use them to store any herbs and spices that you buy in bulk. The flavour of herbs and spices is preserved best when they are stored in airtight containers.

When you cannot use the fresh form of a herb, substitute a powder. Garlic and onion powders (and celery seed) are far lower in sodium content than their salt equivalents. The sodium content of the blend is far higher than necessary. If you find that your recipe needs additional salt, add it yourself. You will end up using far less.

Finally, whenever we say 'dash' of salt, we mean what some cooks refer to as a 'pinch'. When we say 'salt to taste', go lightly and let people add a bit more at the table if they wish. We discovered that this instruction resulted in tremendous variation among the 'army' of chefs who helped design and taste our recipes. Until we made our intentions clear, this misunderstanding sometimes resulted in food that was so salty we could not believe the cook had tasted it before emptying the salt shaker!

Since nutrients in herbs and spices are so minimal in the quantities sold, we haven't provided nutritional analyses for our herb blends.

GARAM MASALA

PREPARATION TIME: 3 MINUTES.

A traditional Indian 'masala' is simply a mixture of spices. A 'garam masala' is typically added to a dish just before serving. The preferences of the cook often determine which spices are included in the mixture, and in what quantities. This one is a little sweeter than our Indian Spice Blend (p. 244). If you like it, you may want to double or triple this recipe in order to have plenty on hand.

1 dessertspoon ground
  cardamom
1 teaspoon cinnamon
1 teaspoon cumin

½ teaspoon ground cloves
½ teaspoon fresh-ground
  black pepper
¼ teaspoon nutmeg

1. Combine all ingredients and store in an airtight jar.

Makes about 2 tablespoons.

INDIAN SPICE BLEND

PREPARATION TIME: 3 MINUTES.

Curry powder is actually a combination of several spices, including ginger, coriander, cardamom, cayenne pepper, cinnamon, chillis, mustard seed, turmeric, cumin, black pepper, poppy seeds, fenugreek, fennel, mace and cloves. There are many different versions of the blend, depending on the type of dish and the cook. You can create your own special curry using some of these spices. Or mix the blend below to have on hand 'in a pinch', and use it any time curry powder is called for.

8 teaspoons cumin
4 teaspoons ground
  ginger
2 teaspoons ground
  coriander

2 teaspoons cayenne
  pepper
4 teaspoons turmeric
2 teaspoons fresh-ground
  black pepper

1. Combine all ingredients and store in an airtight spice jar.

Makes about 5 tablespoons.

HERB SALT

PREPARATION TIME: 3 MINUTES.

Though the following combination of herbs is one of our favourites, you can experiment with your own combination of herbs. You will soon find that a Herb Salt is an excellent substitute for plain salt, and instead of about 2200 milligrams of sodium per scant teaspoon, it has only 285 milligrams. Thus a sprinkle (about ⅛ teaspoon) of Herb Salt will give you perhaps 30 or 40 milligrams of sodium, instead of the almost seven times that amount (200 to 300 milligrams) plain salt would provide.

½ teaspoon basil
¼ teaspoon thyme
¼ teaspoon dillweed

¼ teaspoon celery seed
¼ teaspoon salt
¼ teaspoon dried parsley

1. Combine all ingredients and grind with a mortar and pestle. Store in a small herb jar.

Makes about 1 dessertspoonful.

TRADITIONAL ITALIAN HERB BLEND

PREPARATION TIME: 3 MINUTES.

Use this blend whenever Italian seasoning is called for but you don't want to take the time to mince or crush garlic. Add a bay leaf to your recipe along with this blend for the perfect Italian flavour. This mixture will contain 96 milligrams of sodium per scant teaspoon (less than one-twentieth of the sodium content of salt itself, which contains 2200 milligrams sodium per scant teaspoon, so it can be considered a low-sodium seasoning).

4 tablespoons dried basil leaves

1 dessertspoon garlic powder

2 teaspoons fresh-ground black pepper

1 teaspoon salt

1. Combine all ingredients and store in a tightly sealed jar in a cool, dry place.

Makes about 6 tablespoons.

Sandwiches, Sandwich Spreads, and the Working Lunch

My typical quick lunch consists of two slices of whole-grain bread topped with an ounce or two of cheese and a dash of seasoning, then grilled or microwaved for a minute (see Cheese Toast, p. 250).

But you don't have to limit yourself to whole-grain bread as your sandwich foundation. Try wholemeal muffins, rolls or pita (Middle Eastern pocket) bread. Even a whole-wheat or maize meal tortilla can function as sandwich bread.

We prefer cooked chicken, turkey or cheese, and low-calorie tuna salads and spreads such as we show in our recipes, to processed meats such as luncheon meat, ham or salami, which contain salt, sugar and other additives. In addition, processed meats are usually higher in fat than in any other nutrient. Because a high consumption of the saturated fats found in meat appears to be related to a high blood cholesterol level, in turn a risk factor for cardiovascular disease, some food processors have taken to producing reduced-fat processed meats. But be sure to read the labels: reduced-fat processed meats can still contain a lot of fat.

Read about the Combination Sandwich (p. 249) for basic preparation tips for sandwiches.

And now, a brief word about lunch in general. What do

you do if you're an office worker whose usual lunch consists of either a hamburger and chips or a quick chocolate bar and a drink from a vending machine? Many of us are hampered by lack of time for lunch and less than adequate kitchen facilities in our workplaces.

Of course, more and more restaurants are becoming health-conscious, and offer good low-calorie selections that go way beyond the boring old 'diet special' of cottage cheese and a limp lettuce leaf. If you are lucky enough to have a good health food restaurant near you, you're ahead of the game. And remember that at many self-service counters it is possible to make a sensible low-calorie, high-fibre choice.

Bringing your own lunch is one of the best alternatives. Then you really have control of what you're eating. Sandwiches, fruit and salads in plastic containers last until lunchtime without refrigeration, and don't require heating up.

In some workplaces simple kitchen facilities are provided, or employees might club together to buy appliances like a hot plate, a toaster oven, a small refrigerator or even a microwave. Having these expands the lunch possibilities tremendously. Soups, stir-fries, leftovers – indeed, whole meals, can be stored in the refrigerator and prepared later for a quick, low-cost lunch.

A refrigerator is especially handy for those who like to bring yogurt for lunch or for a snack. And do bring a snack! Mid-afternoon 'blahs' are conducive to raids on the chocolate machines. Fruit and homemade muffins are tops on our list for snacks, or high-fibre cereal and skimmed milk.

So, although we present sandwiches in the following section, many of our recipes, especially soups, stews, stir-fries or leftovers, can do double duty as all or part of a nutritious lunch.

MEAT SPREAD

PREPARATION TIME: 8 TO 10 MINUTES.

8 ounces (225 g) cooked
  meat OR poultry
1 small onion, diced

3 tablespoons wheatgerm
  OR cooked red beans
2 dessertspoons soy flour

247

Herb Salt (pp. 244–5) OR   *Freshly ground black*
   other herb blend to taste   *pepper to taste*

1. Blend all ingredients in a food processor. Moisten as needed with tomato ketchup, mustard or salad dressing.

Makes about 10 ounces (300 g). Serving size is about 2 ounces (56 g).

Per Serving: 99 calories, 38 mg cholesterol, no dietary fibre, 2 g fat, 85 mg sodium. (With cooked red beans: 97 calories, 39 mg cholesterol, 1 g dietary fibre, 2 g fat, 85 mg sodium.)

TURKEY MELT

PREPARATION TIME: 10 MINUTES.   COOKING TIME: 20 MINUTES.

The original recipe called for ham. You can, of course, use lean ham, but try it with turkey, as suggested below, or chicken, for less sodium and fat content. Serve over whole-grain toast.

1 teaspoon vegetable oil
4 ounces (110 g) fresh
  mushrooms, sliced
1/3 ounce (10 g) butter OR
  margarine
1 dessertspoon flour
8 fluid ounces (225 ml)
  skim OR *low-fat milk*
3 tablespoons white wine

1/4 teaspoon nutmeg
1/4 teaspoon tarragon
1 ounce (28 g) Gruyère
  cheese, grated
Diced cooked turkey to fill
  a 16-fluid-ounce
  (450-ml) measure (about
  10 ounces/300 g)

1. Brush a pan with the oil, and heat over medium heat. Add the mushrooms, cover, and reduce heat slightly. Let cook for several minutes, until mushrooms are tender, stirring occasionally.
2. Meanwhile, melt the butter or margarine in another pan. Stir in the flour and let cook, stirring constantly, until golden brown. Stir in the milk, wine, nutmeg and tarragon.
3. Combine the cheese and turkey, and stir into the

248

milk mixture. Add the mushrooms, and heat the mixture through without boiling.

4 servings. Serving size is an 8-fluid-ounce (225-ml) measure.

Per Serving: 235 calories, 74 mg cholesterol, 1 g dietary fibre, 11 g fat, 147 mg sodium.

COMBINATION SANDWICH

This is another frequent suggestion on the original *Rotation Diet* menus. The label 'combination sandwich' refers to any combination of ingredients between 2 slices of whole-grain bread such as any slice of meat and cheese, or spreads with vegetables or cheese.

The way to prepare sandwiches with limited calories is to use lean cuts of meat or poultry, and only limited amounts of mayonnaise or ketchup. You may use as much mustard as you like since it is very low in calories. Then you add lettuce, tomato or other *free vegetables* as desired.

Two slices of whole-grain bread, with one ounce each of meat and cheese, will contain approximately 295 calories. Mayonnaise is about 33 calories a scant teaspoonful, ketchup 16 calories a dessertspoon, and mustard is negligible. Along with the *free vegetables*, or a piece of fresh fruit, a Combination Sandwich gives you a satisfying lunch for about 350 to 380 calories. (Compare the calorie content of this lunch with the 650 or so calories you obtain in a typical hamburger roll. The hamburger will have about twice the fat content of your lean slice of meat, and lashings of mayonnaise or ketchup may be used to enhance the flavour.)

For variety, try one of the following spreads. They make especially attractive open-faced sandwiches. Serve with sprouted seeds, a slice of tomato or cheese; place under the grill or in the oven for a hot sandwich.

CHEESE TOAST

PREPARATION TIME: 3 MINUTES.   COOKING TIME: 3 TO 5 MINUTES.

2 slices whole-grain bread   *2 slices tomato (optional)*
1 ounce (28 g) cheese,
sliced thin, to cover 2
slices of bread

1. Place the bread on a foil-lined baking sheet. Arrange the cheese, and tomato slices if desired, on top of the bread, and place under the grill for a few minutes, until the cheese is melted.

VARIATIONS: Before grilling sprinkle the cheese toast with basil, chilli powder, cumin or other herbs and spices.

Serves 1.

Per Serving: 248 calories, 26 mg cholesterol, 3 g dietary fibre, 11 g fat, 452 mg sodium.

SHRIMP SPREAD

PREPARATION TIME: 15 MINUTES.

1 pound (450 g) shrimps   *1 clove garlic, crushed*
8 ounces (225 g) low-fat   *1 teaspoon dried tarragon*
cottage cheese   *Dash of Worcestershire*
2 ounces (56 g) St Ivel or   *sauce (optional)*
other cream cheese   *Salt and fresh-ground*
4 fluid ounces (110 ml)   *black pepper to taste*
plain low-fat yogurt

1. Put the shrimps into a mixing bowl and roughly chop.
2. Put the cottage cheese and the St Ivel cream cheese in a blender or food processor and blend until smooth. Pour into mixing bowl.
3. Add the remaining ingredients, mixing well. Chill and serve.

Serving size is a 2-fluid-ounce (55-ml) measure.

Per Serving: 60 calories, 48 mg cholesterol, no dietary fibre, no fat, 160 mg sodium.

TUNA SALAD

PREPARATION TIME: 8 TO 10 MINUTES.

This is our basic tuna salad. As a halfway measure for reducing the amount of mayonnaise in our diet, we mix a little mayonnaise (for flavour) with yogurt and mustard. This same dressing goes equally well with cooked chicken, turkey, salmon, crab or shrimps. You can vary it by adding a dash of tarragon, dillweed or other herbs and spices. Use about a pound (450 g) of cooked or tinned seafood.

On a day when you feel like splurging, add a dessertspoon or two of chopped nuts or olives.

2 medium tins (8 ounces/ 225 g) each water- packed tuna, drained
4 fluid ounces (110 ml) plain low-fat yogurt
2 dessertspoons mayonnaise
1½ teaspoons Dijon mustard

1 hard-boiled egg, chopped
1½ stalks celery, chopped
1 tablespoon fresh parsley, chopped
Fresh-ground black pepper to taste

1. Combine all ingredients in large bowl. Serve chilled on lettuce leaves or in half a melon or large tomato.

4 servings. Serving size is an 8-fluid-ounce (225-ml) measure.

Per Serving: 253 calories, 134 mg cholesterol, 1 g dietary fibre, 8 g fat, 331 mg sodium.

TUNA SALAD WITH FRUIT VINAIGRETTE DRESSING

PREPARATION TIME: 5 MINUTES.

We suggest a raspberry vinegar for this salad, although

251

you may use any fruit vinegar; substitute ordinary wine vinegar if that's all you have on hand or if you don't like fruit vinegars.

1 medium can (8 ounces/ 225 g) water-packed tuna, drained
½ apple, unpeeled, chopped
1½ ounces (40 g) sultanas

2 fluid ounces (55 ml) fruit OR *red wine vinegar*
½ teaspoon Dijon mustard
½ teaspoon dillweed
½ teaspoon celery seed

1. Combine all ingredients. Serve on lettuce leaves or mixed greens, if desired.

2 servings. Serving size is an 8-fluid-ounce (225-ml) measure.

Per Serving: 283 calories, 74 mg cholesterol, 2 g dietary fibre, 2 g fat, 741 mg sodium. (Two leaves of lettuce, about 1 ounce, will add 4 calories, no cholesterol, no dietary fibre, and 2 mg sodium.)

MEXICAN BEAN SPREAD

PREPARATION TIME: 8 TO 10 MINUTES.

This is good as a dip and is great grilled with a slice of cheese or tomato and sprinkled with oregano. In a hurry, use tinned beans.

1 pound (450 g) dark-red kidney beans, cooked and drained
1 small onion
2 tablespoons tomato ketchup

⅛ teaspoon cayenne pepper
Herb Salt (pp. 244–5)
Freshly ground black pepper

1. Blend the above ingredients in a food processor or blender, adding more ketchup if needed for desired consistency.

Makes just over a pound (450 g). Serving size is about 2 ounces (56 g).

Per Serving: 78 calories, no cholesterol, 6 g dietary fibre, no fat, 456 mg sodium.

CURRIED TURKEY SALAD

PREPARATION TIME: 10 TO 15 MINUTES.

Diced cooked turkey to fill a 16-fluid-ounce (450-ml) measure (about 10 ounces/300 g)
4 fluid ounces (110 ml) plain low-fat yogurt
1½ tablespoons mayonnaise
1½ ounces (40 g) sultanas
2 ounces (56 g) nuts OR
seeds (walnuts, peanuts, sunflower seeds, etc.), finely chopped
1½ stalks celery, chopped
½ teaspoon Indian Spice Blend (p. 244) OR other curry powder
Fresh-ground black pepper to taste

1. Combine all ingredients in large bowl. Serve chilled on lettuce leaves, in half a melon or large tomato, or surrounded by other fresh vegetables.

4 servings. Serving size is about an 8-fluid-ounce (225-ml) measure.

Per Serving: 261 calories, 54 mg cholesterol, 2 g dietary fibre, 13 g fat, 125 mg sodium.

CRABMEAT SPREAD

PREPARATION TIME: 8 TO 10 MINUTES.

8 ounces (225 g) crabmeat
4 stalks celery, diced
1 small onion, diced
Herb Salt (pp. 244–5) to taste
½ green pepper, diced
4 ounces (110 g) bean OR other sprouts
8 ounces (225 g) low-fat cottage cheese

1. Blend all the ingredients with enough salad dressing to moisten. (We use about 2 dessertspoons of mayonnaise.)

253

Makes about 1¼ pounds (565 g). Serving size is about 2 ounces (56 g).

Per Serving: 32 calories, 13 mg cholesterol, no dietary fibre, no fat, 215 mg sodium. (With 2 tablespoons mayonnaise: 49 calories, 14 mg cholesterol, no dietary fibre, 2 g fat, 228 mg sodium.

Beverages

We must start by talking about plain, fresh WATER!

Although it may not have occurred to you, water is our most essential nutrient. No beverage (including those in this chapter) should replace plain, fresh water as the primary beverage in your diet. Aim for eight 8-fluid-ounce (225-ml) glasses per day.

For many people this is very hard advice to follow. Water doesn't taste very good any more when it comes out of the tap. In fact, the consumption of soda pop is greater than that of water in the United States.

Won't diet drinks do? In my opinion, no. Perhaps in moderation they don't do any harm, but intensely sweetened drinks of any kind seem to dull our sensitivity to sweetness and keep alive a sweet tooth in those who may find it hard to manage their weight.

But plain water won't do for all occasions and we are constantly asked, 'What am I supposed to drink?' Well, coffee or tea may do no harm provided you limit yourself to 2 or 3 cups per day, and many nutritionists believe it's okay to count them among the recommended daily total of 64 fluid ounces (almost 2 litres) of fluids. But what about treats and special occasions? Isn't there anything you can drink that's really tasty and not bad for you?

This chapter contains some suggestions for making

flavoured teas and coffees and for other beverages that are satisfying and good for you, such as some tasty blended fruit drinks. Notice the use of vanilla flavouring: it makes beverages taste sweeter without adding any calories and it reduces the need for sugar. Other extracts can do the same. In cold weather you will find that Herb Rum Tea is even more satisfying on snowy nights than it is on rainy nights. It's a favourite of mine after a long walk or run in chilly weather, and like all our recommendations, good for entertaining.

An important consideration for making beverages is the taste of the water you're using. If your tap water doesn't taste particularly good, it may be adding an off-flavour to other beverages that you make with it. That may be why you prefer sweetened bottled drinks to water or the drinks that you blend yourself. Try some bottled spring water for tea, coffee and the other beverage suggestions in this chapter. If you notice a pleasant improvement, you might consider using bottled water for drinking and cooking. Or you may want to purchase an activated-charcoal filter for your kitchen tap to remove chlorine and other objectionable organic matter. Be sure to get one that's bacteriostatic, to prevent bacteria from multiplying in water from which chlorine has been removed. You will find it easier to replace sweet-flavoured beverages in your diet if your water tastes fresh and clean. You can also try soda water or carbonated mineral water.

Two warnings: I do not recommend that you use distilled water as your primary source of fluids. Tap and spring water contain a number of essential minerals that are removed in the distillation process, and appliances that soften water may add a considerable amount of sodium. Be sure that your water requires softening before you buy this type of water conditioner. The activated-charcoal filters that I advise for making tap water more palatable do not remove essential minerals, nor do they add unnecessary sodium.

Fruit and vegetable juices are good, and for variety, there are many blended juices available in supermarkets and health-food stores if you don't want to combine your own. Fruit juice blended with herb tea also makes a satisfying punch, and the possibilities for combining are practically endless. If you are interested in limiting your calorie intake, however, we recommend you turn to whole fresh fruit rather than juice. Most people end up consuming fewer calories when they eat fresh fruit, which contains considerable fibre, than they do when they drink juice, which is almost devoid of fibre.

BANANA-STRAWBERRY FROZEN DELIGHT

PREPARATION TIME: 7 TO 8 MINUTES. FREEZING TIME: 2 HOURS.

2 medium bananas,
* peeled*
4 fluid ounces (110 ml)
* evaporated skim milk*
¼ teaspoon vanilla extract
Strawberry, banana OR
* almond extract*
* (optional)*

10 ounces (300 g) frozen
* whole unsweetened*
* strawberries*

1. Wrap the peeled bananas in plastic wrap and place in the freezer for at least 2 hours, until frozen.
2. Cut the frozen bananas into chunks. Place the chunks in a blender or food processor.
3. Combine the milk and the extract(s) and pour over the Bananas. Blend until smooth.
4. Reserve a couple of strawberries to slice for a garnish, if desired. Gradually add the remaining strawberries to the blender or food processor, blending briefly after each addition. Serve immediately.

4 servings. Serving size is about 6 fluid ounces (180 ml).

Per Serving: 102 calories, 1 mg cholesterol, 3 g dietary fibre, no fat, 39 mg sodium.

HERB RUM TEA

PREPARATION TIME: 8 TO 10 MINUTES.

Also known as 'Chilly, Rainy Night Tea'. We combine a

favourite tea, such as Earl Grey or Darjeeling, with a favourite herb tea (usually mint, lemon or almond). Then we put a teaspoon of rum in a mug and pour in the hot, brewed tea. Try adding a whole clove, a piece of cinnamon stick or an orange or lemon slice. A great warmer-upper.

COFFEE SUGGESTIONS

For those who are used to drinking coffee with sugar and/or cream, here are a few hints that may help you reduce or completely omit those high-calorie additions. When brewing coffee, add to the grounds one or more of the following:

A dash or two of ground cinnamon, cardamom or other sweet spices
A piece of vanilla bean (about ⅛-inch (2 mm) per cup)
A bit of orange peel
Ground almonds (about ¼ teaspoon per cup)

We also suggest that you use dairy products rather than the non-dairy substitutes if you don't take coffee black. The substitutes may contain even more saturated fat than the dairy product; and, in our opinion, the substitute can't compare in flavour. (Most creamers/powders contain about 10 calories per teaspoon, twice as much as whole milk.)

COOL COFFEE SPECIAL

PREPARATION TIME: 15 TO 20 MINUTES.

For a refreshing dessert drink, try this with either regular or decaffeinated coffee, or a blend of the two, which is how we drink it. You can substitute instant coffee if you prefer.

16 fluid ounces (450 ml)   *16 fluid ounces (450 ml)*
  hot brewed coffee   *cold skim milk*

16 fluid ounces (450 ml)   *3 teaspoons sugar*
  cold water   *½ teaspoon vanilla extract*
2 eggs, separated

1. Put the hot coffee in a large jug.
2. Add the cold milk and cold water and stir. Beat the egg yolks and add to the coffee mixture. Stir in the sugar and vanilla.
3. Beat the egg whites until stiff. Gently fold them into the coffee mixture. Serve over ice.

6 servings. Serving size is about an 8-fluid-ounce (225-ml) measure.

Per Serving: 67 calories, 93 mg cholesterol, no dietary fibre, 2 g fat, 66 mg sodium.

GREAT SHAKES

PREPARATION TIME: 8 TO 10 MINUTES.

Here is the basic recipe for a satisfying sweet substitute for the common, sugar-loaded milkshake. Vary this recipe by using any combination of fruit. Our favourites are orange-banana, as shown below, strawberry-banana and strawberry-peach. Try different flavourings as well, such as almond extract, cinnamon, cloves or cardamom. This makes a complete breakfast or lunch for one person, or a dessert drink for one or two people.

8 fluid ounces (225 ml)   *1 medium orange*
  plain low-fat yogurt   *¼ teaspoon vanilla*
1 small banana   *Dash nutmeg*

1. Place yogurt in blender or food processor. Cut the fruit into chunks and add to the yogurt. Blend for 30 seconds. Add vanilla and nutmeg and blend until smooth. Serve immediately.

1 serving. Serving size is 16 fluid ounces (450 ml).

Per Serving: 310 calories, 14 mg cholesterol, 6 g dietary fibre, 4 g fat, 160 mg sodium.

FRUIT 'N' JUICE SHAKE

PREPARATION TIME: 5 TO 10 MINUTES.

This recipe combines whole fruit with fruit juice for a refeshing, low-calorie 'shake'. You can use your imagination with this one; for starters, try banana, orange, apple, and/or strawberries; mix and match your favourite fruit flavours.

10 fluid ounces (275 ml)   1 medium piece of fruit,
  fruit juice   sliced

1. Combine the ingredients in a blender, and blend for about 30 seconds.

2 servings. Serving size is about 8 fluid ounces (225 ml).

Per Serving (using orange juice and pineapple): 82 calories, no cholesterol, 1 g dietary fibre, no fat, 2 mg sodium.

SPICED TEA

PREPARATION TIME: 10 MINUTES.

1½ pints (570 ml) brewed   1 to 2 teaspoons sugar
  tea   1 teaspoon ground cloves
2 cinnamon sticks   1 to 2 teaspoons lemon
8 fluid ounces (225 ml)   juice OR *4 slices of fresh*
  unsweetened orange   lemon
  juice

1. When brewing the tea, place the cinnamon sticks in the teapot. When the tea is ready, discard the cinnamon sticks.
2. Add the remaining ingredients and serve, or chill first and serve over ice cubes if you want iced tea.

4 servings. Serving size is about 10 fluid ounces (275 ml).

Per Serving: 38 calories, no cholesterol, no dietary fibre, no fat, 9 mg sodium.

IRISH SPICED COFFEE

PREPARATION TIME: 10 MINUTES.   COOKING TIME: 10 MINUTES.

This is a dessert drink which is satisfying served alone or with a barely-sweet confectionary such as Sweet Pineapple Squares (p. 277) or Carrot-Nut Tea Bread (p. 272).

16 fluid ounces (450 ml)
  strong black coffee
  (regular or
  decaffeinated)
1½ teaspoons sugar
2 whole cloves
1 stick cinnamon

1 teaspoon finely grated
  lemon peel
1 teaspoon finely grated
  orange peel
2 fluid ounces (55 ml) Irish
  whiskey

1. Bring the coffee, sugar, cloves, cinnamon and lemon and orange rind almost to the boil. Cover and let stand for a couple of minutes, then remove the cloves and cinnamon stick and discard.
2. Add the whiskey, and serve. Or chill – it is delicious cold, for a summer dessert drink.

VARIATION: For an exotic chilled dessert, add to the recipe 1 envelope of unflavoured gelatine, as follows:

1. Follow step one.
2. Soften the gelatine in the Irish whiskey. Then add the hot coffee mixture and stir until the gelatine dissolves.
3. Pour into 2 small serving dishes or parfait glasses, and chill overnight. Garnish with a curl of lemon or orange peel, if desired.

The taste and texture will surprise you!

2 servings. Serving size is about 8 fluid ounces (225 ml).

Per Serving: 90 calories, no cholesterol, no dietary fibre, no fat, 3 mg sodium.

Cakes, Desserts and Biscuits

WARNING! It is dangerous to read this chapter without also reading the next chapter!

If you put the recipes of this chapter into practice, and if you are a sedentary person, you must go all the way: you must develop the active life-style that will permit you to enjoy them without gaining weight!

We have made a special effort to include desserts that are relatively low in fat and sugar and high in more valuable nutrients, so that you will see that a treat need not necessarily be a 'cheat'. Our goal is to reduce fat, sugar and salt in basic cake and pudding recipes by significant amounts, often by as much as 50 per cent in comparison with other recipes of a similar nature.

Sometimes we combine more healthful ingredients with the less healthful processed ingredients that have worked their way into our style of food preparation because they are easier to use, 'fluffier' or in other ways more satisfying to the human preference for fat and sugar. We blend whole-grain flour with white or use only whole-grain flour when appropriate, and we use honey and molasses when they enhance flavour rather than relying on white sugar. (If you find that 100 per cent whole-wheat flour makes a cake too heavy for you, try using wholemeal cake flour or an 81% or 85% variety.

We also suggest skim and low-fat milk in place of whole milk, low-fat yogurt and single, whipping or sour cream instead of double whenever these will do the job satisfactorily.

Some of our recipes, such as the Oat Nut Biscuits (p. 273), use vegetable oil instead of solid shortenings such as butter or margarine. You can often make this substitution with perfectly acceptable results. Although the calorie content in all fats is about the same, the amounts and types of fats you use, expecially in desserts, which tend to be relatively high in fat, can make a difference to your health.

Fats are present in foods in three forms: saturated, monounsaturated, and polyunsaturated. *Saturated fats* have a chemical structure that tends to make them harden at room temperature; lard, butter, some margarines and some vegetable oils are saturated fats.

Research has shown that there is a link between high intake of fat in the diet and the risk of certain forms of cancer. *Saturated fats* raise the blood level of cholesterol, which is a primary risk factor for heart disease. On the other hand, monounsaturated and polyunsaturated fats either reduce or have no effect on blood cholesterol.

The typical Western diet contains 40 to 50 per cent calories from fat, yet health authorities recommend 30 per cent or less. Saturated fats should equal no more than 10 per cent of total calories for the day, or, in other words, one-third of the 30 per cent total of all fat calories per day. Many western diets contain 17 per cent.

Foods contain various combinations of the different types of fats, but in any given food there is usually more of one type. Animal fats, for instance, are primarily saturated. Even some vegetable fats are highly saturated, such as coconut oil, palm oil and cocoa butter.

Polyunsaturated fats, which tend to lower blood cholesterol, are usually liquid at room temperature. They are: corn oil, safflower oil, sunflower oil, soybean oil or margarines made from these oils. However, hydrogenation, the process which 'saturates' or hardens vegetable fats when making spreads from them, gives these fats some of the same characteristics as animal fats. Check labels for hydrogenated margarines that have been chemically saturated. The softer the margarine, the better. Margarine in a tub, for example, is more likely to be polyunsaturated than margarine in a solid block, although cheaper soft margarines are often not polyunsaturated.

Monounsaturated fats, which also tend to have a cholesterol-lowering effect, are olive oil and peanut oil. Avocados, too, have mainly monounsaturated fat, but they are high in total fat and calories compared with other fruits and vegetables, so eat them in moderation.

When vegetable oil is called for in a dessert recipe, I usually use corn oil. I normally use olive or peanut oil for sautéing, and I sometimes use a little butter with these oils, since nothing can quite equal the flavour that butter imparts to many foods.

Although our desserts are relatively low in fat, sugar and salt, we make no effort to reduce every recipe to, say, 30 per cent of total calories from fat. THAT IS THE AVERAGE, TOTAL TARGET FOR A DAY, NOT FOR EVERY SINGLE MEAL OR DISH. If you eat a well-balanced diet throughout the day, with plenty of fresh fruit and vegetables, low-fat meats and milk products, and if you avoid fried foods, your basic diet, before dessert, may contain as little as 20 to 25 per cent fat. Thus, there is no need to fear an occasional dessert of 300 calories in which 50 per cent of the calories come from fat: your total fat for the day will still fall within the guidelines of a nutritious diet.

However, we must issue one more warning. In spite of the lowered fat and sugar, the recipes in this chapter are really good! Don't have too many, or too much, around at one time!

During the period in which we were developing and testing recipes in great numbers, we had to sample eight in one evening. (That was our 'biscuit-testing' week.) To resist overeating at least a little under these circumstances would have required the willpower of a saint. Neither of us qualified!

Finally, a word of advice when you decide to 'go all the way' at your favourite restaurant and indulge in the super-rich cheesecake or the layer cake in which the layers of filling are thicker than the layers of cake. If you are an active person in good health, we don't think an occasional indulgence of this sort is harmful. We sometimes do it ourselves, and, having relatively low cholesterol levels and no hypertension, we don't feel guilty about it. You don't need to kick yourself, either. But we *don't* go overboard on a regular basis, and you won't want to either, especially in your own cooking, once you see how you can reduce the fat in your own recipes.

Take a look at Coffee Chocolate Cheesecake (pp. 268–9), for example. There is simply no need to use cream cheese and thick cream in your own baking once you learn how to use lower-fat ingredients for desserts in the appropriate proportions. I challenge anyone to make a better cheesecake, no matter how much fat you use! And do write to me if you can devise a better cheesecake! I love cheesecake and promise to find a way to share your expertise with others who share your (and my) predilections.

APRICOT-BANANA BREAD

PREPARATION TIME: 15 MINUTES. BAKING TIME: 55 TO 60 MINUTES.

This makes a lightly sweet, wholesome dessert bread.

2 medium bananas,
  mashed
8 whole dried apricots,
  chopped
6 ounces (175 g) whole-
  wheat flour
1½ teaspoons baking
  powder

½ teaspoon salt
Dash nutmeg
6 tablespoons vegetable
  oil
6 tablespoons honey
1 egg

1. Heat the oven to 350°F (Gas Mark 4/180°C).
2. Combine the bananas and apricots in a small bowl.
3. In another bowl, combine the dry ingredients. Add the oil and the honey, then beat in the egg. Add the banana-apricot mixture, blending well.
4. Spray a loaf pan with nonstick vegetable cooking

265

spray, or oil very lightly by rubbing a bit of oil on the pan with a paper towel. Pour the batter into the pan, which will be about one-third full.

5. Bake for 55 to 60 minutes or until slightly browned, and a toothpick inserted in the middle comes out clean.

Makes 10 slices just under 1 inch (2 cm) thick. Serving size is 1 slice.

Per Serving: 195 calories, 27 mg cholesterol, 3 g dietary fibre, 8 g fat, 189 mg sodium.

CHOCOLATE CHIP BISCUITS

PREPARATION TIME: 15 MINUTES.   BAKING TIME: 8 TO 10 MINUTES.

We think our version of this traditional American recipe came out just fine; we cut the fat by one-quarter and the sugar by half.

6 ounces (175 g) margarine, softened
3½ ounces (95 g) brown sugar
4 ounces (110 g) granulated sugar
½ teaspoon vanilla essence
1 teaspoon water
2 eggs
5 ounces (145 g) whole-wheat flour
4 ounces (110 g) plain white flour
1 teaspoon bicarbonate of soda
1 teaspoon salt
8 ounces (225 g) chocolate chips
6 ounces (175 g) chopped nuts

1. Preheat the oven to 375°F (Gas Mark 5/190°C).
2. In a large bowl, combine the margarine, sugars, vanilla and water. Beat in the eggs.
3. In another bowl, combine the flours, baking soda and salt. Gradually add this to the wet ingredients, blending well. Stir in the chocolate chips and the nuts.
4. Drop by rounded teaspoonsful onto Teflon or ungreased baking sheets. Bake until golden brown, about 8 to 10 minutes.

VARIATION: For Orange Chocolate Chip Biscuits, add a couple of teaspoons of grated orange rind to the batter before baking.

Makes 3 dozen biscuits, about 2 inches (5 cm) in diameter.

Per Biscuit: 131 calories, 15 mg cholesterol, 1 g dietary fibre, 8 g fat, 133 mg sodium.

CHOCOLATE DROP-PEANUT BUTTER BISCUITS

PREPARATION TIME: 30 MINUTES.   BAKING TIME: 10 MINUTES.

What a combination: chocolate chips AND peanut butter! Children of all ages are attracted to these peanut butter biscuits with the four chocolate chips in the middle.

3 ounces (80 g) margarine
2½ ounces (70 g) brown sugar
3 ounces (80 g) granulated sugar
1 egg, beaten
6 tablespoons peanut butter
1 dessertspoon skim milk
1 dessertspoon water

½ teaspoon vanilla extract
4 ounces (110 g) plain flour
3 ounces (80 g) whole-wheat flour
1 teaspoon bicarbonate of soda
½ teaspoon salt
3 ounces (80 g) chocolate chips

1. Preheat the oven to 375°F (Gas Mark 5/190°C).
2. Cream the margarine and sugars in a large bowl. Beat in the egg, peanut butter, milk, water and vanilla.
3. In another bowl, combine the flours, baking soda and salt. Add gradually to the wet ingredients, mixing well.
4. Form the dough into small balls, about 1 inch (2 cm) in diameter. Place the balls on an ungreased baking sheet, and make a depression in each ball by pressing your thumb in the centre. Drop 4 chocolate chips into each ball.

5. Bake for about 10 minutes, until the biscuits begin to brown on the bottom.

Makes about 3 dozen biscuits, about 1½ inches (4 cm) in diameter.

Per Biscuit: 79 calories, 8 mg cholesterol, 1 g dietary fibre, 4 g fat, 76 mg sodium.

PEACH COBBLER

PREPARATION TIME: 15 MINUTES.   BAKING TIME: 30 MINUTES.

8 peaches, fresh or tinned unsweetened, drained and sliced
2 dessertspoons lemon juice
3 ounces (85 g) whole-wheat flour
2½ ounces (70 g) brown sugar

1 teaspoon cinnamon
1 ounce (56 g) butter OR margarine
4 tablespoons plain low-fat yogurt (optional)
Dash cinnamon (optional)

1. Preheat oven to 375°F (Gas Mark 5/190°C).
2. Place the peaches in a 9-inch (23-cm) pie pan or shallow casserole dish and sprinkle with lemon juice.
3. In a bowl, blend the dry ingredients. Cut in the butter with two knives or pastry blender to make a coarse, crumbly texture. Spread over the peaches.
4. Bake about 30 minutes.
5. If desired, top each serving with a dessertspoon of yogurt and a dash of cinnamon.

6 servings.

Per Serving: 161 calories, 10 mg cholesterol, 4 g dietary fibre, 4 g fat, 40 mg sodium.

COFFEE-CHOCOLATE CHEESECAKE

PREPARATION TIME: 30 MINUTES.   BAKING TIME: 1¼ HOURS.

This cheesecake tastes as good as it sounds . . . maybe even better!

18 digestive biscuits, crushed

1 ounce (28 g) butter OR hard margarine, melted

3 ounces (80 g) semisweet chocolate chips OR Menier chocolate

15 ounces (425 g) part-skim ricotta cheese

6 fluid ounces (180 ml) plain low-fat yogurt

2 eggs OR substitute 4 egg whites

4 tablespoons coffee liqueur

2 ounces (56 g) brown sugar

2 ounces (56 g) granulated sugar

1 dessertspoon cornflour

Fresh strawberries (optional)

1. Preheat the oven to 350°F (Gas Mark 4/180°C). Combine the crumbs and the melted butter or margarine in a small bowl. Press firmly into the bottom of a 10-inch (25-cm) springform pan. Bake for 10 minutes, then set aside and let cool. Leave oven on.
2. Melt the chocolate in a double boiler.
3. Whir the ricotta cheese and yogurt in a blender or food processor, adding small amounts at a time. Blend until smooth. Add the eggs and blend briefly.
4. Combine the cheese mixture and melted chocolate in a large bowl. Stir in the coffee liqueur, sugars and cornflour and pour over the baked crust.
5. Bake for 1 hour and 15 minutes, or until cake sets in the middle. Turn off oven, leave cake inside with oven door open and let cool for 2 hours.
6. Chill for at least 4 hours. Release sides of pan, and garnish the cake with fresh sliced strawberries if desired.

12 servings.

Per Serving: about 204 calories, 63 mg cholesterol, 1 g dietary fibre, 9 g fat, 150 mg sodium.

Note for the British reader. The original recipe calls for graham cracker crumbs (9 squares). Using digestive biscuits the calorie count will be a little higher.

CRÊPES WITH FRESH STRAWBERRIES (JULIAN'S)

PREPARATION TIME: 30 MINUTES.   COOKING TIME: 15 MINUTES.

This recipe uses barley-malt sweetener in place of sugar. If you cannot find it use sugar instead. Try serving this dessert after the Grilled Duck Breast (pp. 128–9).

The crêpes:
1 egg
2 egg whites
10 fluid ounces (275 ml)
   skim milk

1½ ounces (40 g)
   unbleached white flour
1 teaspoon vanilla extract

The filling:
8 ounces (225 g)
   strawberries for
   strawberry purée (see
   step 3)

12 ounces (350 g) low-fat
   cottage cheese
24 fresh strawberries,
   sliced in halves

The sauce:
8 fluid ounces (225 ml)
   plain low-fat yogurt
2 dessertspoons fresh
   orange juice
1 teaspoon orange rind
1 teaspoon lemon rind

1 tablespoon honey
A pinch or two of barley-
   malt sweetener
Fresh mint, if available,
   for garnish

1. Combine all the crêpe ingredients in a blender and blend for 2 minutes. Set aside and let the mixture rest for 2 hours.
2. Cook the crêpes in a 5-inch (12-cm) nonstick crêpe pan for 30 seconds each. (The batter should yield 12 crêpes.) Set aside and let cool.
3. Meanwhile, whir enough fresh strawberries in a blender to make 6 fluid ounces (180 ml) of purée. Set aside. Prepare the sauce by combining all ingredients in a small bowl, mixing well.
4. Spread 2 dessertspoons of cottage cheese over half of each cooked crêpe. Add 1 dessertspoon of strawberry purée and 4 strawberry halves. Fold the crêpe in half. Spread about 2 dessertspoons of the sauce over and around each crêpe. Garnish with a sprig of fresh mint.

12 servings. Serving size is 1 crêpe.

Per Serving: 77 calories, 26 mg cholesterol, 1 g dietary fibre, 1 g fat, 156 mg sodium.

HONEY-ORANGE BRAN BREAD

PREPARATION TIME: 15 MINUTES.   BAKING TIME: 50 MINUTES.

8 ounces (225 g) plain flour
1 teaspoon baking powder
½ teaspoon bicarbonate of soda
½ teaspoon salt
½ teaspoon ground cinnamon
⅛ teaspoon ground cloves

3 ounces (80 g) All-Bran
8 tablespoons honey
6 fluid ounces (180 ml) orange juice
1 egg
2 dessertspoons vegetable oil
1 teaspoon grated orange peel

1. Heat oven to 350°F (Gas Mark 4/180°C).
2. In a small mixing bowl, combine the flour, baking powder, soda, salt, cinnamon and cloves. Set aside.
3. In a large mixing bowl, combine the cereal, honey and orange juice. Let stand for 2 minutes. Beat in the egg, vegetable oil and orange peel. Add the flour mixture. Stir only until moistened. Spread the batter evenly into a lightly greased large loaf pan.
4. Bake for 50 minutes, or until knife inserted in centre comes out clean.

Makes 1 loaf of 16 slices. Serving size is 1 slice.

Per Serving: 120 calories, 20 mg cholesterol, 2 g dietary fibre, 2 g fat, 290 mg sodium.

ALMOND DROPS

PREPARATION TIME: 25 MINUTES.   BAKING TIME: 15 MINUTES.

Here is an example of a cookie in which we revise the original recipe by blending flours, reducing salt by half, and sugar and fat by 25 per cent. Try this approach with

271

your own recipes. These biscuits are great with a cup of fresh coffee.

5 ounces (145 g) whole-wheat flour	*6 ounces (175 g) margarine*
6 ounces (175 g) plain white flour	*1 egg*
½ teaspoon bicarbonate of soda	*4 tablespoons skim milk*
½ teaspoon salt	*1 scant teaspoon almond extract*
6 ounces (175 g) granulated sugar	*3 ounces (80 g) almonds, chopped or slivered*

1. Preheat oven to 325°F (Gas Mark 3/170°C).
2. In a large bowl, sift flours, baking soda, salt and sugar together. Cut in the margarine with a pastry blender or two knives until the mixture looks like fine oatmeal.
3. Lightly beat together the egg and the milk, and add to the above mixture, along with the almond extract and almonds. Mix well, and shape into small balls, about ¾ inch (2 cm) in diameter. Place them on an ungreased baking sheet, and press them down with your hand to flatten them slightly.
4. Bake for about 15 minutes, or until golden brown on the bottom. Cool on a wire rack.

Makes about 4 dozen biscuits, about 1 to 1½ inches (2 to 3 cm) in diameter.

Per Biscuit: 68 calories, 6 mg cholesterol, 1 g dietary fibre, 4 g fat, 67 mg sodium.

CARROT-NUT TEA BREAD

PREPARATION TIME: 15 MINUTES. BAKING TIME: 45 TO 55 MINUTES.

This is a mildly sweet quick bread.

2 eggs	*4 tablespoons vegetable oil*
6 ounces (175 g) granulated sugar	*4 tablespoons water*

272

5 ounces (145 g) whole-wheat flour
2 ounces (56 g) plain white flour
1 teaspoon bicarbonate of soda
1 teaspoon baking powder
1 teaspoon salt
1 teaspoon cinnamon
3 medium carrots, grated
3 ounces (80 g) chopped nuts
Nonstick vegetable cooking spray

1. Preheat the oven to 375°F (Gas Mark 5/190°C). Spray a large loaf pan with cooking spray and set aside.
2. Beat together the eggs, sugar, oil and water.
3. In another bowl, combine the flours, soda, baking powder, salt and cinnamon. Add the dry ingredients to the liquid ingredients.
4. Stir in the grated carrots and the chopped nuts. Pour the batter into the pan.
5. Bake for 45 to 55 minutes, testing for doneness by inserting a knife or toothpick into the centre of the loaf to see if it comes out clean. The top should be evenly browned when done.

12 servings. Serving size is 1 slice about ¾ inch (2 cm) thick.

Per Serving: 193 calories, 44 mg cholesterol, 2 g dietary fibre, 10 g fat, 287 mg sodium.

OAT NUT BISCUITS

PREPARATION TIME: 10 MINUTES. BAKING TIME: 12 TO 15 MINUTES.

We mixed this dough in a matter of minutes one night. A slightly crumbly and crisp biscuit.

4 fluid ounces (110 ml) vegetable oil
4 ounces (110 g) brown sugar
6 ounces (175 g) granulated sugar
1 egg
4 tablespoons water
½ teaspoon vanilla extract
1 teaspoon rum (optional)
10 ounces (300 g) rolled oats
3 ounces (80 g) whole-wheat flour
½ teaspoon bicarbonate of soda

273

1½ ounces (40 g)
  chopped walnuts OR
  other nuts

1. Heat oven to 350°F (Gas Mark 4/180°C).
2. Combine oil, sugars, egg, water, vanilla and rum in a large bowl, blending well. (A fork works fine for this.)
3. Stir in the remaining ingredients.
4. Drop by heaped teaspoonfuls onto an ungreased baking sheet, and bake for about 12 to 15 minutes.

Makes approximately 3 dozen biscuits, about 2 inches (5 cm) in diameter.

Per Biscuit: 96 calories, 8 mg cholesterol, 1 g dietary fibre, 4 g fat, 15 mg sodium.

MANDEL BREAD

PREPARATION TIME: 25 MINUTES. BAKING TIME: 35 TO 45 MINUTES.

Actually, this is not a bread, but biscuits that are first baked in a loaf form, and then cut into slices or bars, and baked again. A traditional Jewish recipe, modified for lower fat and sugar content, this is another winner with a good cup of fresh-ground coffee.

6 ounces (175 g)
  margarine, softened to
  room temperature
6 ounces (175 g)
  granulated sugar
4 eggs
½ teaspoon vanilla
1 teaspoon ground
  cinnamon

8 ounces (225 g) whole-
  wheat flour
8 ounces (225 g) plain
  white flour
1 teaspoon baking powder
3 ounces (80 g) almonds,
  chopped

1. Heat oven to 375°F (Gas Mark 5/190°C).
2. In a large bowl, cream together the margarine and the sugar. Beat in the eggs, vanilla and cinnamon.
3. In another bowl, combine the flours and baking powder. Add to the wet ingredients, mixing well. Stir in the almonds.

4. Form the dough into a long loaf about 1 inch (2 cm) high and 4 inches (10 cm) wide.
5. Place on an ungreased baking sheet, and bake until browned on the bottom, about 25 minutes.
6. Remove the bread from the oven, place it on a cutting board, and cut it into 26 ½-inch (1-cm) thick slices. Arrange the slices on the baking sheet, and bake until toasted on one side. Turn them over, and toast the other side. Cool on a wire rack.

Makes about 26, about 3 × 1½ inches (7 × 3 cm).

Per Biscuit: 163 calories, 42 mg cholesterol, 2 g dietary fibre, 8 g fat, 87 mg sodium.

BISCUIT-CRUST FRUIT 'PIZZA'

PREPARATION TIME: 35 MINUTES.   BAKING TIME: 10 MINUTES.

A thick biscuit crust is made attractive with a creamy topping and a stunning arrangement of colourful fresh fruit. You can prepare the crust ahead, since it needs to be refrigerated for several hours. Once the fruit is cut up, it tends to begin turning brown, so the 'pizza' is at its best served the same day, although the cut-up fruit will keep in a bowl of water mixed with about a tablespoon of lemon juice. Then drain the fruit well and put it on the crust just before serving.

This is a great recipe for children because it looks so good.

The crust:
3 ounces (85 g) caster sugar
2 ounces (56 g) soft light margarine
2 tablespoons skim milk
½ teaspoon vanilla extract
¼ teaspoon almond extract

5 ounces (145 g) whole-wheat flour
3 ounces (80 g) plain white flour
½ teaspoon cream of tartar
½ teaspoon bicarbonate of soda

The topping:

6 ounces (175 g) soft white
  cheese
¼ teaspoon vanilla extract
2 dessertspoons sugar OR
  honey
Mixed fresh fruit of choice
  (e.g., 8 ounces (225 g)
pineapple chunks, 2 kiwi
fruit, 1 sliced banana, 4
ounces (110 g) fresh
strawberries, 4 ounces
(110 g) mandarin
oranges)

1. For the crust, cream the sugar and margarine together until fluffy. Add the milk and extracts.
2. In another bowl, sift the dry ingredients and add to the creamed mixture until well blended. Cover and refrigerate for 4 to 6 hours.
3. Heat the oven to 375°F (Gas Mark 5/190°C).
4. Press the dough into a 12- or 13-inch (30- or 33-cm) pizza pan, or use a similar-sized square pan if necessary. Press the edges of the dough slightly upward to resemble a pizza crust.
5. Bake for about 10 minutes, or until golden.
6. Meanwhile, prepare the topping by creaming together the soft cheese, vanilla and sugar or honey.
7. Let the crust cool, and spread the topping over it.
8. Slice your favourite fruits into bite-sized pieces, and decorate the pizza with fruit in any pattern you like. Use your imagination! One of our favourite combinations is a mix of fresh pineapple, kiwi fruit, bananas, strawberries and mandarin oranges. We've also used grapes, peaches or other berries in season.

8 servings. Serving size is ⅛ pizza.

Per Serving (using the selection of fruits suggested above): 350 calories, 17 mg cholesterol, 4 g dietary fibre, 17 g fat, 276 mg sodium.

SWEET PINEAPPLE SQUARES

PREPARATION TIME: 20 MINUTES.   BAKING TIME: 40 MINUTES.

3 ounces (80 g) whole-
wheat flour
1 ounce (28 g) soy flour
3 ounces (80 g) all-purpose
flour
2 scant teaspoons baking
powder
½ teaspoon salt
2 dessertspoons brown
sugar

1 egg
2½ fluid ounces (65 ml)
honey
2½ fluid ounces (65 ml)
vegetable oil
1 16-ounce (450-g) tin
crushed unsweetened
pineapple, plus juice
Nonstick vegetable
cooking spray

1. In a large bowl, sift together the dry ingredients.
2. In another bowl, beat the egg, then beat in the honey and the oil. Measure the oil first, then use the same jug for the honey and it will slip out easily.
3. Drain the pineapple carefully to get 5 fluid ounces (145 ml) juice. Add the juice to the egg, honey and oil mixture. Blend mixture into the dry ingredients.
4. Spray an 8-inch (20-cm) square baking pan with nonstick vegetable cooking spray. Spread the batter in the pan, and top with the pineapple. Bake at 350°F (Gas Mark 4/180°C) for about 40 minutes. Cut in squares to serve.

12 servings of about 2 × 2⅔ inches (5 × 7 cm).

Per Serving: 180 calories, 22 mg cholesterol, 2 g dietary fibre, 7 g fat, 140 mg sodium.

CURRIED FRUIT COMPOTE

PREPARATION TIME: 10 MINUTES.   COOKING TIME:
1 HOUR AND 20 MINUTES.

This is a 'day before' recipe. It's best after it has been baked, chilled overnight in the refrigerator, and reheated, as directed. It's also good cold, so you may find it mysteriously disappearing from your refrigerator before you have a chance to reheat it.

You may use 1½ teaspoons of a commercially prepared curry powder, of course, but we highly recommend making the investment in the various spices and
mixing your own. Try the special blend we've selected,
and see how you like it. Once you discover the difference
between this and the commercial blends, you may end
up always preparing your own, as we do.

*1 16-ounce (450-g) tin
unsweetened peach
slices
1 16-ounce (450-g) tin
unsweetened pear
halves
1 16-ounce (450-g) tin
unsweetened apricot
halves
1 16-ounce (450-g) tin
unsweetened stoned
dark cherries
1 16-ounce (450-g) tin
unsweetened pineapple
chunks
3 ounces (80 g) almonds,
chopped or slivered*

*4 ounces (110 g) brown
sugar
½ teaspoon ground
cinnamon
½ teaspoon ground
coriander
¼ teaspoon ground
cardamom
¼ teaspoon ground
ginger
¼ teaspoon cumin
¼ teaspoon turmeric
⅛ teaspoon cayenne
pepper
1 ounce (28 g) butter* OR
margarine, melted

1. Drain all liquid from each tin of fruit. Pour the fruit
   into a 9 × 13-inch (23 × 33-cm) baking dish and stir.
   Top with almonds.
2. In a small bowl, combine the brown sugar, spices
   and melted butter. Sprinkle this mixture over the
   fruit.
3. Bake at 350°F (Gas Mark 4/180°C) for 1 hour. Let
   cool at room temperature, then refrigerate overnight. Twenty minutes before serving, reheat at
   350°F (Gas Mark 4/180°C) until bubbly.

*16 servings. Serving size is about a 4-fluid-ounce
(110-ml) measure.*

Per Serving: 144 calories, 8 mg cholesterol, 3 g dietary
fibre, 5 g fat, 39 mg sodium.

LEMON PUDDING

PREPARATION TIME: 20 MINUTES.   COOKING TIME:
                                            25 TO 30 MINUTES.

*8 ounces (225 g)
  granulated sugar
1 ounce (28 g) butter* OR
  *margarine, softened
Grated rind of 2 lemons
3 tablespoons lemon juice*

*3 tablespoons whole-
  wheat flour
4 eggs, separated
Nonstick vegetable
  cooking spray*

1. Heat oven to 350°F (Gas Mark 4/180°C).
2. Cream together the sugar and butter. Add the lemon rind, juice, flour and egg yolks, blending well.
3. Beat the egg whites until stiff, and fold into the batter.
4. Spray an 8-inch (20-cm) square baking dish or 8 small ovenproof dishes with nonstick cooking spray, and pour the batter in. Place in a larger oven-proof baking dish that has about 1 inch (2 cm) of hot water in it.
5. Bake for 25 to 30 minutes (15 to 20 minutes if the individual serving dishes are used), or until set and slightly browned on top.

VARIATION: Substitute grated rind of one orange for the lemon rind, and 3 tablespoons orange juice for the lemon juice.

8 servings. Serving size is about a 4-fluid-ounce (110-ml) measure.

Per Serving: 176 calories, 145 mg cholesterol, no dietary fibre, 6 g fat, 65 mg sodium.

COCOA-COURGETTE CAKE

PREPARATION TIME: 20 TO 25 MINUTES.   BAKING TIME:
                                            ¾ TO 1 HOUR.

This cake is moist, lightly sweet, with a satisfying, rich texture.

10 ounces (300 g)
granulated sugar

4 fluid ounces (110 ml)
vegetable oil

½ teaspoon vanilla extract

1 egg

2 egg whites

4 fluid ounces (110 ml)
low-fat milk

½ teaspoon baking
powder

1 teaspoon bicarbonate of
soda

4 ounces (110 g) plain
white flour

6 ounces (175 g) whole-
wheat flour

3 tablespoons cocoa
powder

½ teaspoon cinnamon

½ teaspoon salt

8 ounces (225 g)
courgettes, grated,
unpeeled (about 2
medium)

Nonstick vegetable
cooking spray or oil

1. Heat oven to 350°F (Gas Mark 4/180°C). Grease a large loaf tin.
2. Combine first 6 ingredients in a large bowl.
3. In another bowl, sift together the dry ingredients, and add alternately with the grated courgette to the first mixture. Press into the loaf tin.
4. Bake for 45 minutes then test to see if done. Remove from oven when a toothpick inserted in the centre of the cake comes out clean. The cooking time will depend upon whether you use a deep or shallow tin. Let stand 5 to 10 minutes before removing from the tin.

24 servings.

Per Serving: 136 calories, 11 mg cholesterol, 1 g dietary fibre, 5 g fat, 90 mg sodium.

DATE BRAN BARS

PREPARATION TIME: 15 MINUTES.   COOKING TIME: 30 MINUTES.

4 ounces (110 g) plain
white flour

1 teaspoon baking powder

5 ounces (145 g) chopped
dates

4 fluid ounces (110 ml)
boiling water

1 ounce (28 g) margarine, softened	4½ ounces (125 g) All-Bran
½ teaspoon vanilla extract	3 ounces (80 g) chopped nuts
1 egg, slightly beaten	
3 fluid ounces (70 ml) orange juice	

1. Heat oven to 350°F (Gas Mark 4/180°C).
2. In a small mixing bowl, stir together the flour and baking powder. Set aside.
3. Stir together the dates and the boiling water. Set aside.
4. In a large mixing bowl, combine the margarine, vanilla and egg. Beat well. Alternately add the flour mixture and the orange juice. Mix well. Fold in the dates, cereal and nuts. Spread the mixture evenly in a lightly greased 8 × 8 × 2-inch (20 × 20 × 5-cm) baking tin.
5. Bake for about 30 minutes or until a wooden tooth-pick inserted in the centre comes out clean. Cool in the pan; cut into 24 bars.

24 servings of about 1⅓ × 2 inches (3 × 5 cm).

Per Serving: 80 calories, 10 mg cholesterol, 2 g dietary fibre, 3 g fat, 170 mg sodium.

CHEWY BRAN-RAISIN BARS

PREPARATION TIME: 15 MINUTES.   STANDING TIME: ABOUT
1 HOUR.

6 ounces (175 g) All-Bran	3 tablespoons peanut butter
2½ ounces (70 g) raisins OR sultanas	½ teaspoon vanilla flavouring
3 ounces (80 g) chopped nuts	¼ teaspoon ground cinnamon
½ ounce (14 g) margarine	
4 fluid ounces (110 ml) honey	

1. Stir together the cereal, raisins and nuts. Set aside.

281

2. In a large saucepan, combine the margarine, honey and peanut butter. Stir over medium heat until the mixture is well blended. Remove from heat. Stir in the remaining ingredients.
3. Press the mixture into a lightly greased 9 × 9 × 2-inch (23 × 23 × 5-cm) pan. Let cool. Cut into 20 bars when cooled. Store covered in the refrigerator.

MICROWAVE DIRECTIONS: In a large glass mixing bowl, combine the margarine, honey and peanut butter. Cover loosely with wax paper or microwave-safe plastic wrap. Microwave on full power for about 2 minutes until the mixture is well blended. Stir in the remaining ingredients. Press the mixture into a lightly greased pan as above.

20 servings of about 2¼ × 2 inches (6 × 5 cm).

Per Serving: 110 calories, no cholesterol, 3 g dietary fibre, 4 g fat, 90 mg sodium.

ORANGE-CHOCOLATE PUDDING

PREPARATION TIME: 25 MINUTES.   REFRIGERATION TIME: 2 HOURS.

4 ounces (110 g) dark chocolate
2 tablespoons brown sugar
14 fluid ounces (390 ml) low-fat milk

2 tablespoons cornflour
2 fluid ounces (55 ml) orange juice

1. Combine the chocolate, sugar and milk in a large saucepan. Heat slowly over medium heat, stirring constantly (preferably with a wire whisk, if you have one; otherwise use a spoon) until chocolate is melted and milk is just beginning to scald, not boil.
2. Measure the cornflour into a bowl, and pour in about one-third of the hot chocolate mixture. Whisk vigorously until the cornflour is dissolved, then whisk back into remaining hot chocolate mixture in the saucepan.

3. Cook over very low heat for about 8 more minutes, stirring constantly. As the pudding thickens, you may need to switch to stirring with a spoon (if you've been using a whisk).

4. When the pudding is thick, remove from heat and stir in the orange juice. Pour into a serving bowl or individual cups. Chill for at least 2 hours, and serve.

VARIATIONS: Use 16 fluid ounces (450 ml) of low-fat milk, and add ¼ teaspoon of almond extract in place of the orange juice for Chocolate-Almond Pudding. Garnish each serving with a teaspoon of toasted almonds if desired. For Mocha Pudding, use vanilla extract instead of almond, and add a couple of teaspoons of strongly brewed coffee.

4 servings. Serving size is about a 4-fluid-ounce (110-ml) measure.

Per Serving: 263 calories, 10 mg cholesterol, 1 g dietary fibre, 12 g fat, 62 mg sodium.

POPPY SEED CAKE

PREPARATION TIME: 20 MINUTES.   BAKING TIME: 45 MINUTES.

Believe it or not, we often come up with a recipe that works perfectly the first time we try it! This confection had all our taste-testers smiling (mouths full) right away.

Nonstick vegetable cooking spray
Whole-wheat flour
2½ fluid ounces (70 ml) vegetable oil
6 ounces (175 g) granulated sugar
2 eggs, separated
½ teaspoon vanilla essence

5 ounces (145 g) whole-wheat flour
½ teaspoon salt
½ teaspoon bicarbonate of soda
5 fluid ounces (145 ml) plain low-fat yogurt
2 ounces (56 g) poppy seeds

1. Spray a small loaf tin with nonstick vegetable

cooking spray, and dust lightly with whole-wheat flour. Heat oven to 350°F (Gas Mark 4/180°C).

2. Blend the oil and sugar in a large bowl. Add the egg yolks one at a time, beating well. Add the vanilla.

3. In another bowl, sift together the flour, salt and bicarbonate of soda. Alternately fold the flour mixture and the yogurt into the oil and sugar mixture. Set aside.

4. Beat the egg whites until stiff. Fold into the batter. Fold in the poppy seeds. Pour the batter into the pan.

5. Bake for about 45 minutes, until top is nicely brown and a toothpick inserted in the centre comes out clean.

20 servings. Serving size is 1 slice about ⅜ inch (1 cm) thick.

Per Serving: 106 calories, 28 mg cholesterol, 1 g dietary fibre, 5 g fat, 87 mg sodium.

GINGERSNAPS

PREPARATION TIME: 20 MINUTES. BAKING TIME: 10 TO 12 MINUTES.

Compared with chocolate chip biscuits, gingersnaps generally run a poor second in popularity. Not these! They disappeared first in our tasting session.

4 fluid ounces (110 ml) vegetable oil

4 ounces (110 g) granulated sugar

2 ounces (56 g) brown sugar

3 tablespoons light molasses OR *black treacle*

1 egg, well-beaten

6 ounces (175 g) plain white flour

2½ ounces (40 g) whole-wheat flour

¼ teaspoon salt

2 scant teaspoons bicarbonate of soda

1 scant teaspoon cinnamon

1 scant teaspoon ground cloves

1 scant teaspoon ground ginger

1. Preheat the oven to 350°F (Gas Mark 4/180°C).

2. In a large mixing bowl, combine the oil, sugars and molasses. Beat in the egg.
3. In another bowl, combine the flours, salt, bicarbonate of soda and spices. Stir into the wet ingredients, mixing well.
4. Form the dough into balls about 1 inch (2 cm) in diameter, and place them about 2 inches (5 cm) apart on ungreased baking sheets. Bake for about 10 to 12 minutes.

Makes 3 dozen biscuits, about 2 inches (5 cm) in diameter.

Per Biscuit: 75 calories, 8 mg cholesterol, no dietary fibre, 3 g fat, 64 mg sodium.

WHOLE-GRAIN GOODY

PREPARATION TIME: 20 MINUTES. BAKING TIME: 25 TO 30 MINUTES.

This has a nutty flavour and a chewy texture because of the rolled oats. It goes almost too well with a glass of milk.

3 eggs
2 ounces (56 g) brown sugar
3 tablespoons molasses OR *black treacle*
3½ ounces (95 g) rolled oats
5 ounces (145 g) wholewheat flour
½ teaspoon baking powder
Grated rind of 1 orange
Juice of ½ orange
½ teaspoon vanilla extract
1 teaspoon rum
4 fluid ounces (110 ml) cultured buttermilk
1 ounce (28 g) butter OR *margarine, melted*
2 ounces (56 g) seedless raisins OR *sultanas*
Nonstick vegetable cooking spray

1. Heat the oven to 375°F (Gas Mark 5/190°C).
2. Beat the eggs with the sugar and molasses until smooth.
3. In another bowl, combine the oats, flour and baking powder.
4. Add the orange rind and juice, the vanilla and the rum, and mix well. Stir in the buttermilk, butter and raisins. Add to the egg-sugar mixture, blending well.

285

5. Pour into a pie tin that has been sprayed with nonstick vegetable cooking spray or greased very lightly with oil.
6. Bake for 25 to 30 minutes, until set.

8 servings.

Per Serving: 232 calories, 111 mg cholesterol, 3 g dietary fibre, 6 g fat, 101 mg sodium.

The Rotation Diet Activity Programme or How to Have Your Cake and Eat It, Too

I simply could not imagine writing a book that had any-thing to do with health and weight management and failing to discuss the importance of physical activity. At the beginning, on page xii, I made a very important point: if you are, or have been, a *sedentary* overweight person, I don't believe there's a cookbook in existence that can show you how to sustain a significant weight loss and maintain desirable weight unless you are willing to change your ways and become active. Without additional physical activity, no matter what style of cooking you choose, you will have to deprive yourself for ever and ever of most of the really good tasting things you can put on your table.

The human body was *not* designed for sedentary living! From the beginning of our existence on this planet until the invention of modern transport and the availability of elec-tricity in our homes, the average person had to move the energy equivalent of seven to eight miles of walking every day, *just to get the job of living done.* Today we can get by with a mile or two, and, compared with life just 100 years ago, that's an energy expenditure difference of several hundred calories each day!

Our appetites for fat and sugar, however, have not dimi-nished to compensate for our decrease in physical activity! Quite the contrary: for many of us, when there is little physical work to do, appetites seem to increase. If any-thing, high-calorie foods are more available to more people in the Western world now than has ever been the case in the history of humankind.

Thus, we have an epidemic of *overnutrition* – OBESITY – as *the* major nutrition problem. Fortunately, the problem has a solution.

In order to match appetite and energy expenditure, to put them in sync, the average sedentary person needs to add about 45 minutes of some sort of brisk physical activity to his or her daily routine. In about 45 minutes of brisk walking, a person who weighs just under 11 stone (about 68 k) will burn about 200 calories over and above the cal-ories required to just sit still; if you weigh more than 11 stone (70 k), you burn more in physical activity; if you weigh less, you burn less.

THAT 200 CALORIES IS VERY IMPORTANT FOR WEIGHT MAINTENANCE. That's because it takes about 200 calories a day to keep 40 to 50 pounds (18 to 23 k) of fat alive in the human body. Fat is relatively inactive tissue and only about 200 calories of your total daily food intake will be used to keep 40 to 50 pounds alive, on the average. I cannot be more exact in this estimation because there is a great deal of metabolic variability. At the extremes, some people may need only 100 calories a day to maintain 40 to 50 pounds of excess fat, while others may need 300; metabolic needs really do vary by that amount.

Let's assume you have lost extra pounds. The key to weight maintenance without deprivation at the dinner table, is to exercise enough EACH DAY to burn up the same number of calories it used to take to keep you fat! It's simple arithmetic: if you were 40 to 50 pounds overweight and are now at desirable weight and want to stay that way, exercise 200 calories-worth every day. IF YOU DON'T, THE FAT WILL CREEP BACK ON AGAIN, ON THE AVERAGE OF 200-CALORIES-WORTH EVERY DAY. That's an average of about 2 pounds (1 k) a month. It means that some time within the next year or two, all the weight you struggled to lose will be back on again, unless you restrict yourself to an extremely low food intake for the rest of your life – and who can do that? And who would *want* to?

Physically active people can eat like normal human beings.* Yes, there is room for dessert every day, especially if you make it one of the healthier, less fatty desserts included in the previous chapter. I know I am being repetitious, but if it helps just one person who has lost a significant amount of weight to stay motivated, it's worth warning you once again: if you do not become active and stay active, YOU ARE GOING TO GET FAT ALL OVER AGAIN.

End of lecture. Time now for a few words of encouragement and a little practical advice.

The best activities for weight management, as well as for cardiovascular health, are those in which you continuously move your whole body through space, or those which move the large muscle groups in your thighs and buttocks. Walking, bicycling, swimming, rowing (in a boat, or with a machine using your legs as well as your arms), are at the top of the list. I don't recommend jogging for overweight people because of the risk of injury. Bouncing on a mini-trampoline is fine, but be careful not to become too vigorous until your legs become accustomed to this type of exercise.

You get the best effects, while assuring cardiovascular and pulmonary conditioning as well as safety, when you exercise within what is called your **target** or **training range**. This range is between 60 and 85 per cent of your maximum heart rate. For most people, maximum heart rate will be about 220 minus their age. For example: the average maximum speed that the heart is capable of beating is about 180 beats per minute at maximum exertion for people 40 years old.

To determine your own target heart rate for physical activity, subtract your age from 220. Then multiply that figure first by .60 to get the bottom of the range, and then by .85 to get the top. Thus, for someone 40 years old, the range will be .60 × 180, or 108 beats per minute, to .85 × 180, or 153 beats per minute at the maximum. When that person

---

* Women of about 9 stone (58 k) who follow the Rotation Diet Activity Programme will require an average of about 1800–2000 calories per day to maintain their weight. Men at about 11 stone (70 k) will require an average of around 2400. Heavier people will need more, lighter people less.

goes for a *brisk* walk, swim or other aerobic activity, he or she should strive to keep the heartbeat between 108 and 153 beats per minute.

Most experts feel that you can improve cardiovascular endurance by exercising within your target range a minimum of three times a week for 20 minutes at a time. You should warm up for at least 5 minutes before working up into that range, and cool down afterwards for about 5 minutes before stopping, by walking or doing some other exercises less vigorously. A few minutes of gentle stretching exercises in addition may help to prevent injury, especially if you tend to be tight in the joints.

However, weight management requires more than cardiovascular conditioning in terms of time and frequency, as I have said. While it is important for cardiovascular health that you exercise within the target range at least three times a week, it is quite acceptable for weight control that you exercise on other days as well, at the bottom of that range or even below, for comfort.

THE FIRST RULE OF PHYSICAL ACTIVITY IS TO GO AS VIGOROUSLY AS YOU CAN *WITHOUT HURTING YOURSELF*.

We advise people who are sedentary to start slowly and increase gradually. Aim for 15 minutes a day during your first week, increase gradually toward a goal of 30 minutes a day the second week and end up at 45 minutes a day in the third week. Taking a day off is, of course, in order, if you don't feel well or have over-exerted on a previous day!

It may seem strange to you that we suggest you check with your doctor before doing something so simple as going out for a walk, BUT WE DO! We do because we want you to get as vigorous as you can *without hurting yourself*. Sedentary, overweight people should check with their doctors before going on any diet or starting any activity programme. Obesity is related to a number of physical illnesses, some of which may be undetected unless you have had a recent physical examination. These include heart disease and hypertension as well as diabetes. Although physical activity can be helpful in dealing with these illnesses, their presence, as well as the presence of a number of other physical problems (arthritis, kidney disease, other circulatory problems) will require a physician's supervision as you become more active.

It seems best from both a physical and psychological standpoint to exercise for at least 30 minutes at a time. That amount of activity may stimulate your metabolism to burn a few more calories round the clock, and it seems to be the amount of time required in order to feel truly relaxed and refreshed.

However, don't be concerned: you can break up your activity to fit your schedule and still get at least 98 per cent of all its benefits. Just get out of your chair for 5 minutes on the hour each hour during the working day, climb a flight of stairs or two and walk the hallways as vigorously as you can without causing chaos! You will end up burning close to the extra 200 calories a day that helps guarantee weight maintenance. Also, the break will refresh you and you will probably be more productive during the rest of the hour.

Time of day for physical activity has little practical meaning, although some research suggests you may burn a few more calories exercising between 4 and 8 p.m. when the metabolic rate tends to be a bit higher for most people. If you exercise in the morning, you will be more alert and ready for productive work; if you exercise late in the afternoon, you will be relaxed and refreshed at night, and you'll probably sleep better, *unless* you have over-exerted yourself. Indeed, just about everyone who completes the working day feeling tired, and perhaps irritable, reports feeling incredibly better after some exercise. (And their spouses and friends report that they are much easier to live with, too!)

Physical activity may not feel good at first if you are overweight or out of shape. Terri and I have both been overweight and inactive. So we both know from experience that once you've got used to daily physical activity, it will become one of the high points of your day.

Here are a few facts to help you stay motivated for physical activity until the pleasure of doing it takes over.

When you go for a walk at just 3 miles per hour, you burn about three times the calories that you burn sitting still. If you walk briskly at 4 miles per hour, you burn almost five times the calories burned when you sit still.

The average person can count on burning a total of

around 100 calories for every fifteen minutes of brisk activity, that is, while doing things that are equivalent to walking at 4 miles per hour. A good game of singles tennis, played at a strong intermediate level, is about equivalent. Badminton and squash are even more vigorous. Doubles tennis, on the other hand, may be good for your social life but, unless played very vigorously, doesn't burn nearly as many calories as continuous walking.

Perhaps the reason that jogging is so effective in weight management (and remember, we DO NOT recommend jogging for overweight people; get down to desirable weight first) is that even at a 6-mile-per-hour pace, which is quite gentle once you get into it, you burn from nine to ten times the calories of sitting still. Jogging at that pace will burn 100 calories, or more, every ten minutes. It adds up to a total of 600 to 800 calories an hour. And, for many people, this level of activity, at this intensity, does leave a residual metabolic elevation that burns up 50 to 100 more calories than normal, as the body recovers from activity over the next several hours.*

A time for activity always goes down first on my daily calendar, and on Terri's. It means more to us than just improving our physical condition and increasing our flexibility. As the years go by and I have grown busier and busier, the time I take for a jog or a walk has become more and more important. It's the most creative and refreshing part of my day. Although we encourage people to get active together when they first start and to form 'buddy systems' to support and motivate each other, physical activity may well become a time for you to be alone, to relax, and to completely separate yourself from the rest of the day's activities.

So, we hope you will use and enjoy our recipes for good healthy cooking AND for physical activity. It's the only way you can have your cake and eat it, too!

---

* In the examples we have just given, we are referring to total calories burned in activity. This *includes* the amount it would have taken if you had just sat still. Earlier, when we spoke of the need to exercise for around 45 minutes a day, we spoke of 200 calories being burned in that period of time *in addition* to the sitting requirements. For simplicity's sake, and in view of the great metabolic variability, we are rounding figures to the nearest 100 in these last examples.

Sample Menus for Weight Loss and Weight Maintenance

OVERVIEW OF THE QUICK-WEIGHT-LOSS ROTATION DIET

Included in this chapter (pp. 303–10) are sample menus for 600-, 900-, 1200-, 1500- and 1800-calorie rotations on the Rotation Diet. These menus are different from, but interchangeable with, the original Rotation Diet menus.

In order to have the instructions for implementing the Rotation Diet for quick-weight-loss all in one place and easily available for reference, we must of necessity repeat certain nutritional guidelines and cooking suggestions that appeared separately in various parts of this book. We hope the integration will be useful to you and that you forgive the occasional redundancy.

The Rotation Diet is a twenty-one-day, quick-weight-loss diet that is safe for overweight people who are otherwise in good health. The average weight loss is approximately 12.5 pounds (5.7 k) during this three-week period. Heavier people lose faster than lighter people, and men tend to lose faster than women of equal weight.

For women: During the first three days of the diet, the core menu contains approximately 600 calories. During the next four days it contains approximately 900 calories.

In Week 2 you go up to 1200 calories and then, in Week 3, you repeat Week 1.

In addition to the core menu (see pages 303–6), you may eat unlimited *free vegetables* with any meal or as snacks, and you choose a *safe fruit*, also to be used as a snack, whenever you feel hungry or need a lift. (Additional information on *free vegetables* and the *safe fruit* is on pages 295–6.) In Week 4 you make a transition to maintenance, eating approximately 1200 calories for three days, followed by 1500 for about four days. Then you increase until your weight stabilizes.

It is very important that you take a 'vacation' from dieting and allow your weight to stabilize for one to two weeks before repeating the Rotation Diet. This prevents the metabolic slow-down that can occur with prolonged dieting, and the vacation will help you maintain your motivation. You will learn how to maintain your losses and avoid feelings of deprivation.

On the average, women who implement the complete Rotation Diet recommendations for the correct balance of foods plus 45 minutes a day of physical activity will find that their weight stabilizes when they eat around 1800 to 2000 calories per day.

For men: Men add 600 calories a day to the basic menus for women. Thus, the calorie levels for men are 1200 calories for three days, 1500 calories for four days followed by 1800 calories for a week. In Week 3, you return to Week 1 levels. Then, in the fourth week, men also take a 'vacation' from dieting by going up to 1800 calories for three days, 2100 for about four days and then stabilizing somewhere around 2400 calories. Additional instructions appear on pages 297–8.

SUBSTITUTIONS are allowed on the Rotation Diet if you don't like a particular food or if a particular food does not agree with you. However, you must substitute within the same food group. That is, if you don't care for the vegetable that appears on any menu, substitute another vegetable; if you don't care for one protein food (fish, poultry or meat), substitute another and so on. **Substitution lists appear in this chapter, on pages 312–22.**

Serving sizes are given with the food items on the daily

menus. It is a good idea to weigh and measure your food for the first few days of the diet if you are unsure of the 'look' of these portion sizes. However, if you don't wish to weigh and measure, choose a moderate 'restaurant-size' portion, such as you would find at a cafeteria, and you will be fairly accurate. A dish followed by an asterisk (*) in the sample menus means the recipe – with other nutritional information – appears in the recipe section of this book.

THE ROTATION-DIET INSURANCE POLICY

So that everyone can follow the Rotation Diet and never feel hungry, we have designed an 'insurance policy' that will help you overcome temptation and achieve good results. This insurance policy has two clauses.

Clause #1 is *free vegetables*. If you are ever tempted to eat anything that isn't in the diet during the next three weeks, you may eat all you want of the *free vegetables* with any meal and at any time of the day as snacks (see the list that follows). They contain vitamins, minerals and beneficial amounts of fibre, with fewer than 25 calories per 4-fluid-ounce (110-ml) measure. Eat them plain or use only no-cal salad dressing on the 600-calorie days, and no- or lo-cal dressing on any other days.

Unlimited Free Vegetables

asparagus	aubergine	bean sprouts
beetroot	broccoli	brussels sprouts
cabbage	carrots	cauliflower
celery	chard	chicory
courgettes	cucumbers	dandelion greens
French beans	endive	escarole
green pepper	kale	lettuce
mange-tout peas	mushrooms	okra
onions	parsley	radishes
rhubarb	runner beans	spinach
spring greens	tomatoes	turnips
turnip greens	watercress	

Clause #2 in our insurance policy is the *safe fruit*. Start by choosing *one* fruit from this list, *or any other fresh fruit that is easily available to you*, as your *safe fruit*. Carry one with you at all times as a snack. Eat up to *three* servings a day, in addition to whatever different fruits are called for in the menus of the Rotation Diet, when you need a lift, feel unbearably hungry or are tempted to stray from your diet for any reason. (A serving size is one piece of fruit, or standard 'restaurant' portion for such fruits as strawberries, melon, etc.)

Safe Fruits

apple	banana	blackberries
canteloupe	cherries	currants
grapefruit	grapes	honeydew melon
kiwi	mango	orange
papaya	peach	persimmon
pineapple	plum	raspberries
strawberries	tangerine	watermelon

Weight loss tends to be quicker if you limit yourself to one fruit as your safe fruit, because you will probably get bored with it and hence will not overeat. But to be sure you can stick with the diet and not go back to high-calorie snacks, *feel free to substitute any fresh fruit at any time as your safe fruit if it means you will be able to avoid junk-food snacks for the full three weeks of the diet.* Indeed, many people can eat almost unlimited quantities of fresh fruit during the Rotation Diet and, although they may not lose an average of two-thirds of a pound a day, will still lose a considerable amount of weight.

HOW TO COOK FOR THE ROTATION DIET

To ensure the quickest and safest possible weight loss, prepare everything on these daily menus simply, without additional fat or sugar. Some recipes do call for fat and/or sugar, but these menus have been analysed to fall within the calorie guidelines. This advice is especially for menu items for which there is no recipe. It is the added fat and sugar in your diet that provide concentrated calories and no bulk.

Use low-fat products and remove the skin from chicken, preferably before cooking as the skin contains much of the fat. Use the portion sizes in the menus and recipes as a guide when eating out. Weights in the menus are all cooked weights for cooked foods such as meat, fish and poultry, which shrink when cooked.

The portion sizes in the menus are for women. You may add unlimited free vegetables and as many as three extra servings of fruit each day and still stay within the guidelines of the diet. Fruits and vegetables provide a great deal of bulk but minimal calories; make up your mind to use fruit and vegetables, not junk food, for snacks, and it will help you be successful on the Rotation Diet. Fresh is best, but frozen and tinned fruit, un-sweetened, in fruit juice, still have high bulk and low calories.

When a side salad is called for, start with an 8-fluid-ounce (225-ml) measure of any fresh salad vegetables of your choice. (Remember, vegetables don't make you fat; you really can eat unlimited quantities of them.) 'No-cal' salad dressings have fewer than 10 calories per des-sertspoon, while 'lo-cal' dressings have about 35. No-cal salad dressings can be added at any time, so they are not always indicated.

As a general rule, whether dieting or not, we suggest that you add little or no salt to your foods. Our recipes call for a 'touch' of salt, just to help enhance the flavour of the herbs and spices.

INSTRUCTIONS FOR MEN AND FOR COUPLES USING THE DIET TOGETHER

The diet for men contains 1200 calories for the first three days and 1500 calories for the next four days. Men can use the basic Rotation Diet menus for women by adding approximately 600 calories each day according to the following instructions. This also permits couples to use the diet together by simply preparing larger quantities of the basic foods. (Men can also use the 1200-, 1500- and 1800-calorie menus that we've supplied as examples and guides for the construction of additional menus.)

To the 600- and 900-calorie-diet menus for women, men should add, each day:

— two more servings of grain (bread, cereal or crispbread)
— 50 per cent larger portions of meat, fish or poultry
— ⅓ ounce (10 g) of butter or 1 dessertspoon of oil or regular salad dressing
— three *safe fruits* (these are optional for women, but should be included to be sure men add the extra 600 calories to their diets).

SPECIALLY RECOMMENDED FOODS FOR THE ROTATION DIET

The menus are designed to maximize nutritional value while maintaining variety and good taste. Certain substitutions can, however, make the diet even more healthful.

For example, fortified breakfast cereals (of course, NOT the sugared variety) can always be substituted for a grain product at breakfast, or whenever bread or crispbreads are called for. Check the labels of your favourite cereals. Look for fortification at around 25% of the recommended dietary allowances for most vitamins and minerals. For instance, the Special K Breakfast, which was especially designed with weight management in mind, would be a good choice with fruit. Remember that you can increase the fibre content of your own favourite cereal by adding fruit or by adding 1 to 2 tablespoons of a high-fibre cereal. Our favourites for this latter purpose are All-Bran and Brand Buds. (You can, of course, use your own favourite fibre cereals for additional fibre.)

Fish and poultry can always be substituted whenever beef is called for. This will greatly lower the saturated fat and cholesterol in your diet – two of the goals for reducing the risk of cancer and heart disease. You may also substitute tofu, complementary-protein foods such as beans and rice, or any grain served with beans, seeds or nuts in place of meat. (Complementary-protein cooking is discussed on pages 156–7.

We do not feel, however, that you have to eliminate beef in order to design a healthy diet. We choose lean cuts such as topside, sirloin, and silverside, and fillet and skirt steaks in our own cooking. We use mince that is truly lean (10% fat or less, by weight). We do not recommend sweetbreads because they tend to be higher in either fat or cholesterol.

If the shop where you usually buy your meat does not normally serve well-trimmed beef you must request a lean trim or trim your beef yourself. In some of the fatty cuts, as much as 80% of the calories come from fat, not protein!

Although trimming well will remove a large percentage of the fat from meat, there is still a considerable amount intertwined with the muscle in best quality steaks and roasts. You can tell this from the white streaks or 'marbling'. Nowadays beef is specially bred to produce less marbling. You will have to ask your butcher for help and information.

THE VEGETARIAN ROTATION DIET

Many vegetarians easily use the Rotation Diet by substituting their usual protein foods whenever meat, poultry or fish is called for. Use standard 'restaurant'-size portions of complementary protein foods, dairy products, tofu or other soy products. For example, a 4-fluid-ounce (110-ml) measure of beans with the same measure of rice would be about the equivalent of a serving of meat, fish or poultry.

BEVERAGES

Drink eight 8-fluid-ounce glasses of water a day. *Drinking plenty of water is one of the most important things you can do in your efforts to lose weight and keep it off, as well as in your pursuit of overall good health.* Use only no-cal beverages (black coffee, black tea, herbal teas, soda waters, water with a twist of lemon or lime, low-sodium bouillons) except when milk is called for. Limit your use of caffeinated coffee or tea to two cups each day, because more may cause stomach upset on low-calorie days. Also, too much caffein can add to nervousness, irritability and other health problems. If decaffeinated coffee and tea do not upset your stomach, you can use these beverages, but only in moderation, since the health implications of decaffeinated beverages are still in question. Finally, if black coffee upsets your stomach, one or two teaspoons of milk will not hurt.

Artificially sweetened diet drinks and artificial sweeteners and sugar should also be used in moderation. Our experience indicates that people who have been accustomed to drinking large quantities of sweet-flavoured drinks are better able to manage their weight when they reduce or eliminate their consumption and start drinking plain water or unsweetened herbal teas.

If you find the taste of your tap water objectionable and have difficulty drinking it, ice or refrigerate it, add a twist of lemon, or drink soda water. Clean, fresh-tasting water is a pleasure to drink, so you also might look into bottled mineral water or a much more reasonably priced alternative: a portable or kitchen-sink filtration unit that removes chlorine and objectionable organic matter from your tap water.

HOW TO BE COMFORTABLE ON THE ROTATION DIET

The Rotation Diet is a fun diet and a 'feeling-good' diet! You do not have to be uncomfortable in order to succeed. If you feel tired, grouchy or headachy, INCREASE YOUR CALORIES. Dip into the *free vegetables* and your *safe fruit*. Have a bowl of cereal and milk. If necessary, go up to 1200 calories a day if you are a woman or 1800 if you are a man. *You will still lose weight* in a way that will amaze you if you just substitute healthy low-calorie, high-fibre foods, such as safe fruits and free vegetables, for desserts, sweets, junk-food snacks and alcohol.

VITAMIN AND MINERAL SUPPLEMENTATION

We strongly recommend the use of a multiple vitamin and mineral supplement, especially for people who will use the Rotation Diet several times in a row. Choose a supplement that provides approximately 100 per cent of the Recommended Dietary Allowances (RDAs) of the essential vitamins and minerals. Calcium and iron may require additional supplementation in the form of separate calcium and iron tablets. Do not use megadoses of vitamins without the advice of a physician, and if you need help, discuss the choice of a supplement with your doctor, chemist or nutritionist.

READ THIS BEFORE USING THE ROTATION DIET

The Rotation Diet is safe for overweight people who are otherwise in good health; however, no one should undertake this or any other weight loss programme without consulting his or her doctor.

The Rotation Diet should not be used by:

Pregnant or nursing women
Children or teenagers
Diabetics
Underweight or normal-weight adults
People recovering from surgery or trauma

People at present under a physician's care and taking prescription medication should check with their doctor before changing their diet in any way. Dietary changes can cause changes in the effects of medication.

The Rotation Diet is not appropriate for highly active people; for example, those who run five miles or more a day. In order to lose weight, such people should not cut their normal intake by more than 500 calories per day.

301

People who are not overweight should not use the Rotation Diet. Normal-weight persons who wish to reduce body fat and tone up their bodies, should consult a fitness expert and embark on a well-rounded physical conditioning programme.

THE ROTATION DIET ACTIVITY PROGRAMME

Physical activity is absolutely essential for weight management and overall good health.

Be sure to read about physical activity on pages 290–1 for more tips on getting started safely and comfortably. IF YOU ARE A SEDENTARY PERSON WITH A WEIGHT PROBLEM, YOU MUST MAKE A LIFETIME COMMITMENT TO AN INCREASE IN PHYSICAL ACTIVITY.

Briefly, the Rotation Diet activity programme requires you to increase total *daily* physical activity by 15 minutes each week until you reach a daily average of about 45 minutes in Week 3. Week 1 calls for 15 minutes per day; in Week 2 you build up to 30 minutes per day; and in Week 3 you reach your goal of 45 minutes per day.

If you feel that your physical condition prevents you from engaging in the Rotation Diet Activity Programme, we recommend that you discuss with your doctor what, if anything, in the way of exercise might be suitable and enjoyable for you. If you are an overweight person who cannot be active and must control your weight through diet alone, you may never be able to increase your intake to the maintenance levels attainable by more active people. Thus you will be restricted to a low-calorie, potentially inadequate diet. Under these conditions, you will do well to seek the advice and supervision of a registered dietician, who can help you design the most satisfying diet possible.

SAMPLE ROTATION DIET
QUICK-WEIGHT-LOSS MENUS

Here are some sample menus for quick weight loss. In order to maximize nutritional value on 600- and

900-calorie days, we suggest a fortified breakfast cereal with milk in these menu examples. **You may, however, substitute according to the substitution guidelines given on pages 294 and 298–9. Use the following sample daily menus to help you construct additional menus, using the substitution lists for variety.** Be sure to eat a wide variety of foods: many different fruits and vegetables, along with whole-grain products, skim or low-fat dairy products and lean meats. The complete Rotation Diet can be found in *The Rotation Diet* by Martin Katahn, Ph.D., published by the Bantam Press.

Recipes for dishes followed by an asterisk (*) are recipes included in this cookbook.

The serving sizes in the *recipes*, however, may not always correspond exactly to the suggested serving size on these *menus*. This will be true most frequently in the menus containing fewer than 1500 calories per day. The serving sizes in the recipes are the typical sizes used in nutrient analyses and are geared more towards weight-maintenance diets than calorie-restricted diets. You're on your honour to adjust portion size when you use these Rotation Diet menus for losing weight!

SAMPLE 600-CALORIE DAY FOR WOMEN

Breakfast
1 ounce (28 g) fortified cereal
8 fluid ounces (225 ml) skim or low-fat milk
½ cup strawberries or other fresh fruit*
no-cal beverage

Lunch
6 fluid ounces (180 ml) plain low-fat yogurt
½ banana, sliced
1 tablespoon high-fibre cereal or wheatgerm
no-cal beverage

* For cup measurements please see Standard Measures for the British Edition, p. x

Dinner
Grilled or poached fish (3 ounces/80 g cooked):
Grilled Cod with Shallots*, Lime-Steamed Fish Fillets*
or any other fish fillet
½ cup cooked brown rice
1 cup broccoli, steamed
tossed salad with unlimited free vegetables
no-cal salad dressing
no-cal beverage

SAMPLE 900-CALORIE DAY FOR WOMEN

Breakfast
1 ounce (28 g) fortified cereal
8 fluid ounces (225 ml) skim or low-fat milk
½ cup sliced peaches or other fruit
no-cal beverage

Lunch
2 ounces (56 g) salmon (tinned)
unlimited free vegetables
1 teaspoon mayonnaise or 1 dessertspoon Paprika
Dressing*
1 slice whole-grain bread
1 orange
no-cal beverage

Dinner
Baked chicken (3 ounces/80 g cooked):
Happy Heart Chicken*, Lime-Light Chicken* or Patti's
Roast Chicken*
½ cup pasta, brown rice or other cooked grain
Cheese-Baked Cauliflower*
1 cup greens (spinach, kale, cabbage or other)
1 apple
no-cal beverage

SAMPLE 1200-CALORIE DAY

This is an example of a basic Week-2 day on the Rotation Diet for a woman, or a Day 1, 2 or 3 of Week 1 for a man.

You may add ⅓ ounce (10 g) of butter or margarine or 1 dessertspoon of oil and include 3 servings of a safe fruit. Or, in place of 2 servings of fruit, you can have an ounce (28 g) of breakfast cereal and 4 fluid ounces (110 ml) of low-fat milk. With these additions, we aim for a total of between 1200 and 1300 calories per day.

Breakfast
1 whole-grain scone or small roll
1 dessertspoon peanut butter
8 fluid ounces (225 ml) skim or low-fat milk
½ cup fresh fruit:
Creative Fruit Salad* or other mixture of fruit
no-cal beverage

Lunch
Barley Chicken Soup* or Spinach-Egg Drop Soup*
Toasted Open-Face Sandwich:
1 ounce (28 g) cheese, 1 slice whole-grain bread, 1
tomato slice
1 orange
no-cal beverage

Dinner
Baked Skirt Steak* or some other lean meat (4½
ounces/125 g cooked)
Sweet Spiced Beets*
Shades of Green*
½ cup sliced peaches
no-cal beverage

SAMPLE 1500-CALORIE DAY

This is an example of a menu appropriate for women on the first three days of Week 4 as they make a transition to maintenance. It is also appropriate for men on Days 4 to 7 of Week 1 during the fast-weight-loss period. As usual for all menus of 1200 calories and above, you add ⅓ ounce (10 g) of fat and your safe-fruit snacks to the stated menu.

Breakfast
8 fluid ounces (225 ml) skim or low-fat milk
1 cup hot cereal
cinnamon
2 dessertspoons raisins or sultanas
½ grapefruit
no-cal beverage

Lunch
4 sardines
sliced tomato
unlimited free vegetables
1 slice whole-grain bread
1 apple
no-cal beverage

Dinner
Baked Bass with Lemon-Wine Bouillon* or
some other fish fillet (4½ ounces/125 g cooked)
Broccoli with Water Chestnuts*
1 or 2 courgettes
½ cup cooked brown rice
2 Gingersnaps*
8 fluid ounces (225 ml) skim or low-fat milk

SAMPLE 1800-CALORIE MENUS

Here are some examples of 1800-calorie menus that are appropriate for most women who implemented the complete Rotation Diet and Activity Programme for weight maintenance. You add to these menus additional fat or oil, up to a total of ⅓ ounce (10 g) or 1 dessertspoon per day, and your fruit or cereal snacks. You may also be able to add an occasional higher calorie dessert or a glass of wine. HOWEVER, YOU MUST EXPERIMENT TO

FIND YOUR CORRECT MAINTENANCE LEVEL. As you begin to increase your food intake, get on the scales every day. If you go up 2 or 3 pounds and stay up for two or three days, YOU HAVE EXCEEDED YOUR MAINTENANCE LEVEL. Sorry, you will have to cut back. Catch it quickly! Additional instructions follow the menus.

For men: These menus can be used during Week 2 while you are on the quick-weight-loss Rotation Diet. When you reach Week 4, add calories slowly until you reach maintenance. Additional instructions follow the menus.

1800-CALORIE MENU #1

Breakfast
Great Shake* or
8 fluid ounces (225 ml) plain low-fat yogurt with 1 cup berries
1 slice Buttermilk Corn Bread* or any Muffin* recipe
no-cal beverage

Lunch
Japanese-Style Crab Salad* or
2 ounces (56 g) water-packed tuna or salmon
2 slices whole-grain bread
unlimited free vegetables
lo-cal salad dressing
choice of fruit
no-cal beverage

Dinner
Baked Horseradish Chicken* (4½ ounces/125 g baked chicken)
Spinach Bake*
Honey-Nut Glazed Carrots*
2 Chocolate Chip Biscuits*
8 fluid ounces (225 ml) skim or low-fat milk

1800-CALORIE MENU #2

Breakfast
8 fluid ounces (225 ml) skim or low-fat milk
4 ounces (110 g) fortified cereal
½ cup fresh fruit
Honey Bran Muffin* or
1 slice whole-grain toast with 1 teaspoon margarine or
butter
no-cal beverage

Lunch
Chunky Tomato Soup* (12 fluid ounces/330 ml)
Spinach Salad:
1½ cups fresh spinach, ¼ cup sliced mushrooms, ½
cup mandarin orange sections, 1 dessertspoon slivered
almonds with Poppy Seed Dressing* or another
dressing
5 whole-wheat crispbread
no-cal beverage

Dinner
White Bean Casserole*, Tofu Cannelloni* or
Swiss-Mozzarella Bake* (or ½ cup beans, ½ cup
cooked rice, 2 ounces (56 g) cheese)
1 cup Courgettes with Dill*
1 cup Side Salad*
no- or lo-cal dressing
1 slice Poppy Seed Cake* or choice of fruit
8 fluid ounces (225 ml) skim or low-fat milk

1800-CALORIE MENU #3

Breakfast
8 fluid ounces (225 ml) skim or low-fat milk
½ banana
1 dessertspoon peanut butter
2 slices whole-grain bread
no-cal beverage

Lunch
Oriental Tofu Soup*, Winter Bean Soup* or another
soup
(12 fluid ounces/330 ml)
Combination Sandwich*
unlimited free vegetables
1 orange
no-cal beverage

Dinner
Fish Fillets *Véronique* (6 ounces/175 g cooked fish)
1 medium baked potato
Artichoke-Spinach Salad*
no- or lo-cal dressing
Serving of Curried Fruit Compote*
or Peach Cobbler*
8 fluid ounces (225 ml) skim or low-fat milk

1800-CALORIE MENU #4

Breakfast
'English Danish':
4 ounces (110 g) low-fat cottage cheese
¼ teaspoon ground cinnamon
½ cup fresh or unsweetened sliced peaches or other
fruit
on
2 halves whole-grain roll
8 fluid ounces (225 ml) skim or low-fat milk
no-cal beverage

Lunch
Tuna Salad with Fruit-Vinaigrette Dressing* (2 ounces/
56 g fish)
1 whole-grain 6-inch (15-cm) pita bread
unlimited free vegetables
½ canteloupe melon
no-cal beverage

309

Dinner
Veal *Scaloppine* Dijon* (4½ ounces/125 g cooked
meat)
1 cup cooked pasta
1 cup courgettes
1 cup Side Salad*
no- or lo-cal dressing
1 slice Coffee Chocolate Cheesecake*
8 fluid ounces (225 ml) skim or low-fat milk

GENERAL MAINTENANCE GUIDELINES FOR WOMEN

The preceding 1800-calorie menus are meant to serve as illustrations of a healthy weight maintenance diet. Design your own by building your daily diet around the following selection of foods. Use the Food Substitution Lists (pp. 312–22) for information on serving sizes and nutritional equivalence.

- Four servings per day of whole grains or their equivalents.
- Two to three servings of skim or low-fat milk products.
- Five to seven ounces (145 to 200 g) of lean meat, fish or poultry (cooked weight) per day. Or use complementary protein substitutes of grains and legumes.
- Two servings of vegetables, including a dark green vegetable for vitamin A and extra calcium.
- Two servings of fruit, including a citrus fruit for vitamin C.
- To this basic diet you may add ⅓ ounce (10 g) of butter or margarine or 1 dessertspoon of oil, regular salad dressing or any other fat per day.
- These selections will total between 1200 and 1400 calories. To arrive at about 1800, add unlimited free vegetables and safe fruit snacks, or another serving or two of a grain product, up to a total of about 300 calories more (see the following substitution lists for approximate calorie contents). This leaves you room for between 100 and 200 calories in desserts

(pp. 262–86) or one to two glasses of dry wine at dinner (about 90 calories per 4-fluid-ounce (110-ml) serving).

MAINTENANCE GUIDELINES FOR MEN

- Six servings per day of whole grains or their equivalents.
- Two to three servings of skim or low-fat milk products.
- Eight to ten ounces (225 to 300 g) of lean meat, fish or poultry (cooked weight) per day. Or use complementary protein substitutes of grains and legumes.
- Two servings of vegetables, including a dark green vegetable for vitamin A and extra calcium.
- Two servings of fruit, including a citrus fruit for vitamin C.
- To this basic diet you may add ⅓ ounce (10 g) of butter or margarine or 1 dessertspoon of oil, regular salad dressing or any other fat per day.
- Depending upon whether you select the smallest suggested quantity of leanest meats and skim milk products, or the upper limit, calories in the above recommendations can vary from a low of around 1325 to a high of 1750. The average male will need between 2100 and 2400 calories per day to maintain his weight. To arrive at your maintenance level, add unlimited free vegetables and safe fruit snacks, or another serving or two of a grain product, up to a total of about 300 calories more (see the following substitution lists for approximate calorie contents). This should leave you room for between 200 and 300 calories in desserts (pp. 262–86) or one to two glasses of dry wine at dinner (about 90 calories per 4-fluid-ounce (110-ml) serving).

FOR EVERYONE

- *Desserts, high-calorie snacks and alcoholic beverages should never replace the foods in this basic dietary plan.* They can be added as treats to this diet at a level that doesn't lead to weight gain.

311

FOOD SUBSTITUTION LISTS

Milk and Dairy Products

Whether you are using the Rotation Diet for quick weight-loss or following our suggestions for weight maintenance, our menus include skim or low-fat dairy products daily. The maintenance menus recommend two to three servings a day.

Milk is the leading source of calcium in the diet. However, since not everyone wishes to have two or three glasses of milk each day, the following list indicates possible substitutions for milk, from the daily group of foods, that are approximate equivalents in terms of calories. The dairy products in this list contain from about 80 to about 115 calories per serving, with an average of about 105 calories. Skim-milk products have the fewest calories, and those with 5 per cent butterfat will have the most.

Substituting another dairy product for milk may, however, compromise calcium content to a certain extent. For this reason, we list the calcium content of the items in parenthesis for comparison.

Women need over 1000 milligrams of calcium a day for strong, healthy bones and men need around 800 milligrams each day. If your calcium consumption consistently falls short of recommended levels, you may require a calcium supplement. You do not need to obtain all of your calcium from milk products. Deep green vegetables such as kale, spinach and other greens are also good sources of calcium, as are fish with bones, such as sardines and tinned salmon.

Type of Dairy Product	*Calcium Content*	*Amount for Calorie Equivalent**
Skim or non-fat milk	(302 mg)	8 fl oz (225 ml)
Low-fat (1%) milk	(300 mg)	8 fl oz (225 ml)
Lo-cal (1.8%) milk	(270 mg)	8 fl oz (225 ml)
Powdered, non-fat dry (before adding 8 fl oz (225 ml) water)	(316 mg)	4 T dry

Tinned, evaporated		
skim milk	(368 mg)	4 fl oz (110 ml)
Buttermilk	(285 mg)	8 fl oz (225 ml)
Plain, low-fat yogurt	(415 mg)	6 fl oz (180 ml)
Cheeses		
Greater than 5% butterfat, such as:		
Emmenthal/Gruyère	(272 mg)	1 oz (28 g)
Parmesan	(207 mg)	3 D
Cheddar	(204 mg)	1 oz (28 g)
Less than 5% butterfat, such as:		
Mozzarella		
(part-skim)	(183 mg)	1¼ oz (35 g)
Ricotta (part-skim)	(169 mg)	2 oz (56 g)
Cottage (low-fat)	(155 mg)	4 oz (110 g)
Neufchatel	(63 mg)	1½ oz (40 g)

*Note: T = level tablespoon; D = level dessertspoon; t = scant level teaspoon.

FAT FACTS: The fat content of dairy products varies with the amount of butterfat. Skim and low-fat products have had some or all of the butterfat removed. Limit your consumption of dairy foods made from whole milk or cream; although these provide approximately the same vitamin and mineral content as their low-fat counterparts, an equivalent serving size gives you substantially more calories, fat and cholesterol.

Protein Foods

This list encompasses substitutes for various protein foods such as beef, pork, poultry and fish. Also included are plant-protein sources with comparable calories for the given serving sizes. Substitutions for approximate protein equivalence are listed in quantities for one ounce (28 g) cooked. Although the serving size at meals varies from 3 to 4.5 ounces (80 to 125 g), sometimes even 6 ounces (175 g), depending on whether you're a man or a woman or which calorie rotation you're on, you can work out protein equivalency ounce by ounce.

Always choose lean, well-trimmed cuts of meats, which will contain about 55 calories per ounce. (The fatty cuts, untrimmed, have over 100 calories per ounce.) Most types of fish tend to contain fewer calories than meats. Remove skin from poultry before cooking. Bake, grill, boil or poach rather than fry. Avoid adding fat when cooking; avoid high-fat sauces and gravies. Follow the Rotation Diet menus and recipes for specific serving sizes; in general, women may include 5 to 7 ounces (145 to 200 g) of protein foods per day (except on 600- and 900-calorie days while on the weight-loss diet) and men may include 8 to 10 ounces (225 to 300 g) a day.

Type of Protein Food	*Amount for Protein Equivalent*
Beef, lean (less than 10% fat), well-trimmed cuts such as: skirt steak, fillet or rump steak, topside or silverside	1 oz (28 g)
Lamb, lean cuts such as: leg, best end, loin, shank, shoulder	1 oz (28 g)
Pork: leg, tenderloin, lean ham, lean rib or loin chops	1 oz (28 g)
Veal: leg, loin, best end, shoulder, cutlets	1 oz (28 g)
Poultry, without skin: chicken, turkey, guinea fowl, pheasant	1 oz (28 g)
Fish, fresh or frozen, any kind	1 oz (28 g)
Tinned tuna, salmon, crab	4 D
Oysters, scallops, shrimps	1 oz (28 g)
Sardines, drained	3 sardines (or 1 oz/28 g)
Egg (high in cholesterol)	1
Peanut butter (high in fat)	1 D
Cheeses, less than 5% butterfat	1 oz (28 g)
Legumes, dried beans or peas (cooked)	4 D
Tofu	3 oz (80 g)

FAT FACTS: Many Westerners get as much as 40% of the total fat they eat from meat, primarily red meats. Limit red meat to three or four times a week, replacing it with lower fat, lower cholesterol animal alternatives such as fish and poultry, and plant proteins such of tofu. Experiment with our recipes that use meat as a garnish rather than as the centre of the meal.

Vegetables

Here again is your complete unlimited *free-vegetable* list! It contains all the vegetables that have 25 or fewer calories per ½ cup serving. Exchange any vegetable in this list for any other that appears in the list.

You will note that there are some vegetables that contain fewer than 25 calories for a full 1-cup serving! They are marked with an asterisk. Some vegetables not listed here contain more calories and are included in the Grain List, since they are considered 'starchy' vegetables. Use the other 'starchy' vegetables in the Grain List as a substitute for breads.

asparagus	aubergine	bean sprouts
beetroot	broccoli	brussels sprouts
cabbage	carrots	cauliflower
celery	chard	chicory*
courgettes	cucumbers*	dandelion greens
French beans	endive*	escarole*
green pepper	kale	lettuce*
mange-tout peas	mushrooms	mustard greens
okra	onions	parsley*
radishes*	rhubarb	runner beans
spinach	spring greens	tomatoes
turnips	turnip greens	watercress*

*Serving size = 1 cup

FIBRE FACTS: On average, most of the above vegetables contain about 2 grams of fibre per serving. We need 20 to 35 grams of fibre a day for good health; many people in the Western would get less than 10!

FAT FACTS: Vegetables are essentially fat free. Don't mess up nature's blessing by covering them with added fats or high-fat sauces. Season with your favourite herbs and spices, and use the recipes appearing in this cookbook. If you do season with butter or margarine, go easy; ⅓ ounce (10 g) will flavour four to six servings of vegetables.

Fruits

The portion sizes for fruits in the following list all contain about 40 calories. You can see that there is considerable difference in portion sizes for 40 calories, since fruits vary in the amount of sugar they contain per unit of size or weight.

Choose fresh fruits rather than tinned fruit or fruit juices whenever possible. Fresh fruit is a good source of fibre and 'fills you up'. The fibre content has been included for most of the listed fruits. When using tinned fruits, choose those preserved in their own juice or in water. Fruits tinned in syrup may have as much as twice the calories of their fresh equivalents.

Although the quantities listed are equal to about 40 calories, people often choose larger pieces of fruit. A large apple is about twice the size of a small apple and, therefore, would have around 80 calories (in fact, it is sometimes almost impossible to find a 40-calorie apple). Our daily calorie calculations in the Rotation menus reflect these larger servings, since they are customary. The list below is meant to serve as a basic guideline to illustrate the portion size for equivalent calories in various fruits.

Fruit	Amount (average 40 calories)	Fibre (gms)
Apple stewed	1 small	1.5
(unsweetened)	½ cup	1.7
Apricots, fresh	2 medium	1.6
Apricots, dried	4	3.4
Banana	½ small	1.5
Blackberries	½ cup	3.8
Canteloupe (6-inch/15-cm diameter)	¼ melon	1.0
Cherries	10 large	1.2
Cranberries, no sugar	½ cup	4.0
Dates, dried	2	2.4

Fruit cocktail or fresh mixed fruit	½ cup	2.1
Figs, fresh	1	2.0
Grapefruit	½	2.6
Grapes (large)	12	.6
Grapes (small, seedless)	40	.9
Honeydew melon	⅛ medium	1.5
Mandarin orange sections (tinned)	½ cup	.1
Mango	½ small	1.0
Nectarine	1 medium	.5
Orange	1 small	1.2
Papaya	¾ cup	1.8
Peach	1 medium	1.3
Pear	1 small	2.8
Persimmons	½ cup	.4
Pineapple	2 slices	1.5
Plums	2 medium	2.0
Prunes	2 medium	1.3
Raisins	2 D	2.0
Raspberries	½ cup	4.6
Strawberries	¾ cup	3.9
Sultanas	2 D	2.0
Tangerine	1 medium	.3
Watermelon	1 cup	.5

Juices (unsweetened; fibre content is negligible in juice):

Apple, cider or juice	2½ fl oz (65 ml)
Cranberry juice	2 fl oz (55 ml)
Grape juice	2 fl oz (55 ml)
Grapefruit juice	4 fl oz (110 ml)
Lemon juice	6 fl oz (180 ml)
Lime juice	4 fl oz (110 ml)
Orange juice	4 fl oz (110 ml)
Pineapple juice	2½ fl oz (65 ml)
Prune juice	2 fl oz (55 ml)
Tomato juice	8 fl oz (225 ml)
Vegetable-juice cocktail	8 fl oz (225 ml)

FIBRE FACTS: Fresh fruits, especially those that have peels and seeds you can eat, are excellent sources of fibre. Try to obtain at least 5 grams of fibre a day from this naturally sweet group food.

FAT FACTS: Fruits contain no fat, with the exception of avocados, coconuts and olives (found in the Fat Substitution List). A rich source of many vitamins and minerals, and convenient to carry everywhere with you (they come in their own natural wrappers!), fruits are the perfect alternative to higher fat, higher calorie desserts or snacks.

Grains

Over three-quarters of the world's population centre their diets on starches or grains (and they tend to be thinner than those who don't). Grains are sources of carbohydrate, protein, vitamins, minerals and fibre. Nutritionists are encouraging the Western population to eat more carbohydrate-rich foods rather than fatty foods because grains contain little fat. And, except for complete protein and vitamin B_{12}, grains have the same nutrient spectrum as the more fatty foods in the meat group.

The following foods are interchangeable in the portion sizes indicated and, apart from the exceptions noted, contain about 70 calories in the indicated serving sizes. Choose whole-grain, unprocessed products whenever possible.

Note that some items, indicated by an asterisk, count as a serving of ¼ oz (7 g) of fat as well as a bread choice. These contain about 115 calories per serving instead of 70 calories, as for a bread serving alone.

Type of Grain	Amount (average 70 calories)	Fibre (grams)
Breads		
Bread, white	1 slice	1.0
Bread, wheat and rye	1 slice	3.0
Bread, pumpernickel	1 slice	2.0
Breadcrumbs	3 T	1.0
Croutons (without fat)	3 T	.5

Type of Grain	Amount (average 70 calories)	Fibre (grams)
Rolls		
Hot dog	½	1.0
Hamburger	½	1.0
Hard	2-inch (5-cm) diameter	1.0
Muffins		
Plain*	1 small	1.0
Bran*	1 small	2.0+
Cornbread*	2 × 2 × 1-inch (5 × 5 × 2-cm) square	2.0
Tortilla	1, 6-inch (15-cm) square	2.0
Girdle Pancake*	1, 5-inch (12-cm) diameter (½ inch/1 cm thick)	1.0
Waffle*	1, 5-inch (12-cm) diameter (½ inch/1 cm thick)	1.0
Crispbreads		
Allinson's Wholemeal	5	1.9
Hovis Wheatslice	3	1.8
Krisprolls, wholegrain		
Pretzels, very thin	2	1.2
sticks	25	.1
Ryvita	3	3.9
Saltines	5	trace
Soda Crackers	4, 2½-inch/6-cm square	trace
Cereals		
All-Bran	1 oz (28 g)	3.0
Bran Flakes, Raisin Bran	1 oz (28 g)	3.0
Cooked cereals rice, porridge, barley	½ cup	2.0
Cereals, dry unsweetened, ready-to-eat	¾ cup	1.0
Maize meal, dry	2 D	2.0
Cornflour	2 D	0

Type of Grain	Amount (average 70 calories)	Fibre (grams)
Flour, white plain	2½ D	.2
Flour, whole-wheat	2½ D	1.8
Pasta, cooked (lasagne, macaroni, noodles, spaghetti)	½ cup	.2
Pasta, cooked, whole-wheat	½ cup	2.8
Popcorn, popped, no fat added	2 cups	2.0
Rice, white	½ cup	.2
Rice, brown	½ cup	2.0
Wheatgerm	4 D	.7

Starchy Vegetables

Beans, peas, lentils, dried and cooked**	½ cup	4.0
Sweetcorn:		
on the cob	1 small ear	2.1
whole kernel	½ cup	2.1
Mixed vegetables	½ cup	2.5
Parsnips	⅔ cup	3.0
Peas, green	½ cup	3.8
Potato, white	1 small	3.1
Potato, mashed	½ cup	3.7
Potatoes, french fries*	8 pieces	.4
Yam or sweet potato	¼ cup	2.0

FIBRE FACTS: Whole, unprocessed grains provide an excellent source of dietary fibre. Including a serving or two at each meal can help to achieve a healthy fibre content in your diet each day.

*These items, prepared according to standard recipes, contain about 35 calories of fat in addition to the basic calories contained in the grains from which the product is produced.
**Legumes (beans, peas, any variety of plants that have seeds growing in pods) are a significant source of protein as well as carbohydrate. Although the protein is incomplete, that is, not completely available to the body as is the protein in milk, eggs or meat, combining legumes with grains, nuts or seeds, or a small amount of meat or dairy products, makes them as nourishing as meat, with far less fat, cholesterol and calories.

FAT FACTS: Prepared or commercial bread or grain products can contain substantial amounts of added fats. And since humans like fat, food processors tend to 'sneak' it into their recipes in order to increase their products' attractiveness to the consumer. If you truly want to reduce the fat in your diet, forego sweetened bought cakes and biscuits or cake-like breads, except on special occasions. The bread and muffin bun recipes in this book illustrate how delicious these can be with minimal amounts of fat.

Fats

Fats provide more than twice as many calories per equal weight as carbohydrates or proteins. Western diets typically contain more than 40 per cent calories as fat. Many overweight people get over half their daily calories from fat. For weight maintenance as well as for the prevention of cardiovascular disease and certain forms of cancer, health authorities recommend that fewer than 30 per cent of calories should come from fat.

In general, avoid using more than 135 calories of added fat each day (½ ounce/14 g). Cutting back on fats in the diet is essential to long-term weight management as well as to good health. Cut fat whenever possible in your own recipes. The recipes in this book are all lowered in fat, compared with standard recipes of a similar nature.

There are about 45 calories in the serving sizes for fats in the following list. Note that the list is divided into two categories. The first listing contains fats and fatty foods that contain little or no saturated fat and cholesterol. If and when you use added fats in cooking, vegetable oils such as corn, safflower, sunflower, soybean, olive or peanut, are the preferred choices. The second listing includes foods that contain significant amounts of saturated fat and cholesterol. Unfortunately, butter is in this list. Because butter has such an attractive flavour, we frequently blend a little with a vegetable or fruit fat from the first list, such as olive oil, when we want a touch of butter flavour in our recipes.

High-Fat Foods	*Amount (45 calories)*
Avocado, 4-inch (10-cm) diameter	⅛
Vegetable oil	1 t
Margarine, reduced-calorie	2 t
Margarine, regular	1 t
Mayonnaise	1 t
Nuts, pecans, walnuts	4 whole or 1 D
Olives	5 small
Peanuts, shelled	1 D
Sunflower seeds	1 D

Salad dressings	
Italian, French, oil and vinegar, blue cheese, thousand island	2 t
Tartar sauce	2 t

The following fat choices contain significant amounts of cholesterol and/or saturated fat. Use them sparingly.

Very High-Fat Foods	*Amount (45 calories)*
Bacon, crisp	1 slice
Butter	1 t
Chocolate, unsweetened	1 t
Coconut, shredded	2 D
Cream cheese	1 D
Cream:	
double, unwhipped	1 D
double, whipped	2 D
whipping, unwhipped	2 D
Gravy	2 T
Lard	1 t
Sour cream	2 D
Whipped topping, commercial	3 D

Index

331